Once Bitten, Twice Shy

CATHERINE SPENCER

SOPHIE WESTON

Harlequin Books

TORONTO • NEW YORK • LONDON
AMSTERDAM • PARIS • SYDNEY • HAMBURG
STOCKHOLM • ATHENS • TOKYO • MILAN
MADRID • WARSAW • BUDAPEST • AUCKLAND

ONCE BITTEN, TWICE SHY

Copyright © 1996 by Harlequin Books S.A.

ISBN 0-373-15260-4

The publisher acknowledges the copyright holders of the individual works as follows:

LOVE'S STING
Copyright © 1994 by Kathy Garner

THE WEDDING EFFECT
Copyright © 1995 by Sophie Weston

CONTENTS

LOVE'S STING
CATHERINE SPENCER

She had made a gross miscalculation when she'd decided she could handle seeing Clint again. He'd changed. The old appeal was still there, possibly more potent than ever, but there was an added dimension Sharon hadn't counted on. There was steel underneath all that charm, and she wasn't at all sure she could deflect its determined sense of purpose.

THE WEDDING EFFECT
SOPHIE WESTON

"You're in no danger from me." He sent Penny a wry look. "I like my affairs to be a little less of an assault course."

She stared.

"I mean," Zoltan said, his eyes glinting, "that it takes more than twenty-four hours to seduce a porcupine. Even for one of my famous charm." He smiled kindly. "And, no matter what your family might have told you, I haven't got more than twenty-four hours. So you can relax," he added acidly. "You're quite safe—at least from me."

<u>LOVE'S STING</u>
CATHERINE SPENCER

Catherine Spencer, once an English teacher, fell into writing through eavesdropping on a conversation about Harlequin romances. Within two months she changed careers, and sold her first book to Harlequin in 1984. She moved to Canada from England thirty years ago and lives in Vancouver. She is married to a Canadian and has four grown children—two daughters and two sons—plus three dogs and a cat. In her spare time she plays the piano, collects antiques and grows tropical shrubs.

CHAPTER ONE

APART from herself, two distant cousins and the maid hired for the occasion, everyone else at the bridal tea was gathered in the reception rooms of the Dunns' gracious house. Busy admiring the latest wedding gifts, they didn't hear the hiss of the door swinging open, and remained blissfully ignorant of Sharon's return from the kitchen, cake tray of *petits fours* balanced on one hand. Which was probably why Miss Jubilee Bodine felt at liberty to give voice to words never intended for Sharon's ears.

'How long do you suppose we can keep the news from her that Our Boy is back in town?'

The meaning of her question was as unmistakable as the resonant whisper she'd developed since her hearing had started to fail. As far as the Bodine sisters were concerned, there was only one person on the face of the earth whom they referred to as 'Our Boy', and the fact that he must be thirty-eight by now didn't hinder them a bit.

He was the sun, moon and stars in their heaven, all rolled up into one. He was Clinton Bodine, their great-nephew, their adopted child, the light and life of their declining years. And he was Sharon's ex-husband, whom she'd hoped never to see again, least of all here in a town she'd thought he despised almost as much as he despised her.

'Hush, Jubilee!' Miss Celeste Bodine shook a finger and jerked her head towards the door at her back. 'Sharon might hear.'

But the warning came too late. From the other end of the dining-room, Margot looked up, saw Sharon, and groaned audibly. The chatter dribbled into silence. All eyes turned to discover the cause of the bride's distress and came to rest on Sharon, poised in the doorway, the *petits fours* in danger of sliding from their doilied silver platter to the polished oak floor.

Laden cake forks hovered at open jaws, a lapse of manners not normally countenanced in the refined social circles of Crescent Creek. Miss Celeste clapped a hand to her mouth. Miss Jubilee turned raspberry-red. Vera Dunn, the mother of the bride, continued to pour tea into a china cup, even though it was already full to overflowing. Margot's brown eyes widened in dismay, then lowered guiltily.

The only person not frozen with shock was Fern, who, in love with the importance of being a bridesmaid for the first time in her short, sweet life, continued to hum Wagner's 'Wedding March' and pace studiously back and forth on the terrace beyond the open French doors of the dining-room.

Among the adults, Sharon recovered first. 'What did you say, Miss Jubilee?'

'Sharon ... !' Margot stuffed wafer-thin champagne flutes into their tissue-lined gift box with little regard for their fragility, and came towards her with hands outstretched.

'Darling girl!' Miss Celeste whimpered, horrified.

Miss Jubilee muttered, 'Eh?' and tried to look a little deafer than she really was.

Sharon stared her straight in the eye. 'Did I understand you correctly?' she asked, enunciating each syllable clearly. 'Did you say that Clint is in town?'

'Yes,' Miss Jubilee mumbled, paling rapidly.

'When did you learn he was coming back?'

The old lady stared down at her gnarled fingers and blinked. The silence took on a heavy, smothering air of foreboding that made it hard to breathe normally.

'Miss Jubilee?' Sharon prompted, a shade more gently. The old sweetie was eighty-two, after all.

'The . . . other day.'

'And when did he arrive?'

'Last night.'

Good grief; considering that only one flight a day landed at Crescent Creek's decrepit little airport, it was a miracle they hadn't bumped into each other before now!

'Sharon——' Margot tried again, a note of pleading in her voice.

Sharon silenced her with a slashing motion of her free hand. 'And when were you going to let me in on the news?'

Miss Jubilee's shoulders lifted helplessly. 'He asked us not to mention it to you.'

And of course, it had never occurred to either aunt to disregard his wishes. If Clint had ordered them to burn their house to the ground, they'd probably have done so.

Sharon swallowed an exasperated sigh. 'Why not? Don't you think, considering I was once married to him, that I had a right to know something that's obviously common knowledge to everyone else here?'

'Oh, dear!' Miss Celeste wrung her hands. 'Please, darling girl, don't let Clinton's presence spoil the wedding for you.'

Apprehension raced up Sharon's spine. 'How could it?' She swung her gaze to the bride, her friend since college days, the one person who knew why it was imperative that Clinton Bodine be kept as far away from Sharon as possible. 'He's not invited to the wedding—is he?'

Silence, except for Fern's absorbed humming.

'*Is he, Margot*?'

Margot dipped her head in shame.

The *petits fours* slid on to the floor then, and rolled under the table. 'Oh, dear heaven!' The words fluttered past the constriction in Sharon's chest, and all the prettily patterned dresses of the ladies merged into a blur of dizzying colour.

Someone took the silver platter from her hand. Someone else pressed her into a chair. Margot stroked her face. Miss Celeste urged her to sip tea.

'How *could* you?' Sharon whispered, pushing Margot away.

'I was going to tell you . . . I didn't know myself until . . . Sharon, what could I do? Tell him he wasn't allowed back in town?'

'I would have, in your place,' Sharon raged quietly. 'And you can bet your last miserable dollar he wouldn't be a guest at my wedding.'

'Alan wanted to invite him, and I could hardly refuse. It's his wedding too, after all.' Margot sighed unhappily. 'I had no choice.'

'Well, lucky for me, I do! I'm out of here, first thing tomorrow.'

Margot's wail brought all eyes swinging their way once more. 'I knew that's how you'd react! That's why I didn't want to tell you.'

'What else did you expect?' Sharon glared, deliberately fuelling her anger at the betrayal, because if she didn't she knew she'd collapse in a babbling heap of hysteria. Then everyone would know what she was trying so desperately to conceal: that it wasn't animosity or bitterness towards her ex-husband that left her in such a state; it was mortal fear.

'Darling girl,' Miss Celeste ventured, her sweet face crumpling, 'it's been ten years. Can't you forget and forgive?'

Not in this lifetime! Sharon thought miserably. To her dying day she'd remember the hunted look on Clint's face the day he'd stood before the marriage commissioner and repeated his wedding vows. And she'd never forgive the expression that had flared in his eyes when he'd learned that she'd miscarried the baby. A man granted a last-minute reprieve from the hangman's noose couldn't have appeared more relieved!

'For our sakes?' Miss Jubilee begged. 'We've seen him so seldom, ever since...'

'Please don't go,' Margot implored.

Never an easy woman, Vera Dunn was a dragon when crossed. She was crossed now. 'You can't go,' she declared in that bossy way that had always set Sharon's teeth on edge. 'I won't allow it.'

'Oh, yes, I can,' Sharon retorted.

'What, and disappoint your little daughter when she's been looking forward to this wedding for so long? Surely you wouldn't do that—not to mention letting down the rest of the wedding party? After all, Sharon, everything has been arranged for months, and the numbers simply won't add up if we lose our little bridesmaid.'

As though on cue, Fern pushed her way through the crowd and came to lean against Sharon's knee. She gazed at her with clear green eyes inherited, thank God, from her mother's side of the family. 'Mommy? Are you sick?'

Oh, yes! Sick to the soul. 'No, darling.'

'Your mother,' Mrs Dunn announced, pink-cheeked with annoyance, 'is thinking of taking you home and missing the wedding, Fern. What do you have to say about that?'

'My mommy won't do that,' Fern said with childlike certainty, and fixed trusting eyes on Sharon. 'She promised I could be a bridesmaid, and she never breaks her promises, do you, Mommy?'

Sharon slumped in the chair. 'Not if I can help it.'

'Good. Then it's settled.' Mrs Dunn brushed one palm against the other dismissively, as though to say that now that Sharon had had her little fit she should stop being tiresome and remember who really belonged in the lime-light. 'Perhaps it's time we switched from tea to sherry. Margot, dear, why don't you pour Sharon's first? It might settle her nerves.'

'Sharon?' Margot hesitated uncertainly.

Sharon waved her away. 'Pour your own, and make it a stiff one. You're going to need it,' she promised, 'before I'm through with you, because the subject is not closed, Margot, not by a long shot.'

The bridal tea droned on interminably, the precursor not of a week of celebration, as Sharon had expected, but of prolonged stress and uncertainty. Cameras clicked; murmurs of approval hummed as gifts were handed around for inspection. Speculation arose about the honeymoon destination. Traditions were discussed as if

their preservation were of cosmic importance: the
wedding-dress was new, the heirloom pearls old, but what
about something borrowed, something blue?

Sharon endured it all, veiling her agitation behind an
air of tranquillity that fooled everyone but Margot. As
soon as she could decently do so, she escaped into the
garden and hid in the rose arbour, unable to put off a
moment longer deciding how she was going to deal with
the situation suddenly confronting her.

She could run away, of course. She had before, but
then so had he, so no one had paid much attention. But
if she were to go this time, abandoning her best friend
and depriving her of one of the bridesmaids, just because a man she'd once been married to showed up,
people would surely wonder. Wondering led to gos-
siping, which was only a hop away from conjecturing,
and there was always the outside chance that someone
would put two and two together and come up with four.

If that should happen, the repercussions would be disastrous, which left her with only one alternative. She
had to stay, face Clint, and do whatever was required
to protect her secret.

He'd never thought he'd live to see the day that Crescent
Creek would look good to him. While the rest of the
world grappled with war and upheaval, this town went
steadily about its business, protected by a sort of time
warp in which golf handicaps and soirées created the
headlines, and poverty and corruption were relegated to
the back pages, as befitted matters occurring elsewhere.
The closest to political graft that anyone here had come
was the time the ex-mayor used his influence to get his
wife elected president of the horticultural society.

Clint stretched out in the hammock strung between two ancient copper beeches, folded his hands behind his head, and wondered how long it would be, in a town this size, before he and Sharon came face to face. An hour? A day?

One thing he knew for sure: he wasn't about to wait until the wedding to see her. Their first meeting in ten years was not going to take place before a crowd of gaping witnesses nodding wisely and whispering behind their hands as though they saw more happening than quite met the eye. It was going to be conducted privately, at a time and place of his choosing.

A very odd thing had happened on the afternoon he'd run into Alan Wilson during a four-hour stop-over in Chicago's O'Hare Airport and learned of his old football mate's upcoming marriage to Margot Dunn, Sharon's best friend. Memories he'd sworn he'd successfully buried had suddenly risen up to confront him with shocking clarity, and he'd known at that moment that the running must come to an end.

It hadn't taken much interrogative skill to find out that Sharon was invited to the wedding. What *had* taken some doing was hiding his response to the information. Possessed by a burning curiosity to see again the woman he'd once promised to love and cherish, for better or worse, for the rest of his life, he'd wangled an invitation for himself out of the bridegroom, then rationalised his behaviour by telling himself that Fate had intervened and handed him a golden opportunity to lay the past to rest. There was no question but that he'd have to do that, if he seriously intended to abandon his vagabond ways and settle down peacefully in Crescent Creek.

The last thing he'd ever expected was that his and Sharon's paths would cross again, after all this time, in the same small town where they'd met. Would he recognise her? he wondered. She'd been nineteen the first time he'd seen her, and so bloody beautiful and self-assured that he'd been more than ready to believe her when she'd told him she was twenty-three. But that was ten years ago, and people changed...grew fat and sloppy.

The idea of Sharon growing fat or sloppy had him laughing out loud. A less likely candidate he could hardly imagine. When he'd met her she'd just won an apprenticeship with an Italian fashion designer and, according to Alan Wilson, she'd gone on to make quite a name for herself in the world of *haute couture*. She'd probably become cold and hard. In a cut-throat business like hers, it would be difficult not to, and she'd always been ambitious.

He stretched again, and closed his eyes, picturing the eager young woman she'd once been, so poised on the outside, so defenceless within. She'd been so young, had had such a zest for life. What drove her today? Success? Money?

It was good, he supposed, that she'd been able to forge ahead with her career, and male ego made him wonder if she'd ever regretted what she'd given up in return.

Disturbed from his afternoon nap at Clint's feet, Jasper, the aunts' overweight basset hound, flopped over the side of the hammock and waddled off around the side of the house, baying joyfully. The tidal wave of motion that resulted tipped Clint off, too, and tumbled him on to the grass. It needed cutting, he noticed, and made a mental note to take care of it later. Right now he had other obligations. Jasper's greeting signalled the return of the aunts, who'd no doubt be itching to regale him with details of the bridal tea.

It was just as well they were home. Too much lying around, swigging Celeste's home-brewed cider, could add inches to a man's waist without his even noticing. And Clint was damned if he was going to come face to face with Sharon after ten years to have her look him over pityingly and wonder aloud if he'd ever thought of going on a diet.

Slapping the flat of his hand against the ridged muscle of his stomach, he loped over the grass to the rear porch. Had she been at the tea, too? And if so, would his aunts volunteer the information, or would he have to weasel it out of them, a syllable at a time?

He wasn't left wondering too long.

'Oh, Clinton! The most awful thing happened at the tea,' Aunt Celeste panted, meeting him at the back door. 'Come and sit with us while Jubilee and I tell you about it.'

He slung an arm around her stooped shoulders and walked through the house with her to the cool, high-ceilinged living-room. 'You spilled tea on Mrs Dunn's silk carpet and she's having you burned at the stake.'

'Worse,' Aunt Jubilee confessed from the sofa, fanning herself with her hat. 'Sharon was there, and she knows. She overheard me talking about your being home for the wedding.'

Cursing inside, he smiled reassuringly and bent to help Celeste ease off shoes that were at least half a size too small for her feet. 'So?'

'She was terribly upset,' Celeste said. 'She threatened to leave town.'

'Tomorrow,' Jubilee put in gloomily. 'If the new airport at Harperville were open, she'd probably have gone tonight.'

But the Harperville airport wasn't due to open for another six months, and the next flight out of Crescent Creek didn't leave until noon tomorrow.

Clint made his plans for early the following morning.

After she'd dressed for dinner, Sharon slipped into the adjoining room and stood by the bed, watching her child with the same sense of wonder that had touched her the day she'd held her in her arms for the first time. Fern's dark blonde eyelashes lay long and thick on her cheek, her curled fingers snuggled beneath her chin. Her mouth, pursed sweetly in sleep, formed a perfect bee-sting.

'My miracle baby,' Sharon whispered, her heart so full that she thought it would burst. She turned away, stifling a sigh of regret for the wisdom of hindsight come much too late.

When Margot had asked her to design her trousseau and bridal ensemble, Sharon had been happy to comply, though she'd never intended actually coming to town for the wedding itself. But Margot had then complicated matters terribly by asking Fern to be a bridesmaid, and Sharon had been forced to admit to her friend that she was afraid to come back to Crescent Creek, a town that held few fond memories for her and more grief and regret than any person deserved in one lifetime.

'What if Clint chooses the same time to pay his aunts one of his infrequent visits?' she'd protested. 'Two hundred and twenty miles from Vancouver isn't that far off the beaten track for a world traveller like him, after all, and, although he professed to hate its small-town mentality, Crescent Creek *is* the only real home he's ever known, Margot.'

But Margot had pooh-poohed the notion. 'You're overreacting, Sharon. The last anyone heard of Clint,

he was up to his neck shipping refugees from some
country under siege in Eastern Europe—and that's about
as far removed from here as he can get. And anyway,'
she'd concluded with inimitable good sense, 'what do
you think he'd do if, by chance, he did happen to show
up? Corner you and insist you give him a blow-by-blow
account of your every movement since the divorce? He
probably wouldn't be interested and, even if he were,
it's none of his business, as he'd be the first to admit.'

It had seemed a plausible argument at the time, and
a risk worth taking for a friend who had remained constant through the best and worst days of Sharon's life.
Returning the favour by agreeing to attend her wedding
was an admittedly small price to pay for Margot's loyalty.

Someone tapped softly on Fern's bedroom door.
'Sharon?'

Margot's voice, almost timid with apprehension, left
Sharon feeling ashamed. Mrs Dunn was right. She had
no business spoiling this week for her friend, and no
right to blame her for Clint's whereabouts or inclinations.

'Sharon?' Another light tap. 'Are you there?'

'I'm here.' Dropping a kiss on Fern's cheek, Sharon
flung a silk shawl around her shoulders and opened the
door.

'I thought we might talk—about what...' Margot's
soft brown eyes pleaded for understanding.

'About Clint's being at the wedding,' Sharon finished
for her. 'Look, Margie, I'm sorry if I took it out on you
this afternoon, but I was——'

'Shocked. I know. So was I, when I first heard.'

'Actually, "flabbergasted" might be a better word.
I'm afraid I reacted very badly. Your mother will never
forgive me.'

'I won't forgive you, if you run out on me before my wedding!'

'I'm not going anywhere—at least not until I see you safely off on your honeymoon.'

'Oh, thank you!' Margot sagged against the door. 'I keep having the most awful attacks of wedding nerves, and you're the only one who'll keep me sane on the big day.'

'In that case, you can relax. I'm not the type to run away—not any more.'

It was true. She was no longer the nineteen-year-old pregnant wife of a man who felt as though he'd been hog-tied and forced into marriage; she was the successful widow of a man who'd loved her enough to accept her previous mistakes without once reproaching her for them. If Jason were alive today, he'd tell her to stand her ground. Clint Bodine had forfeited the right to dictate the terms by which she conducted her life.

Margot touched her hand in sympathy. 'I'm sorry you had to find out the way you did, with everybody listening in and watching.'

Sharon glanced at her sharply. 'Why? Did someone say something?'

'Nothing worth repeating or worrying about, and we're already late for dinner, so let's go down.' But although she sounded confident, Margot slewed her glance away and fixed it on the stairs.

It was a mannerism that Sharon knew well, and it caused a tremor of alarm to ripple over her. She grabbed at her friend's sleeve, preventing her escape. 'There's something you're not telling me. What is it?'

Margot chewed her lip, then shrugged. 'All right. People who knew you then think you're still a little in love with Clint. That you never really got over him.'

'Oh, please!' Relief had Sharon hiccuping with laughter as she started down the stairs. 'I got over Clint Bodine the day he walked out of our marriage. If I feel anything at all for him, it's gratitude. Thanks to him, I was free to marry Jason when he asked me.'

'If you say so,' Margot said placatingly.

Sharon clutched the banister and stared over her shoulder. 'For heaven's sake, Margie, my reasons for not wanting to see him again have nothing at all to do with left-over puppy love, as you of all people should know.'

'I suppose. But you were crazy about him, at the time.'

Crazy. It was a good word—the *only* word, in fact— to describe the inexcusable duplicity that had eventually led her to such heartbreak and grief. That she should be forced into another round of deceit now, when she'd thought herself safely past the need, infuriated Sharon beyond measure.

Checking to make sure no one was close enough to eavesdrop, Margot whispered, 'What about Fern?'

'What about her? Clint Bodine isn't interested in children. We both know that.'

'But what if he finds out?'

Hearing her own worst fears put into words threatened to unravel all of Sharon's tightly woven control. 'We can't let him, not after all this time. It would hurt too many people.'

'But what if he guesses?'

'Why should he? No one else has.'

Margot sighed unhappily. 'If only you'd told him the truth from the beginning... But you were so sure you knew what you were doing.'

'I was sure of a great many things then, and I wish I had one tenth the same confidence now.' The evening

was balmy, but she pulled the shawl more snugly around
her shoulders as though to ward off a chill. 'One thing
I do know, though, is that honesty isn't always the best
policy. Sometimes telling the truth does more harm than
good, especially if it comes nearly ten years too late.'

'Hmm.' Margot sounded unconvinced. 'Does that
mean you've already decided how you're going to handle
seeing him again?'

With extreme care, the way a person might handle a
time-bomb that came flying through the window without
advance notice!

'Take him by surprise,' Sharon replied, allowing none
of her trepidation to show. 'I'm going to pay a call on
him, first thing tomorrow, and make it plain that I am
not interested in rehashing the past, that I bear him no
ill will, but that the less I see of him, the better. By some
freak of coincidence we're both guests at your wedding,
Margie; that's all. It starts and ends there.'

And she truly believed every word, because there
wasn't a reason in the world to doubt it.

CHAPTER TWO

THE Bodine sisters' house sat at the top of a winding hill on the east bank of the river that gave Crescent Creek its name. The Dunns' house was situated on the west bank. Leaving Fern to help Margot arrange wedding gifts in the library, Sharon set off first thing the next morning, intent on only one thing: seeing to it that Clint Bodine understood her ground rules and agreed to abide by them without question or argument.

It was a still June morning, with laser beams of sunlight slicing between the branches of the trees and glowing softly on the banks of flowers that lined the curving driveway. Sharon was glad to be alone. The solitude calmed her nerves and gave her an opportunity to rehearse what she planned to say when she arrived at the Bodines' front door.

Her preoccupation, added to the fact that the sun slanted into her eyes when she rounded a bend in the drive, was probably why she didn't see him coming the other way until she'd walked practically into his arms. Maybe it was best that things happened like that, because if she'd realised sooner who he was she might have lost her nerve and run back the way she'd come. As it was, he spoke before she recognised him, by which time it was too late to worry about the wisdom of yesterday's decision, and she was left with no choice but to face the man she'd gladly have avoided for the rest of her life, had such an option been possible.

'Hello, dear heart,' he said, his voice just as she remembered it—sexy and slightly rough, like velvet rubbed the wrong way. 'Where are you racing off to at such an early hour?'

'Looking for you,' she said, so discombobulated by his use of the old familiar endearment that it never occurred to her to quibble about his right to question her or otherwise interfere in her business.

'Well, you've found me.' He held his hands palms up and, although the sun continued to dazzle her, she could tell from his tone that he was smiling. 'Here I am, in the flesh. What did you want to see me about?'

Very slowly, her brain cells filtered back to normality. 'I wanted to talk to you.'

'Really? I'm flattered—especially since word has it that you were ready to fly the coop rather than face me.'

'You were misinformed,' she said, with a trace of asperity.

Legs straddling the ground, he grinned down at her, not the least abashed by her disclaimer. 'Does that mean that you're thrilled to see me, and over the moon that we're both invited to the same wedding?'

'Before you get carried away with conceit,' she replied, slewing her gaze away, because everything about him spelled appeal at its masculine best, and she'd rather die than have him read the knowledge in her eyes, 'let's get two things straight. First, whether or not you're a guest at the wedding is immaterial to me; and second, I wasn't on my way to see you because I'm interested in any sort of social intercourse.'

'Not even for old times' sake?' He practically cooed the words at her.

'Least of all for old times' sake. Just the opposite, in fact, and I hope you'll be gentleman enough to agree to what I'm about to suggest.'

To the left of where they stood, a wrought-iron park bench marked the beginning of a path that branched off from the main driveway and meandered towards the riverbank. At her words, Clint sauntered over to it and flung himself down, arms spread-eagled along its back. 'Forgive me for saying so, but, as I recall, we seldom agreed on anything much in the past. What makes you think it'll be different this time?'

'I'd like to think we're both a bit more mature than we were back then.'

He slithered over to make space for her beside him, and patted the bench invitingly. 'Why don't we find out? Sit down, dear heart, and tell me what's on your mind.'

Not a chance, she thought. Keeping her distance was the only safe route to take when dealing with a man like Clint Bodine. 'I don't think that's a very good idea.'

'Why not?' He grinned lazily at her, and crossed his long legs at the ankles, obviously enjoying her discomposure. 'Still ashamed to be seen with me?'

'I was never ashamed to be seen with you,' she shot back, 'so don't go making things worse than they really were.'

'I didn't think they could be made any worse,' he replied, sobering. 'I'd have said, if you'd bothered to ask, that we'd hit the skids with a vengeance by the time we decided to call it quits and go our separate ways.'

In the distance Sharon heard the slam of a door, followed, a second later, by a car's engine roaring into life. With a stab of alarm, she remembered that when they'd finished arranging the gifts Margot and Fern were driving into town to attend to some last-minute wedding chores.

Controlling the urge to dive for cover behind the trunk of a grand old Ponderosa pine, Sharon gestured towards the glimmer of water just visible beyond a dip in the path. 'Do you suppose we could walk down by the river? I feel foolish standing here, holding this conversation where anyone might see us.'

'You *are* ashamed,' he drawled, but rose to his feet with that same lithe and sexy grace that had contributed to her undoing ten years earlier. 'Either that, or you're afraid. Why, Sharon?'

'I'm past the age where I have to explain myself,' she snapped, so eager to put as much distance as possible between herself and any passing traffic that she would have tripped headlong over an exposed root had Clint not loped past her and caught her.

'And how old do you tell people you are these days, my dear?' he enquired smoothly, guiding her down the last steep stretch of bank to the curve of white sand edging the river.

His hands were capable and sure, darkly tanned against her milk-pale skin. Instruments of proficiency in work, she suspected, and of consummate skill in love, as she very well knew. She wrenched herself free, a flush derived equally from embarrassment and anger sweeping over her face. 'You've never forgiven me for that, have you?'

He shrugged, as though he couldn't be bothered expending the energy required to forgive her anything.

Feeling compelled to defend her past behaviour, she went on, 'Women have lied about their age for centuries.'

'Indeed they have,' he returned, 'but usually because they want to pass themselves off as younger, not older.'

'I fail to see how it makes much difference either way.'

He shook his head reproachfully, disturbing his neatly barbered hair. It was as thick as ever, she noticed, but there were strands of silver interwoven with the blond.

He was older, this one-time idol of hers. Always a handsome man—it was his male beauty, after all, that had caught her eye to begin with—he had, if it was possible, improved with age. The years had graced his features with a maturity that reflected the core of integrity that was perhaps his most admirable trait. The passion that shaped his mouth had become tempered by restraint, the arrogance in his eyes softened by humility.

'I think you know that it does,' he said, 'especially when the deceit results in such far-reaching consequences. I think you know that I would never have made love to you had I known you were only——'

'Made love?' She rounded on him, glad of an excuse to divert her thoughts. 'You seduced me!'

'No more than you seduced me,' he said.

Good grief, he was making her feel ashamed all over again! She pursed her lips disapprovingly and waged silent war on memories that insisted on springing to life in glorious Technicolor. 'This is one of the things I wanted to talk to you about.'

His lazy smile washed over her. 'What? Seducing me?'

He was impossible, and so busy exercising his charming side that it was hard to believe he was capable of chilling distance when roused to anger. 'We can hardly avoid seeing each other at the wedding,' she said coldly.

'Hardly,' he murmured, apparently fascinated by the collar of her blouse.

The buttons couldn't possibly have come undone during her scramble down the path, could they? 'I was hoping,' she continued, surreptitiously checking to make sure she was decent, 'that on those occasions when we can't avoid each other we could try to behave like civilised people and agree not to rake up the past. It's over and done with, and I find it frankly painful to rehash mistakes that can't be rectified.'

He switched his attention to her face and looked at her long and soberly, his gaze so potent that she quailed inside. 'And the others?'

'What?' Disconcerted by the dark, impenetrable blue of his eyes, she fumbled to make sense of his question.

'You said that was one of the things you wanted to talk about. What are the others?'

'Oh, yes.' Dismayed to find herself on the brink of regret for things she couldn't possibly change at this late date, she took a deep breath and stepped backwards, as though doing so might release her from his magnetic force field. 'I don't wish to be unpleasant, nor do I want to do anything to spoil this special time for Margot, but the simple fact of the matter is that you and I mean nothing to each other any longer. The way I see it, we're merely distant acquaintances, under no obligation to pretend an interest in each other that neither of us really feels.'

She knew she sounded about as engaging as a snarling wolverine, but what hurt was realising that he agreed with the estimation. The warmth fled from his gaze and he looked her over very thoroughly, as though she were a particularly repulsive specimen, but all he said was, 'I see.'

'Naturally I wouldn't dream of making a scene if we find ourselves thrown together by accident.'

'Naturally not.'

'I mean,' she continued, all the while wondering why she didn't just keep her mouth shut, since nothing she was saying was coming out right, 'there's been a lot of water under the bridge since ... then.'

'Yes,' he said gravely. 'I understand you married again, since ... then. Rather quickly, too.'

She stiffened. Was he taunting her? Implying that her true vocation was snagging husbands in quick succession by whatever means presented itself?

Deciding she didn't care, she traded level stares. 'Within a few short months, as a matter of fact.'

So what if he thought she'd rushed out with a net and trapped Jason before the ink had properly dried on her divorce papers? Perhaps it was better that way. It left less room for speculation or doubt. And Fern, thank God, had always been small for her age.

'But you've been widowed for some time?'

'Almost two years.'

'I'm sorry. Was it a good marriage?'

'The best. Based on all the right things.'

Not a vestige of emotion crossed his features. 'I see.'

'Like love,' she said, a trifle unhinged by his utter stillness, 'and respect. Admiration and liking.'

'What about sex?'

His audacity slammed her in the midriff and knocked the breath out of her. Caught off guard, she gaped and swallowed like an overwrought goldfish ... and fought to recover herself. 'That too, of course.'

'Children?'

There it was, the question she *had* expected, and had thought herself prepared for. But she found herself shaking inside all over again. Her pulse shot into high gear, and fine beads of perspiration sprang down the length of her spine. 'One,' she managed, over the roaring pound of her heart.

He studied her for a long, quiet moment. Then, 'I'm glad,' he said at last. 'I'm sure that must have helped erase the bad memories left behind by our marriage.'

'It did,' she said defiantly. But the bad memories weren't what filled her mind as her eyes roamed over his tall, elegant frame. All she could recall was the breathless wonder of falling in love with him, and, try as she might, she couldn't conjure up Jason's dear face to rescue her. The sadness lurking in Clint's eyes got in the way.

Suddenly she saw not a man who'd run off to a life of high adventure, but someone who'd known more than his fair share of misery. If she'd lived with doubt and loneliness, he'd seen hell and lived to tell about it. What if she wasn't the only one who'd suffered, merely the only one who'd found consolation?

She smothered a sigh and wished she could hate him. And found herself instead lost in the mists of yesterday, her animosity softening into nostalgia, her reason battered by a surprising rush of desire.

He cleared his throat, as if he'd reached some sort of decision, and she found she was holding her breath, waiting to hear what was coming next. She had to keep her head, had to steer the conversation away from Fern. Anything, even having her heart broken a second time, was better than his suspecting that Fern——

'I'm sure,' he said, 'that it will take a load off your mind to hear that I agree entirely with most of what you've said. I'm too busy looking forward to the future to have any inclination to delve into the past. As far as I'm concerned, you're just another guest at a friend's wedding, and I'll treat you as such. No better, no worse.'

'Thank you. That's what I was hoping for.'

But if that were true, why did she feel as flat as yesterday's champagne, hollow inside, as if she'd just lost a battle, when, in fact, she'd won a major victory?

'See you at the wedding, then.'

'Yes.' It was relief, she told herself, that made her voice quaver like that, and almost reduced her to silly tears. She turned away, hoping he hadn't noticed, but she'd forgotten how observant he was.

'Sharon?' He moved dangerously close. 'Are you crying?'

What was the use of denying it, when her eyes were swimming and she could barely see enough to put one foot in front of the other? 'A little, I guess. First love is so painful, even in retrospect.'

'That's why it so seldom lasts,' he said, and reached out a finger as though to dam the tears that hovered on her eyelashes.

She couldn't endure to have him touch her. He was as potently, dangerously attractive as ever, if not more so. Raw with emotions she didn't pretend to understand, she flinched away from him. 'Go away and leave me alone,' she begged.

He backed off and held up both hands in surrender. 'Whatever you say, Sharon.'

His gentleness completely undid her. Instead of escaping with the dignity befitting a woman of almost thirty, she spun around and bolted back the way she'd come, leaving him standing there open-mouthed, no doubt, and wondering if she'd become completely unhinged.

In a way she had, because, appalling as it might be, the fact was she felt as bereft and desolate as she had the day they'd agreed to end their marriage. She couldn't bear to be the one left to watch him walk away again.

*　　*　　*

'Run as fast as you like, dear heart,' Clint said in soft response to her fading footsteps. 'It won't do you a bit of good.'

Exhaling a long, thoughtful breath, he narrowed his gaze against the glare of sunlight on the river. So, the future wasn't as uncomplicated as he'd thought, after all. No matter. He was used to change, and had plenty of practice adjusting to the unexpected.

He smiled and shook his head ruefully. She'd had him fooled at first, with that tough, lacquered approach. He'd been almost ready to believe what she said and consign her permanently to the past. But he was a man who'd learned to look beyond the obvious and, most of all, to trust his instincts.

He'd seen the way her pulse had raced so agitatedly that it set the open collar of her blouse fluttering. He'd seen how she'd nervously twisted the wedding-ring on her finger. But most of all, he'd seen the fear.

It had been there in her lovely green eyes from the minute she'd almost bumped into him on the drive. There'd been other emotions, too: shock, anger—her glare at his question about her sex life could have turned a man to stone!—and, once, regret, perhaps, and a certain wistful longing. But most of all, there'd been fear.

He knew why he'd deliberately engineered an invitation to the wedding. What he couldn't explain was her panic-stricken reaction to that unremarkable item of news. Was she afraid of him? Or herself?

He didn't know—yet. But he intended to find out, no matter how many barriers she threw up in an effort to deflect him.

The following afternoon the bridal outfits arrived by air courier, and wedding fever in the Dunn household escalated to new heights. Sharon found herself on permanent call, 'Because,' as Mrs Dunn pointed out almost every time she drew breath, 'things must be absolutely perfect.'

Sharon didn't mind being virtually house-bound and spending the next two days in the library, with no time for anything but making last-minute adjustments to hems and suchlike. She thought it would keep her safe from Clint.

She thought wrong. On the third day, with the bridesmaids' outfits at last pronounced acceptable, she came down to lunch with Fern to find him at the other side of the terrace, looking very much at home.

'Clint brought over his aunts' silver epergne,' Margot explained, shooting anxious glances back and forth between him and Sharon. 'Mother's borrowing it for the centrepiece at the reception.'

'I see,' Sharon said with what she hoped was convincing indifference. But what she saw was the way he smiled at Fern, who, accosted by a fit of shyness, half hid behind Sharon.

'So Mother invited him to stay for lunch,' Margot said.

She would! Sharon thought, her heart sinking as he strolled towards her with negligent, unhurried grace. Unobtrusively she reached behind and took Fern's hand in hers.

'Hi,' he said. 'How's it going?'

'Fine.'

'How does the wedding-dress look?'

'Fine.'

'And the bridesmaids'?'

'Fine.'

His eyes teased her unmercifully. 'How about having dinner with me tonight, then driving out to Crescent Point and watching the moon rise?'

Her heart tripped into overtime. The first time they'd made love had been at Crescent Point, with nothing but the rising moon to witness the event. 'Forget it,' she said shortly.

He grinned with unabashed glee. 'For a moment there, I thought you were going to say "Fine" again!'

'Was there something important you wanted to say?' she enquired. 'Or did you just come over here to see how quickly you could annoy me?'

'I was hoping you'd introduce me to this lovely young lady.'

Sharon's heart almost stopped at that, and she stared at him wordlessly, searching for an excuse not to do as he asked. She didn't want him talking to Fern; she didn't want him near her.

But he wasn't about to be put off. 'Sharon?'

'This is my daughter, Fern,' she said stiffly, and tensed, dreading that some eerie, latent intuition might tell him that Fern was his daughter, too.

'How do you do, Fern?' He bent down and enveloped her small hand in his with deferential charm. 'I'm Clint.'

Fern, Sharon noted with dismay, was no more immune to his charm than any other female. She gave him her hand, returned his smile, and murmured hello.

'Are you involved in this wedding, too?' he asked.

'I'm a bridesmaid,' she informed him pridefully.

'The prettiest, I'm sure.'

Fern giggled, falling more securely under his spell, and all Sharon could do was watch helplessly and pray that she could intervene before untold damage occurred. 'It's time to sit down, Fern,' she said, noting with heartfelt gratitude that Mrs Dunn was ushering people inside to the dining-room. 'Come along.'

'Will you save me a dance at the reception?' Clint asked his pint-sized conquest.

Fern released another endearing giggle. 'I don't know how to dance.'

'Neither do I,' Clint admitted, 'but I promise not to step on your toes if you promise not to step on mine.'

I'll break your leg first, Sharon thought balefully. He wasn't going to dance his way into her daughter's heart if she had any say in the matter.

But her ill-wishing fell on Mark, one of the ushers, instead, as she and everyone else learned when the bridegroom showed up halfway through lunch.

'Mark fell and broke his leg water-skiing on the river,' Alan explained. 'I'm afraid he won't be able to make it to the wedding.'

'Not make it to the wedding? But the numbers won't add up!' Mrs Dunn wailed, cutting through everyone else's exclamations of sympathy and getting right to the heart of what really mattered. 'Whatever are we going to do?'

'Fire a bridesmaid?' Alan suggested, attempting to lighten the atmosphere a little.

But while almost everyone else laughed, Mrs Dunn's glance roamed around the table and zeroed in on Fern. 'But of course!' she said. 'It's the perfect solution.'

'I was joking,' Alan protested, as the laughter settled into uneasy silence.

'It's no joking matter,' she declared. 'Fern will have to drop out.'

'Mother!' Margot half rose from her chair. 'You can't be serious.'

'Sharon never really wanted her involved to begin with,' Mrs Dunn said dismissively. 'Isn't that right, Sharon?'

Aware of Fern's strangled gasp of disappointment, Sharon fought to contain her anger at the woman's insensitivity. 'Not at all, Mrs Dunn. We both considered it an honour that she was invited.'

'Phooey! You were all set to rush back to Vancouver the day you heard Clinton was back in town, so don't pretend you weren't.'

'But I decided to stay,' Sharon replied, annoyed that such a juicy little morsel of information had been dropped almost literally on Clint's plate. 'And, if you recall, my reason for doing so was that I didn't want to disappoint Fern.'

Clint, who was seated on the other side of Margot, leaned behind her to exchange a few quick words with her fiancé. The other lunch guests pretended to be interested in the food on their plates, but the atmosphere was fraught with incipient hostility.

Mrs Dunn either didn't notice or didn't care. 'She'll get over it.' She shrugged.

'She won't have to,' Clint announced, concluding his muttered exchange with Alan. 'I'll stand in for the missing usher.'

'No, you won't,' Mrs Dunn snapped. 'You're at least three inches taller than he is. The rented suit won't fit.'

'Then we'll find one that does,' Clint said, overruling her with a smile that left his eyes flinty-cold.

Mottled with rage, Mrs Dunn glared the length of the table. 'This isn't your decision to make, Clinton.'

He usurped her authority with an unimpeachable courtesy that nevertheless brooked no opposition. 'Nor is it yours, Mrs Dunn. Selection of the ushers is the bridegroom's prerogative, a point of etiquette I'm sure you wouldn't dream of contravening, and Alan just accepted my offer to act as Mark's substitute.' The chill melted from his eyes as he shifted his attention to Fern. 'And that means I get to walk the prettiest bridesmaid down the aisle during the recessional,' he declared, increasing the wattage of his smile endearingly. 'I call that a lucky break—for me.'

Just about everyone laughed again at that, and Fern positively glowed with pleasure. But Sharon sat immobilised with horror, regretting that she hadn't acquiesced to Mrs Dunn's high-handed request before Clint opened his mouth and unwittingly trapped her more thoroughly in a web of complications that threatened to grow more tangled with every passing hour.

CHAPTER THREE

IN the well-mannered way that friends of the Dunns always behaved, people began talking about other things and pretended the rather acerbic exchange between hostess and guests had never occurred. Still not an ideal situation, it was nevertheless an improvement over the previous few minutes, and, glad for the reprieve, Sharon sat back and breathed a sigh of relief. Much too soon, as it turned out.

'What with everything else that's happening this week, I'd forgotten that the fair opens today,' Alan remarked. 'I could hear the noise when I drove by the park.'

Sharon didn't need Clint's penetrating stare to remind her that they'd met at Crescent Creek's annual country fair ten summers ago. The mere mention of it was enough to conjure up the memories with dismaying clarity. The sultry heat, the aroma of frying onions and home-made fudge mingling with the smell of diesel oil, the shrieks of terrified glee rising over honky-tonk music blaring from loudspeakers and underscored by the rumble of heavy machinery—it all came back with an immediacy that stunned her.

'Fair? What sort of fair?' Fern, who'd been slumped in her seat with boredom, perked up at Alan's disclosure.

'Don't tell me your mother hasn't mentioned it,' Clint said, his attempt to look guileless foiled by the secretive little smile that crept across his face. 'It's one of the high events of the summer in these parts. All sorts of interesting things have been known to happen during country fair week.'

Hadn't they, though? If she hadn't accepted Margot's challenge to risk her life on some crazy, gravity-defying machine that had left her too giddy to see where she was walking, Sharon might never have stumbled blindly into Clint Bodine's waiting arms. Then he'd have had no reason to cushion her next to his chest, or to suggest, in his smoky, alluring voice, that it might be wiser if he supervised any other rides she planned to try that long-ago day. But, at nineteen, she'd been too foolish to walk away from a dare, and as a result the course of her life and Clint's had been changed for ever.

'Are there merry-go-rounds and stuff?' Oblivious to the nuances of his comment, Fern regarded him from wide, hopeful eyes, and Sharon's heart sank. At the best of times, her daughter was appealing; right then, she was downright irresistible.

Clint, apparently, was no more immune than the rest of the world. 'You bet,' he assured her, abandoning his covert attack on Sharon and devoting all his attention to her daughter. 'Everything from carousels and Ferris wheels to ponies.'

'I've never ridden a pony,' Fern lamented.

'What?' He rounded on Sharon in mock-dismay. 'What sort of mother are you, Sharon, that your little girl's never ridden a pony?'

'There aren't too many horses running loose on Vancouver streets,' Sharon pointed out shortly, and wondered why in the name of sweet sanity she resented his being able to switch off *his* memories so easily.

'Then it's a good thing I can do something to rectify a very serious situation.' He angled an engaging smile Fern's way, captivating her completely. 'Miss McClure, will you allow me to escort you to the country fair and treat you to a ride on the ponies?'

He was as silver-tongued as ever, except this time it was his daughter he was disarming with his smile and his lazy, husky voice. Sharon wished he'd choke on all those perfect, dazzling teeth. Much as she'd like to see Fern having fun, she wasn't about to let Clint Bodine be the one to provide it.

Scraping her chair across the mirrored polish of Mrs Dunn's oak floor, she stood up and held out a hand to Fern. 'That's impossible. We're very busy between now and the wedding.'

Mesmerised by her new ally, Fern gazed at Clint adoringly. 'I'm not busy, Mommy,' she objected, adding with an adult logic that left Sharon at a loss for a suitable reply, 'In fact I don't have anything important to do until the wedding-day, and I'm quite bored.'

'I'll find something for you to do,' Sharon replied, a marked edge in her voice.

'There's no need for that,' Clint said mildly. 'I've already offered to take her off your hands for the afternoon. She'll be perfectly safe with me.'

'No.' Aware that almost everyone else at the table must think her a cold-blooded witch to remain unmoved by such monumental charm, Sharon turned her back on them all and swept Fern through the French doors and out into the garden.

Undeterred, Clint followed. 'You really shouldn't vent your hostility towards me by punishing your daughter,' he chided in a low voice.

'I'm not.'

'Then why won't you let me take her to the fair?'

'Because, in this day and age, smart parents don't send their children off with strangers. And stop interfering in the way I choose to bring up my own child.'

'I'm not a stranger.'

No, you're her father, but you don't know it; that's the whole trouble! 'Nevertheless ...'

His gaze swept over her face, those brilliant, winsome blue eyes examining her feature by feature. 'What are you afraid of, Sharon? That I've turned into some sort of disgusting pervert who can't be allowed around innocent children?'

'Of course not!' But she was grievously afraid that if he ever found out how she'd deceived him he'd exact a terrible revenge.

'Then what's making you so antsy? And don't tell me I'm imagining things, because we both know better.'

He was too perceptive by half, and she much too transparent in her anxiety. 'I suppose it's just that I've become a bit over-protective ever since Jason died,' she parried, struggling to contain the panic that, left unchecked, might prove her undoing. 'Being a single parent is a great responsibility.'

'I can imagine that it must be.'

Perhaps so, but what he couldn't possibly imagine was the relief she felt at just once being able to open her mouth and state a simple fact, untarnished by evasions or half-truths. 'Then surely you can understand why I'm reluctant to let her go off without me?'

'Come with us and you won't have to deal with the problem.'

'I don't think...' Still trapped in his gaze, she searched for an excuse and instead found her thoughts veering again to the first time she'd seen him. He'd been tanned then, too, and his eyes had seemed as deeply blue as tropical seas. She'd floundered into their depths and into love within the space of a heartbeat.

'Come on, Sharon,' he cajoled her now. 'There's been a lot of water under the bridge since we decided to go our separate ways. Give me a chance to show you that I'm not a total jerk. Your little girl is hanging around with nothing to do. *You're* at the beck and call of Margot's mother as if you were a hired hand. Take the afternoon off and come with us to the fair.'

She couldn't afford to divulge the best reason in the world to refuse him. Worse yet, she wanted to go with him. It did no good to tell herself she was flirting with disaster, that the more time she spent around Clint, the greater the danger that he'd uncover her secret. Her heart overrode her head as easily now as it had ten years ago, luring her into dangerous waters without regard for her survival.

As if she'd been primed, Fern dealt a final blow to her resistance. 'Please, Mommy. I promise to be good.'

The child was always good; that was half the problem. She was the best thing that had ever happened to Sharon, the one person who made all the lies and sacrifices worth while. Disappointing her daughter was never easy. Her own imprudent inclinations aside, the guilt of knowing she'd neglected Fern over the last few days made it impossible for Sharon to refuse her now. 'Well, I suppose I could take a couple of hours...'

Something was very wrong. He grew surer of it by the minute. Even on the crowded fairground, with so much noise and activity going on that it was difficult to hear what the other person was saying, Sharon edged away from him as if he had typhoid or something. She even refused to look at him directly, though that could, perhaps, be explained by the fact that her gaze never wavered far from her daughter.

'She's safe for the next five minutes, Mother,' he teased at one point, as Fern rode the children's carousel. 'You can relax and start enjoying yourself.' And just to put his theory to the test, he cupped an impersonally friendly hand around her elbow.

Sure enough, she jumped and shied away as if he'd touched some intensely private part of her. What did she think? That he was such a depraved animal that he might toss her down behind one of the tents and have his way with her?

'This might come as a shock to you, dear heart,' he said mildly, 'but my intention in asking you to come with us this afternoon was not to terrorise you.'

'It never occurred to me that it was,' she said, then put the lie to her assertion by adding another twelve inches between them. It shouldn't surprise him; she'd lied to him before, after all.

The carousel slowed. From her perch on a painted unicorn, Fern waved happily. 'Do you hate me, Sharon?' Clint couldn't help asking.

She shot him an oblique glance from beneath long dark lashes. 'Why should I?'

Let me count the ways! he thought ruefully. 'You once told me that I'd ruined your life. The way you're acting now, I'm inclined to believe you think I'm still doing it.'

'All that happened a long time ago, Clint, and, as you eventually learned to our mutual cost, I was very young.'

'There are some things that time can't change or heal,' he said, wishing to hell he could come up with a more original reply. But he'd never been able to find the right words to make what had happened between them seem less painful. They'd lost their baby, and what remained of their marriage after that had been of so little substance that neither of them could find comfort in it.

As though she'd divined his thoughts, Sharon spoke again. 'You forget that I found Jason. I made a new life for myself after you left me.'

She made it sound like an accusation. 'You say that as if I walked out on you,' he said.

'You did, and it was the kindest thing you could have done. I would never have met Jason otherwise.'

A sudden anger caught him by surprise. This wasn't about Jason, it was about them, and he wasn't going to let her shift the focus to a man who had no part of their history. 'I don't give a flying fig about Jason, Sharon! And I did not leave you or walk out; we ...'

But she moved out of earshot, intent on finding Fern, who'd hopped off the far side of the merry-go-round, a hazardous twenty-five yards away from her mother's vigilant surveillance.

'Where did Mommy go?' Breathless, Fern rushed around to him from the opposite direction, full of exuberance and glee, the way *their* child might have, had things gone differently. Come to think about it, the two children would have been about the same age, give or take a few months. Sharon must have conceived within hours of marrying good old Jason. Clint couldn't believe how much the knowledge soured his mood.

'Mr Bodine? Are you sad?'

It was impossible to remain surly in the face of such a sympathetic audience. He drummed up a smile. 'What makes you think that?'

'You looked a long way off and you didn't answer my question,' she replied, adding with artless candour, 'Mommy does that, sometimes, and it's usually because she's feeling sad.'

'Well, in my case, it's just that I wish you'd call me Clint instead of Mr Bodine. You are my date at the wedding, after all, so I think it would be OK—unless, of course, you'd rather keep things formal and have me call you "Miss McClure" all the time.'

She giggled, a light musical sound that enchanted him. 'I'm too young for that, but it's different with you. You're quite old.'

'Gee, thanks!' His laugh had Sharon scurrying back towards them. 'Here comes Mom,' he said. 'She went looking for you, but you fooled her and came around the other way. What do you want to do next?'

'The ponies,' Fern begged, appealing to him with huge green eyes so much like Sharon's that his heart faltered for a minute. 'Then the Ferris wheel—but only if you go on it with me. I'd be scared by myself.'

'It's a deal. The Ferris wheel is my favourite.'

'No!' Overhearing, Sharon practically arm-wrestled the child away from him, her voice unnaturally shrill. Even she seemed to realise she was overreacting, because she added lamely, 'She might get sick or something.'

'Pigs might fly,' he returned, 'but it isn't very likely.'

He recognised the stubborn set of her mouth and knew she was determined to oppose him even on so insignificant a point as this. 'Nevertheless, I think we should walk around the exhibits for a while, just in case,' she insisted.

'The exhibits are boring.' Fern pouted.

'Then we can go home,' Sharon said. 'I'd find that a perfectly acceptable alternative.'

The child was smarter than he by a country mile. Instead of fighting the issue, she switched tactics and favoured her mother with the sunniest of smiles. 'Some of them are boring,' she amended, 'but most of them are fun.'

Clint nodded towards a huge striped tent on the far side of the park. 'My aunts have a table in the country kitchen,' he told Sharon. 'They're selling home-made preserves and jams, and raffling off the patchwork quilt they made last winter. I know they'd love to have you stop by and visit.'

Just briefly a spark of interest gleamed, before the shutters rolled down over her beautiful eyes again. 'I don't think so, thanks.'

'They're harmless old ladies, Sharon,' he muttered, stifling the surge of annoyance that rose up in him. 'They have no part of your determined resentment of me.'

'It's not that.'

'Then why don't you tell what it is?'

'Fern,' she said, appearing to shuffle through half a dozen excuses before finding one that might hold water. 'I really can see that she might find jams and preserves a bit dull.'

'No problem,' he said easily. 'I'll keep her entertained for ten minutes while you go in and say hello. We'll stay here at the rifle shoot, where I'll do my damnedest to win her a doll or something, and I promise we won't move an inch until you come back.'

'A teddy bear!' Excitement at his suggestion had the child hopping around on one foot like a drunk on a pogo stick. 'A girl in my class has forty-two teddy bears, but I only have eight.'

'Holy cow!'

'Collecting bears is the latest rage among her friends,' Sharon explained, a near-smile softening her mouth at his astonished reaction to Fern's disclosure.

'Then a teddy bear is what I'll aim for, and she can be my cheering section. Go visit the aunts with an easy mind, dear heart.'

'Please don't call me that,' she muttered. 'Fern might hear and ask questions.'

'She'd have to have radar traps for ears to hear in this noise, but would it be so terrible if she found out that we were once married? That there was a time when——?'

Sharon looked aghast. 'Yes!' she hissed. 'She has no idea that... She thinks Jason...'

It was there in her eyes again, that flash of naked fear out of all proportion to the occasion. She reminded him of a doe trying to guard her fawn from hidden danger, and he felt alarmingly protective towards both of them, all of a sudden.

'I wish,' he said, 'that you trusted me enough to tell me what it is about my being here that's really bothering you. You'd have a far better time tomorrow night then, not to mention on the wedding-day itself.'

'Tomorrow night?' Her eyes flickered, seeking a way out of whatever mess she perceived herself to be in.

Confide in me, damn it!

Frustration had him wanting to shake some sense into her. Good God, had he left behind such a bad taste that she viewed him as some sort of monster, incapable of sympathetic understanding? 'The rehearsal dinner,' he reminded her, forcing himself to adopt a moderate tone. 'We're doomed to spend the evening together, whether you like it or not, and I venture to suggest it might be easier on both of us if we cleared the air first.'

'Are you going to win me a teddy bear?' Fern hopped back within hearing range, twitching with impatience, and Sharon seized the opportunity to deflect her attention away from him.

At first inclined to pursue the conversation with Sharon, Clint changed his mind and shrugged in defeat. 'If it's OK with your mom.'

'All right,' Sharon conceded, but reluctantly, as though he'd demanded a king's ransom in exchange for not hounding her. 'But I'd like to watch, if that's all right with you. I'll pay your aunts a visit later.'

His glance fell on the child at her side, and he knew a sharp pang of envy, mixed with an irrational anger, that Sharon had supplanted her loss with another man's child, while he had roamed the earth searching without success for an end to pain and for absolution of his sins. 'Whatever you say,' he acknowledged resignedly. 'She's your daughter, not mine, and you've already made it clear that you call the shots.'

She'd made a gross miscalculation when she'd decided she could handle seeing Clint again. It wasn't nearly as simple and nothing like as uncomplicated as she'd foolishly allowed herself to believe it would be. For a start, he'd changed. The old appeal was still there, possibly more potent than ever, but there was an added dimension Sharon hadn't counted on. No longer the kind who'd walk away from difficulties, he'd grown into a man who stayed with a problem until he'd resolved it, and the realisation petrified her. There was steel underneath all that charm, and she wasn't at all sure she could deflect its determined sense of purpose.

As for the rehearsal dinner, good lord, wasn't it enough that she had to endure the entire wedding-day with him hovering over Fern, without being subjected to the stress of tomorrow evening, too? At his present rate of progress, he'd have Fern so thoroughly bewitched that she'd probably confide the details of her entire life, should he think to ask for them.

Sharon closed her eyes and stifled a groan. Who would ever have thought, back when she first decided on her course of deception, that the lie would come back to haunt her all these years later? Or that a question as simple as, 'How old are you, Fern?' or, 'When is your birthday?' could pose a threat that would destroy the safe little world she'd created for herself and her child?

'Mommy, look!'

Fern's squeal of delight startled Sharon into awareness of what was happening there and then. Clint stood sideways to the row of targets, his blond head cocked at an angle as he took aim and hit every bull's-eye dead centre, as easily as she might have cracked eggs into a bowl.

She wished she could look away, but was too hypnotised by the strength of his deeply tanned forearms, the play of muscle across his back under the thin cotton of his shirt. It wasn't fair that a man could grow more beautiful over time, while a woman showed her age in a thousand subtle ways. Had he noticed that her breasts weren't quite as high and firm as they'd once been, or that her waist wasn't quite as narrow? Did he remember how she'd looked at nineteen? Did he care?

Without warning, memories crowded in again and swept her back through time with dizzying speed: same place, same season, same people...

The sun had set that day unnoticed, outshone by the blaze of attraction between the two of them. At some point Margot had discreetly excused herself, escorted by Clint's friend, both of them fully aware that four made a crowd.

Sharon and Clint had strolled away from the fairground and over the bridge to the deserted side of the river. Above them on the bluff, the town's most exclusive homes, the Dunns' among them, had glimmered with lamplight, but down on the strip of sand it was dim and private.

'What do you want from life?' Clint had asked, looking up at the houses. 'To be rich like them?'

The answers had fallen out of her mouth with easy familiarity. 'No,' she'd said. 'To take the fashion world by storm. To be an international name.'

But under cover of dusk her eyes had looked at him and her heart had said, I want you.

He'd been quiet for a minute or two. When he'd finally spoken, his voice had been even huskier than usual. 'Are you hungry?' he'd asked, folding Sharon's fingers in his.

She'd shaken her head, bewitched, bedazzled. Who needed mortal food?

'Neither am I,' he'd said, and she had known that he was telling only half a truth, that what she heard in his voice went beyond the flirtatious curiosity of youth to full-blown adult desire.

She'd been adept enough at fending off lanky boys with peach fuzz for beards and Adam's apples too large for their throats, but this was no baby-faced adolescent trying to muster up the nerve to kiss her. This was a man, with all a man's appetites, and he wanted her. She had known it instinctively, and the power of that knowledge had shot an arrow of heat from her heart to the pit of her stomach.

He'd smiled at her, his eyes inky pools of twilight. She'd looked into their depths and seen the neat blueprint of her life: the secure, comfortable upbringing by well-to-do, society-conscious parents; attendance at all the best schools, membership at all the right clubs; the coveted apprenticeship with a renowned Italian fashion designer. And all at once, none of it had mattered beside the immediacy and urgency of her desire for him.

He'd stopped in the lee of the bluff, under the glimmering green shadows of a maple tree, and had slid his hand around her neck. Not an unfamiliar experience, she'd have thought; others had done the same before him. But this time was different. He was different. His fingers wove spells over her skin, awaking sensations in other parts of her body—hot, quivering, deliciously frightening sensations that left her mind swirling and clouded her judgement.

When he had finally dropped his mouth to her ear, then down to her neck, it was so unlike anything she'd known before that it might have been the first time she'd ever been kissed. Another hot, damp revelation swept her far away from all the touchstones of familiarity. It had been like falling off the edge of the earth. Every stable facet of her life had spun out of control with the touch of his lips. She'd started shaking like a leaf in a storm, had turned her face to his, blindly seeking a closer contact, and, if it was possible to imprint one's heart on another's mouth, she'd imprinted hers on his.

He had seemed taken aback, had held her away from him, a sudden suspicion banking his fire. 'How old are you, Sharon?' he'd asked, his voice a raspy whisper.

And that was when she'd come face to face with the most dangerous choice she'd had to make in her short and hitherto uncomplicated life. Because she'd known that, desire and attraction notwithstanding, he was a man of conscience. There was an integrity about him that would not allow him to satisfy his own raging needs by taking advantage of someone still half a girl.

Tell him the truth, vanishing sanity had warned her, and you'll be safe. He'll run like the wind and you'll never see him again.

She had opted for the other choice, taken the path that led away from everything circumspect and honourable and familiar. 'Twenty-three,' she'd lied, twining her arms around his neck and pulling his head down so that she could find his mouth again. 'Old enough to know what I'm doing.'

She'd pressed herself against him, the fire raging from her nipples to her knees. When he'd tried to restrain her, muttering about public places and people who might walk by and disturb them, she'd squirmed and undulated, a shockingly wanton hussy bent on having her way.

His resistance hadn't lasted long. She'd gloried in the knowledge of his arousal, and continued to torment him with a recklessness that still made her blush all these years later. She'd let her hands roam shamelessly, and at last pushed him past the point of no return.

'Over here,' he'd urged hoarsely, and had stumbled with her to a pale swath of embankment that jutted out into the river beyond the screen of an overhanging willow tree.

The sand had felt cool and grainy against her skin, but his hands had been warm, his mouth hot and hungry. She hadn't been wearing a bra, just a simple top with shorts and a pair of bikini underpants. He'd pushed them all aside, snapped open his blue denim cut-offs.

She'd lost her nerve then, had wanted to cry out that she'd changed her mind, but it had been too late. The words had choked on a gasp as he entered her. She'd tensed at the stabbing pain, then clung to him in fearful wonder as her body accepted him. He'd groaned, driven by demons of her making, and lost himself inside her.

It had been quick and intense, and when it was over he'd looked down at her and, even though it was almost dark, she'd known that his eyes were flat with disgust—for himself and for her. 'You lied,' he'd said, and rolled over the hard sand, away from her.

Pain, shame and fear finally took their toll, and she'd started to cry.

'Straighten your clothes,' he'd said, unmoved. 'I'm taking you home.'

'What if I get pregnant?' she'd whimpered, when what she'd really wanted to say was, Please fall in love with me, the way I've fallen in love with you.

'God forbid!' he'd replied.

The tears had gushed forth at that, an endless torrent that had alarmed him. 'Hey,' he'd said, hauling her to her feet and brushing the sand from her shoulders. 'Sharon, I'm sorry. It was my fault.'

'I didn't mean to be a virgin,' she'd sobbed, and, after a startled minute of silence, he'd half laughed and put his arms around her.

'We all start out that way,' he'd comforted her. 'It's no big deal.'

'Does that mean I'll see you again?' she'd asked on a breath frail with hope.

Although he still had his arms around her, she'd felt his withdrawal. 'Sure,' he'd said. 'Give me your phone number and I'll call you tomorrow.'

She'd wondered, if her lie had been one tenth as unconvincing as his, why he'd ever chosen to believe her when she'd told him she was twenty-three. Of course he hadn't called, not until three weeks later, and by then the suspicion that there might be consequences to her rash behaviour had begun to crystallise into certainty.

'A girl can't get pregnant the first time,' Margot had assured her naïvely, when Sharon had confided her fears.

But Sharon had grown light-years older than Margot since the day she'd met Clint, and she knew better. Girls who gave themselves easily, irresponsibly to men deserved all the trouble they brought on themselves.

'Mommy! Look what Mr Bodine won for me!'

Fern's squeak of delight echoed down the time tunnel, pulling her back to the uncertain haven of the present. She followed it gladly, relief at being freed from the humiliation of her memories outweighing her apprehension at what tomorrow might hold.

'Two teddy bears?' She hoped her smile wasn't quite as wan as her voice. 'How lovely, sweetheart.'

Clint was watching her far too closely. 'Either you're on the verge of collapse,' he observed, bathing her in a smile that had her heart flopping around like an injured bird, 'or you've just seen a ghost. Which is it, dear heart?'

'The ghost,' she admitted. The only trouble was that ghosts were ephemeral, figments of an overwrought imagination, and Clint Bodine was real, never more handsome or desirable, and never more forbidden.

CHAPTER FOUR

THE rehearsal dinner was held in the Tudor room of the Gables Hotel, the town's second-best establishment after the Crescent Creek country club, where the wedding reception was to take place. Fern didn't attend the dinner after all. She'd been out of sorts earlier, and a good night's rest seemed in order if she was to be at her best for the big day itself.

'But you go out and enjoy yourself, Mrs McClure,' Bertha, the housekeeper, insisted. 'I'll be glad to keep an eye on her. She's overtired, that's all. Too much rich food and excitement, if you ask me.'

That, or divine intervention! Clint wouldn't have the chance to worm incriminating information out of her daughter tonight, at least, and it occurred to Sharon that if she had any brains at all she'd steer clear of him, too. But the idea of spending the evening in Clint Bodine's company attracted her much as a flame drew a moth.

'What if she wakes up and needs me?' she murmured, leaning over Fern and making a last pitiful stab at being sensible.

'I'll phone the hotel,' Bertha said, shooing her towards the door. 'Go out and have some fun. Heaven knows you've earned a night off.'

Back in her own room, Sharon took stock of the clothes she'd brought with her. What had seemed more than adequate a week ago struck her now as woefully uninspired. The aquamarine shantung sheath embroidered with seed pearls was reserved for the wedding

54

itself. The fuchsia *palazzo* pants and matching top were strictly for evenings at the house.

The dress she had originally selected for the rehearsal dinner—a polished cotton rose-covered print with a crinoline skirt and portrait collar—no longer struck the right note. It was too blatantly romantic, too reminiscent of the naïve girl who'd flung herself at Clint Bodine ten years ago.

That left the all-purpose basic black. Pencil-slim skirt that just skimmed her knees, short sleeves, plain scoop neck. Black silk stockings, the old-fashioned kind held up with a scrap of lace that passed for a garter belt, and black peau-de-soie pumps with three-inch heels.

A very tasteful ensemble, no doubt, except that it left her looking like a Russian tragic heroine about to fling herself under the wheels of an on-rushing train, all pale-faced, hollow-cheeked and colourless—except for her eyes, which glowed like agitated fireflies. Something else was needed.

Searching through her accessories, she found a length of black chiffon, shot through with gold thread and spangled with coin-sized gold polka dots. Flung around her shoulders, it relieved her aura of impending doom. Plain gold jewellery, every last ounce eighteen-carat, hanging cool at her throat and ears added a touch of classic elegance which gave her confidence a badly needed boost. A splash of Paloma Picasso, a touch of coral lip gloss, a sweep of mascara, a feathering of blusher, and that was the best she could do, given her limited options. But if she didn't look like a million dollars, at least she no longer resembled someone draped in mourning.

The Tudor Room overlooked the river, and as it was such a fine, warm night tables had been set out on the tiled patio. At least thirty guests were already as-

sembled, and Clint didn't see Sharon arrive. Not that
he would have noticed had there been only a handful of
people present. He was too busy charming Margot's maternal grandmother, a lady who, at seventy-something,
was old enough to know better than to respond to such
overtures by flapping her eyelashes and cooing like a
teenager.

To her credit, the mother of the bride showed more
discernment, and continued to treat Clint with un-
dimmed disapproval. He might look disgracefully
handsome and distinguished in his pale grey suit, but it
took more than a European tailor and a few yards of
fine fabric to sway a woman like Vera Dunn. He was an
interloper at her daughter's wedding, not someone of
her choosing, and she was not about to forgive him
readily for being so crass.

It was an example she would do well to follow, Sharon
had to remind herself more than once as dinner pro-
gressed and Clint, beyond a brief greeting, paid her no
attention whatsoever. She might have excused him for
that, since the seating plan had her placed at a table
reserved for out-of-town relatives of the groom and other
nondescript hangers-on, while Clint, as one of the ushers,
was obliged to sit at the head table. But what she couldn't
forgive was his blatant enjoyment at finding himself
flanked by bridesmaids disposed to hang on his words
as if they had issued from the lips of the Almighty
Himself.

Calling on her extensive repertoire of social graces to
get her through the ordeal of the evening, Sharon tried
to ignore him. It wasn't easy. Despite her best efforts,
she found her glance turning repeatedly to where he
lounged with negligent grace between two pretty bridesmaids, found her ear attuned to the deep, lazy currents

of his laughter. And, worst of all, found herself almost gagging on the bitter dregs of jealousy at his attention not once straying to where she sat.

Dessert was served buffet-style. It was by accident with, perhaps, a little help from design that Sharon managed to wedge herself between Clint and one of his dinner companions, Margot's cousin Genevieve, who appeared too totally under his spell to notice she was in imminent danger of falling out of her low-necked dress.

'Please excuse me,' Sharon murmured, interspersing herself between Clint and the cleavage. 'I'd like to help myself to the fruit *compôte*.'

Clint managed to tear his gaze away from Genevieve long enough to spare Sharon a smile that amounted to little more than a grimace of his finely modelled lips. 'Perhaps I'll do the same,' he said. 'The raspberries are at their best just now.'

'I'd have thought cheesecake was more to your taste,' Sharon couldn't help muttering, with saccharin-coated venom. She was ashamed of herself, she truly was. Genevieve was a nice young woman; that she happened to be generously endowed was no reason to make her the scapegoat of an ex-wife's misplaced envy.

Clint was obviously of the same opinion. His hand closed over Sharon's wrist as she was about to spoon fruit into a stemmed dessert dish. 'Jealous, dear heart?' he enquired softly, his dark blue gaze settling on her with a certain sardonic amusement.

'Hardly!' she scoffed. 'Feast your eyes till they fall out of your head if it affords you pleasure, but don't exhaust yourself too soon. There must be at least five other women still waiting their turn to be ogled.'

'Well, as long as you're not one of them, what do you care?'

'I don't,' she said, and wished it were true. Yet the sad fact was, his words stung her to the quick.

'But?' His fingers continued to restrain her with easy, inflexible strength.

'There are no "buts",' she said, trying to shake him loose.

'Liar,' he mocked. 'You've looked as though you had a sour pickle lodged in your throat from the moment you got here tonight, and, since I'm probably the cause, why don't you spit it out and have done with—if you'll forgive the figure of speech?'

She'd cast sound judgement to the winds and forgive him almost anything—except showing a preference for the company of other women. She must be running a fever!

'I'm worried about Fern,' she improvised. 'You made such a monumental fuss over her yesterday that a person might have been forgiven for thinking you actually cared about her, but it seems to have escaped your notice that she's not here tonight.'

'Oh, I'd noticed,' he said calmly, 'but you *are* here, so there can't be much wrong with her.'

He was too clever for her by half, with a rebuttal ready almost before she'd had time to think up a response to his first charge. 'There isn't,' she admitted. 'She's over-tired, that's all, and so am I.' Catching him off guard, she twisted her wrist free and turned away from the buffet. 'And I've changed my mind. I don't want dessert, after all.'

'You've had enough of this shindig?'

'More than enough.'

Ignoring Mrs Dunn's glare of disapproval, he plopped his own portion of raspberries back into the serving bowl. 'So have I. Let's get out of here.'

'*Together*?' Sharon felt her jaw drop, and snapped it closed again in a hurry.

Clint sighed, as though she was testing his reserve of patience to the limit. 'Yes, *together*. *Alone* together! Or does that offend your sensibilities past bearing too?'

The unpalatable truth was that she'd been pining for his undivided attention all evening. Now that it was offered, however, pride prevented her from accepting it graciously. 'Well, heaven forbid I should be responsible for depriving your besotted fans of your nauseating attentions.'

Annoyance deepened his irises to near-midnight-blue. 'That was a cheap shot, dear heart. I was merely making pleasant conversation with my dinner partners, not stroking their knees under the table.'

This *was* the same man who, when she'd told him she'd miscarried their baby, had suggested that perhaps there'd never been any baby to begin with and that the entire history of her pregnancy had been just another lie to try to tie him to her. He hadn't always been as unflappably reasonable as he now appeared.

'I wasn't suggesting you were,' she said, choking back a hurt whose scars weren't nearly as well-healed as she'd believed.

'What are you doing, then? Trying to convince me that you've turned into a mean-mouthed, first-class bitch?'

'That's absurd!'

'I don't think so. For reasons I can't fathom, you seem determined to make me dislike you. Well, your strategy isn't working, so cut it out.'

'Don't give me orders. I'm not a child.'

'Then stop behaving like one.' His observant, unblinking stare made her regret having wished he'd make her the sole focus of his attention. 'You're a decent, kind woman under all that hostility, Sharon, and there's nothing wrong with letting it show. So stop being tiresome and let's get the hell out of here.'

He took her hand, slid it beneath his elbow, and secured it firmly by pressing her arm close to his side. 'And please,' he went on, 'stop staring at me as if you think I've got a lethal weapon hidden up my sleeve!'

'Give me back my hand,' she squeaked, tremors racing over her at the contact of his body against hers.

'Shut up,' he said, piloting her across the patio and over the lawn towards a gravelled path that ran beside the river.

She did, because it took all her concentration to keep her wits about her. The muscled discipline of his arm holding her fast evoked memories too potent to ignore, and it was all she could do to hide the fact that, left to its own devices, her body would wilt against his in a heap of willing, pliant flesh.

Clint appeared not to notice. The sun had gone down, and across the water the sounds from the fairground echoed faintly on the still air. 'Now what could be nicer than this?' he asked, looking around at the banks of flowering shrubs that soon shielded them from the hotel.

She struggled to come up with some acidic response, something that would at least restore a smidgen of prudence in her, even if it did reinforce his impression that she'd become poisoned with bitterness, but the fight was seeping out of her. Intellect could debate the wisdom of her actions till the earth stopped turning, but what was the use when her body felt so absolutely right snuggled up against his like that, and her heart felt whole for the first time in almost a decade?

'I can't think of a thing,' she replied, accepting what she'd suspected for the last several days: that being ten years older hadn't left her one whit wiser.

'We had too few moments like this,' Clint remarked quietly.

His ability to tune in to her thoughts in a way he'd never managed to do when they were husband and wife further weakened her in susceptibility. Her body relaxed, moulding itself ever more closely to the warm, firm strength of his. 'I know,' she said.

'I sometimes feel,' he went on, with an intensity that hinted at all manner of lonely regrets, 'that I'll spend the rest of my life trying to forget that we lost a child. If I could change just one thing, it would be for you to have carried that baby to term. I've often wondered, if you had, whether things might not then have turned out differently for us.'

They were softly spoken, kindly intended words, but they accomplished what her own impaired common sense had failed to do. The menace that had dogged her ever since she'd heard he was in town rose up like a spectre to fill her with new dread.

He sensed it at once. 'Don't pull away from me,' he begged, in a low, soothing voice. 'I understand that you can't feel the same way. You have Fern, and for you to wish that we'd found a happier ending together must be a bit like un-wishing those years that brought her into your life.'

But he didn't understand at all, Sharon thought despairingly. He didn't understand that every time he showed her kindness or tenderness he mired her deeper in a guilt she'd never expected to feel.

At the time of their separation, she'd been certain her actions had been justified. She'd seen herself as abandoned by a man too insensitive to comprehend the loss she'd suffered. Two months later, when she'd learned the incredible truth—that she'd conceived fraternal twins, lost only one of them, and showed every indication of carrying the second successfully—she had not for a moment thought of trying to find Clint and convey the news to him, too. She had gone ahead with the divorce, determined not to give him the chance to accuse her of entrapment a second time.

That perhaps she'd inflicted her share of wrong on him, or that she hadn't always understood him either, had never once occurred to her. She'd been so consumed by her own unhappiness that she'd had no energy to spare to think about how he might be coping. In fact he'd made it so plain that he was miserable in their marriage that she'd assumed he'd find nothing but relief in having it over and done with. The hindsight of now discovering that she'd misjudged him did nothing but give rise to a lot of useless regrets. She couldn't change history.

'It's too late for any of that,' she said, as much to herself as to him. 'And you're surely not saying you regret regaining the freedom to pursue those ambitions you had to put on hold when we married?'

He considered the question for so long that at first she thought he'd decided not to answer. 'I suppose I'm glad I had the chance to reconcile dreams with reality,' he finally acknowledged, 'but I don't know that I'll ever accept what it cost me.'

'You wanted to save the world from itself,' she reminisced, smiling a little at the memory of him as he'd been then, so full of heroic deeds waiting to be done, and so full of hope and optimism for what he could achieve that the world couldn't help but be a better place for his having touched it. 'You wanted to right all the wrongs, end all the oppression, fight for the underdog, defeat——'

'Spare me the clichés,' he cut in bitterly. 'I was an idealist who thought a twentieth-century Robin Hood was all it would take to change the course of history. I learned differently, and I find talking about it an infinite bore, so let's change the subject. What about you? Was success as grand and satisfying as you thought it would be?'

'Yes,' she said, because there was no way she could tell him that, if she hadn't found out about Fern, no amount of recognition or success would have made up for losing him. 'Yes, it was quite wonderful. I've been very lucky and very happy.'

He steered her over a footbridge that took them across the river and into the park. 'No regrets, then?'

None. Her lips formed the word. Every self protective instinct she possessed cried out for her to say it. He was looking down at the path in front of them, not at her, and it should have been easy to utter such a small white lie when she'd deceived him with far graver untruths. But she made the mistake of looking at his profile, at his dark, thick lashes, his strong jaw, at his mouth, which could turn so quickly from proud to passionate, from laughter to sorrow. And she found herself tongue-tied, unable to free either herself or him.

He knew it immediately. His hand settled in the small of her back, inching her closer despite her objection. 'Sharon?'

'No!' she whispered, still denying the truth. She'd married Jason—a good man, a kind man—had shelved dreams for reality, and exchanged romance for security. She had matured, accepted the cards that Fate had dealt her, and tried to make the best of them. It wasn't fair for adolescent longing to flare up again. Not fair and not wise.

'Don't be afraid of me,' Clint begged. 'I'm not the same man who hurt you before.'

That much was too clearly true. The years had left him twice as appealing, while events in between had wrought chasms neither of them could ever hope to cross. The magic might have intensified, but how could she condone falling in love with him all over again, after she'd robbed him of the right to know his own child?

'You don't understand,' she protested, with an appalling lack of conviction. 'I meant, "no, no regrets".'

They had reached the fairground. The crowds had thinned out, and some of the booths had already closed down.

'I don't believe you,' Clint said, slowing to a stop at the Ferris wheel, which was unloading the last of its passengers for the night.

The operator shook his head, ready to tell them they'd left it too late for a ride, but, turning his back to Sharon, Clint entered into brief conference with him.

Stuffing something into the back pocket of his boiler suit, the operator broke into a sly grin. 'Go ahead, Mister. It's all yours.'

Before she had time to realise what was happening, Sharon found herself led into the waiting carriage. 'I'm not riding on this thing!' she decided somewhat after the fact, as the operator snapped the safety bar into place.

'Oh, yes, you are,' Clint said, settling beside her and resting his arm along the back of the seat. 'I just bought two tickets.'

And with a creak they were off, swinging backwards and up through the dark, with nothing to anchor them to earth but the strains of the theme from *Moulin Rouge* wafting after them.

'Why are you doing this?' Sharon demanded, squirming as far away from Clint as possible in the confined space.

'Because I want you some place where you can't escape me,' he said, slithering after her. 'You've been running away from me ever since I got back to town, and it's time you stopped and told me why you're so afraid to be alone with me.'

'I was alone with you down there,' she protested, turning her head away and peering over the side of the carriage, because she thought anything was preferable to looking him in the eye.

She was wrong again. They were at the very top of the wheel, and the ground below appeared dizzyingly far away. She closed her eyes hurriedly, and prayed for fortitude and an early release from her present predicament.

Clint's hand closed over her shoulder with the weighty authority of a prison guard. 'Not really, Sharon. You were poised for flight the entire time, and if you could find a way out of here now you'd take it in a flash. However, since you are, in effect, my prisoner, I think you must reconcile yourself to providing me with a few answers.'

'I don't have to reconcile myself to anything,' she assured him tartly, opening her eyes and making a feeble attempt to resuscitate her will-power. 'This ride won't last forever.'

'No?' He raised his eyebrows. 'Perhaps you haven't noticed yet, but we aren't going anywhere.'

He was right. They were still poised at the top of the Ferris wheel. 'We've stopped,' she exclaimed, stating the absurdly obvious, and ventured another timid peek over the edge of the carriage. There was no one waiting to get on, and no one left to get off. The operator had retired to his little booth and was sitting with his feet propped up, a cigarette dangling from his mouth. She and Clint were completely alone, completely cut off from the rest of the world. 'Clint, we're the only people left on this thing, and it's not moving.'

He smiled at her gently. 'I know, dear heart. I bribed the man down there. Now stop stalling and let's get down to business.'

She felt her heart gain speed as apprehension took hold. 'What sort of business are you referring to?'

'When you heard I was back in town, why was your first instinct to run?'

'I didn't want...' She swallowed, searching for an acceptable half-truth. 'Didn't want the past dredged up again. It's too painful.'

'That's too bad,' he replied. 'I came back because I wanted to lay my ghosts to rest. It's been ten years, Sharon, and I'm tired of the same old nightmares. I'm thirty-seven, and wise enough to know you can't run away from yourself or your past. You can only come to terms with them.'

He sifted gentle fingers through her hair. 'You've grown into a fine and lovely woman, but you've also become my albatross, dear heart. I hoped, after a few months and a few women, that you'd have the good grace to fade a little from my mind, but you didn't. No matter where I went, nor how dangerous a mission I undertook, you stayed with me. A few times I found myself deliberately courting death because, somewhere between finding you and losing you, life lost its flavour. But I guess there's some truth to that old saying that only the good die young, because I survived regardless, and no amount of kamikaze foolishness altered the fact that we'd lost our child.'

She'd thought that letting him do the talking was the lesser of two evils, but it wasn't. It was heart-wrenching, and she couldn't bear the sorrow she saw carved on his mouth. 'Stop it,' she begged, on a frail, trembling breath. 'It doesn't help to rake over old hurts like this.'

'It doesn't help to hang on to them, either,' he said soberly, and brought his hand to rest at the base of her ear. 'I want you to set me free, dear heart.'

'How?'

'Tell me you're happy and that you've forgiven me, but make me believe it this time, because I can't carry this load of guilty baggage any longer.'

She, forgive him? 'Clint,' she begged, losing the battle with the tears that streamed down her face and turned all the lights of the fairground into one dazzling jewel of colour.

'Tell me, Sharon.'

She opened her mouth, willing to say anything to put an end to his pain, but all that came out was a sobbing wail. She tried to cover her face, but he imprisoned both her hands in his and held them patiently.

'Take a deep breath, then tell me,' he insisted.

She struggled for control. 'There's nothing to forgive,' she finally managed, brokenly. 'Please stop blaming yourself. Please forget about me. Be happy and go on with your life.'

'I can't do that, Sharon, unless you can convince me that you have no regrets about us and that what we once shared is a closed chapter in your life.'

She'd lied to him so many times before, either out of selfishness or fear; why was it so difficult to lie to him now out of kindness? 'I had forgotten you existed until you showed up here,' she whispered, closing her eyes, because he'd have seen the denial in them otherwise. 'You belong to another era and have no part in my present life at all.'

He let go of her hand, carefully cupped her jaw, and turned her face to his. 'Look at me,' he said.

She did. His eyes were very intent, his mouth very tender. 'I'd have to be brain-dead to believe you really mean that,' he murmured, inching his mouth to hers, hesitantly, experimentally almost.

Then, before either of them could react with the proper response, instinct leapt in and took control.

'Sharon . . . ?' he muttered urgently.

'Clint . . . ?' she breathed, as though to confirm a long-withheld dream.

He kissed her then, a wild, swirling kiss, full of rage for time lost, full of promise for time yet to come, full of hunger for the here and now. And the long, lonely years melted away.

It would always be that way between them. Always.

CHAPTER FIVE

MARGOT'S wedding-day promised buttery heat and silk-blue skies, probably because Mrs Dunn's threatened hysteria, should it have dared to rain, intimidated even the weather into co-operating.

The house hummed with activity all morning long as final preparations swung into high gear. If the phone wasn't ringing constantly, the doorbell was. Flowers, telegrams and last-minute gifts were delivered. In between occurred the sorts of minor crises without which no wedding worth its salt could possibly take place.

Mrs Dunn had no qualms about roping in Sharon to act as general dogsbody about the place, and Sharon was happy to oblige. Anything was better than having time to dwell on what had transpired between herself and Clint the night before.

She had no idea how long they'd remained marooned at the top of the Ferris wheel. How one kiss could drift so effortlessly into another, become charged with raging hunger, and deepen to shocking levels of intimacy in less time than it had taken her to sign her divorce papers, left her more than mystified.

If her brain's response to Clint's overture had been one of numbed astonishment, her body had undergone no such inhibition. Suffocating heat had raced through her. Her heart had turned into one vast echo chamber, its laboured beat thundering in her ears. A fine tremor had possessed her, leaving her quivering like a wind-tossed leaf in autumn.

His lips had been firm, warm, compelling. His tongue had been a devil, tempting her to sample forbidden pleasures. Even though he had insisted on nothing in return, her mouth had succumbed to the covert persuasion in his, offering whatever he chose to take.

He had chosen to take liberties. He had touched her, and she'd done nothing to stop him. His palms had slid down her jaw to her throat, embarking on a tactile exploration that, for all its skilled delicacy, invoked such a flood of arousal in her that she had felt near to choking. His fingertips had traced the scooped neckline of her dress, skimmed audaciously to her breasts. Her nipples had responded by blossoming with an eagerness that, in blushing retrospect, was downright wanton. And all the time his mouth had woven its wicked spells, seducing hers without mercy.

'Clint...!' Her protest had emerged as insubstantial as thistledown. She had swatted ineffectually at his hands.

'Hush,' he'd commanded against her mouth, and, instead of restraining him, she'd found her own hands changing course and settling on his chest with the tremulous joy of a lost traveller finding her way home.

She had relished the heat of his body under the cool silk lining of his jacket, had drowned in the scent that was his alone, a mixture of soap and starch and sandalwood. She had loosened his tie, undone his shirt buttons, run her fingers down the lean symmetry of his ribs, and revelled in the uneven acceleration of his heart.

He had repaid her in kind, falling victim to the same onslaught of passion that seared her. If the tiny voice of caution had attempted to speak to either of them, it had been swept rudely aside, completely vanquished by the raging hunger that possessed them.

That the whole encounter had occurred in a space too precarious and narrow to allow for much activity was entirely due to providence. Given more conducive surroundings, she'd probably have let him strip her naked and kiss every bare inch. She had shown, she decided in the cool disdain of hindsight, about as much moral fibre as a piece of cooked spaghetti.

Clint had come to his senses first, stymied more by her tight-fitting skirt than any other consideration, if his impressively articulate cursing had been anything to go by. But not before his wicked hand had forged a path up past her hem and found the strip of soft flesh where her silk stockings came to an end. She could never have looked him in the face again had he gone on to discover how embarrassingly damp and aroused she had become by the whole skirmish.

'You're pinning the corsage to my skin, Sharon!'

Mrs Dunn's pained shriek rescued her from memories too discomfiting to be borne. How could she have allowed an ex-husband such liberties? How could she have reciprocated with such unbridled enthusiasm?

'Sorry,' she mumbled, and managed to stab herself with the pin instead. 'Ouch!'

'Don't get blood on my gown, you inept fool!'

It was a description she deserved, albeit for reasons Mrs Dunn mercifully could never conceive. Given her prior record, she had to be an incredible fool to have believed that she could spend time in the company of Clint Bodine and retain control of her emotions. He had beguiled her once in the space of a few hours, and come close to doing so again.

'Stop dilly-dallying and get on with it, Sharon,' Mrs Dunn complained. 'The wedding's today, not next week. The limousines are waiting, and so is everyone else.'

Including Clint, Sharon thought in resignation.

Though fragrant with roses and jasmine, the church was dimly cool, unlike the day outside. Henrietta Barr, the organist, played Beethoven's 'Ode to Joy' without a single mistake, and followed it with an equally flawless rendition of Pachelbel's Canon in D, no doubt aware that a less than perfect performance would incur the full magnitude of Mrs Dunn's wrath.

Sharon, seated in the second pew on the left, fiddled with the diamond-studded bracelet on her wrist and prayed for the fortitude to survive the rest of the day without further compounding her errors or compromising her integrity. If God would grant her that much, she'd take responsibility for the rest of her life herself, starting tomorrow.

The next flight out of Crescent Creek left at noon tomorrow. Barring a major catastrophe on a par with the eruption of Krakatoa, she and Fern would be on that flight and Clint would again be consigned to the past, where he best belonged. However, if, between now and then, he was crass enough to gloat over what had transpired on that benighted Ferris wheel, she'd shove him and his rented suit head-first in the river.

Not that she really had cause to worry, she conceded wryly, as the grandmother of the bride paraded down the aisle on the arm of the chief usher, to the strains of a prelude by Bach. Apparently as anxious as she to forget the whole shabby incident, Clint was one of the few who hadn't phoned or dropped by the house that morning. She'd heard not a word from him since he'd left her at the Dunns' front door.

He'd been almost as uncommunicative when he'd brought her home, escorting her through the park and up the long driveway to the house in the sort of dazed silence that suggested he was at a complete loss to understand why he'd just succumbed to the same sort of crazy impulse that had landed him in a mess of married misery once before.

Once arrived on the doorstep, he'd taken her key from her hand and inserted it in the lock. It was the time when, given a normal man and woman in a normal situation, she might have asked him in for a night-cap. At the very least, she might have offered her cheek for a kiss. She'd done neither, fumbling her way instead through half a dozen attempts to voice a coolly poised dismissal that had emerged as a string of, 'I don't think—er... It would be best if—er... What I mean is...'

Pathetic!

At first he'd waited for her to wind down with the same weary patience he'd shown after their first sexual encounter ten years earlier. It was the most enduring emotion she seemed able to inspire in him once he'd had his way with her, she reflected gloomily.

Finally he'd cut short her babblings by articulating a strangled, 'Goodnight,' then beating such a hasty retreat that, if she'd pinned any hopes of a reconciliation on their furtive little scuffle above the fairground, they'd have died a fast death on the spot.

Since such an occurrence was not in any way a viable option, she was very glad. Just as she was very glad that when she had arrived at the church door a few minutes ago it had fallen to one of the other ushers to escort her to her seat. Clint had been occupied elsewhere—probably commiserating with the groom—for which she was truly grateful, because she didn't think she could have tolerated walking down the aisle on his arm. That particular stroke of irony would have shattered what frail composure she'd managed to recruit.

'Darling girl!' a familiar voice exclaimed in hushed tones, and Miss Celeste Bodine eased her chubby hips on to the pew beside Sharon. 'You look so lovely. Doesn't she look lovely, Jubilee?'

'A picture. She'll outshine the bride in that dress,' Miss Jubilee boomed, in such carrying tones that Sharon shrank in her seat. 'Don't you think so, Clinton?'

And there he was after all, leaning over his aunts with that charming blend of flirtatious solicitude that unfailingly endeared him to them, and so disgustingly handsome in his white jacket and black tie that Sharon feared she'd melt on the spot.

He looked her over, an evil glint in his larkspur-blue eyes. 'Quite possibly,' he agreed blandly, 'though whoever it was that claimed clothes make the woman missed the mark as far as I'm concerned. It's what lies underneath the outward trappings that really counts.'

Sharon flicked her gaze toward the altar, away from his face and that infuriating knowing smile. Oh, he'd wind up in the river yet!

Clint grinned, slid into the pew behind her, and leaned close enough that the perfume from the fresh violets pinned to the brim of her hat left him almost lightheaded. She stared straight ahead, doing an excellent job of projecting just the right degree of aloof displeasure. A less foolhardy man would have run for cover. He didn't budge.

'I know just what you're thinking,' he whispered in her ear. 'You find me an insufferable boor and would consider it a stroke of the utmost good fortune if I'd quietly slink back under my rock and stop embarrassing you in public.'

'Not just in public,' she muttered through clenched teeth. 'I find you obnoxious at all times.'

'Really?' He exhaled gently against her neck, and felt enormous pleasure when she shivered as though caught in the teeth of a winter gale. 'You have a funny way of showing it.'

'Unless there's a point you're trying to make with all this drivel, shouldn't you be attending to more pressing things, such as ushering guests to their proper places?' she enquired, sitting up a little straighter, squaring her shoulders more firmly, and jutting out her chin in a manner that suggested—in the politest possible terms, of course—that she'd like to roast him on a spit over red-hot coals.

She might have fooled most people, but he wasn't 'most people', and the sooner she accepted that, the better. He saw beyond that perfectly controlled, perfectly lovely facade, and he wasn't deceived for a minute. 'You can spend the rest of the day with your eyes fixed on the flower arrangements as though you expect dancing aphids to spring out at any minute, Sharon,' he said softly, 'but that won't deter me in the slightest.'

'I haven't the faintest idea what you're talking about.'

He lifted a skein of her hair and held it up to the multi-coloured light spilling through the stained-glass windows. It glimmered faintly blue-black, and slid between his spread fingers with the same fluid grace as its owner. She tried to yank herself free, but stopped short when she realised he still held her captive by a strand.

Disregarding Aunt Jubilee's less than subdued snort of glee, he leaned further under the wide brim of Sharon's hat and planted a soft kiss at the base of her ear. 'Do you really think that if you ignore me I'll be persuaded to forget what took place between us at the top of that Ferris wheel?'

'I had hoped you might,' she muttered stiffly.

He let go of her hair. 'Then you sadly underestimate me, dear heart,' he replied. 'What started out less than a week ago as a simple mission to unload my guilt and win your absolution has taken one unexpected turn too many.'

He stood up, did a smart about-turn, and marched back down the aisle, his grin fading into a gravity that more accurately reflected his true state of mind.

In the beginning he had hoped the surprise of his reappearance in her life would take her off guard and hand him an easy victory. What he had not foreseen was his own response to seeing her again, which was turbulent in a way he could neither have explained nor anticipated. So many women grew coarse and unkempt as they grew older—'let themselves go', as the aunts were fond of saying. But Sharon had grown lovelier, and no amount of self-scorn could repress his constant urge to look at her for the complicated pleasure it afforded him. He saw a remote dark-haired, green-eyed stranger who'd once been his wife and once—with tragic brevity—carried his child. He couldn't believe how painful he found that knowledge. Enter problem number one.

Her reaction to seeing him again in some ways struck an odder note still. She appeared weighed down by an even greater guilt than his. On top of that, she was desperate to hide the fact that she was clearly afraid of him. He remembered too well that peculiar brand of wily naïveté that had been her trademark at nineteen not to recognise it in more subtle form today. She was up to something, and it had to do with him. Enter problem number two.

However, since he was not a man to be easily discouraged, he'd laid a trap to outmanoeuvre her. He'd freely admit he had devious intent in mind when he'd arranged for the two of them to be marooned on top of the Ferris wheel. He'd been prepared to spend all night there if that was what it took to get the answers he was looking for.

He'd even gone so far as to decide that the shock effect of a kiss might surprise her into spilling out the secrets she seemed so determined to keep from him. And he'd been damn sure it was all that was needed to settle the ambivalent feelings that plagued him.

But things had gone awry with dismaying speed. A kiss hadn't been enough. A touch hadn't been enough. And when that icy control of hers had crumbled in the heat of a fervour she couldn't disguise, his game plan had backfired with startling consequences. What followed had played havoc with his emotions and hell with his hormones. Ten-year-old feelings had revived, fresh as yesterday. He hadn't been prepared for that, or the fear that suddenly had hold of him.

He didn't understand it. Here he was, a man who'd learned to live by his wits and reflexes—someone who could land an aeroplane on a field the size of a postage stamp, fulfil a mission, take off with enemy artillery blasting around him, and still keep a cool head. Yet the truth was this little bit of a woman scared him witless. He couldn't shake the suspicion that she held his future in the palm of her hand and could destroy him as easily as most people could swat a mosquito.

Enter problem number three, because, no matter how badly he wanted to, he couldn't shrug off the feelings, and he wasn't going to take them home with him when this week was over. He hadn't gone to all the trouble of

tracking her down just to exchange one load of hang-
ups for another.

She could wallow all she liked in outrage and chagrin,
but he wasn't going to be a good sport and disappear
until he'd come up with answers to all his questions.
And if she thought playing the Ice Maiden might dis-
courage him, she should have given it a try *before* last
night, because the performance came too damned late
to be convincing. He was more determined than ever to
get to the bottom of the mystery concerning his beautiful
ex-wife.

'The bride's arrived,' one of his fellow ushers informed him. 'The minister wants us to go around to the
side-door of the vestry, where Alan's waiting to be led
to the slaughter.'

'Good. It's time this show got rolling,' Clint said.

Henrietta Barr paused in her recital, and an expectant
hush fell over the congregation. The minister took up
his position; the groom strode bravely out of the waiting
area, accompanied by his attendants. Sharon took a deep
breath and turned her eyes firmly away from Clint. She
would not dignify his ambiguous little threats by sparing
them another thought.

The opening chords of the 'Trumpet Voluntary'
boomed forth, and the congregation turned to watch the
bridal procession. Fern came first, delicious in flower-
sprigged silk organza, and so starry-eyed with wonder
and excitement that Sharon vowed anew that she'd move
heaven and earth before she'd let anything hurt her
daughter. And it would hurt her, dreadfully, to discover
that Jason wasn't really her father.

Unbidden, Sharon's eyes swivelled to Clint in time to
catch him drop a slow outrageous wink at Fern, who

promptly burst into nervous giggles. The rest of the bridesmaids took up their places and waited for Margot, who drifted down the aisle on her father's arm, looking ethereal in a cloud of silk and lace.

The organ notes faded away as the minister began in one of those rich, solemn voices that lent dramatic impact to the most ordinary proclamations. Fern stared at him, mesmerised, seemingly convinced that he was possessed of supernatural powers. Margot and Alan locked gazes, oblivious to anyone but each other. Mrs Dunn started to cry in the restrained, well-bred sort of fashion acceptable on such occasions. Miss Celeste smiled, and Miss Jubilee blew her nose with the vigour of a trumpeter swan.

Clint chose to stare at Sharon unblinkingly. He had no manners at all, she decided, and tried to look away, but the familiar words of the traditional marriage ceremony reached out to haunt her.

'An honourable estate, not to be enterprised unadvisedly, lightly, but reverently, discreetly...'

'...If you're pregnant, I suppose we'd better not waste any time getting married...'

'Don't feel obligated. I'm a modern, independent woman, and I promise my father won't come after you with a shotgun,' she'd said, knowing full well that she was terrified both at how her parents might react and at what the future held. What she most needed at that moment was to have Clint tell her he loved her and that he was happy and proud to acknowledge her as his wife.

Unlike her, though, he felt under no compunction to mince words. 'There were other things I had in mind, I admit, but...'

'Into which holy estate these persons present come now to be joined...'

She'd never forget her own wedding day. Not joyful with summer sunshine, like this one of Margot's, nor even angry with storms, but prophetically grey and overcast. Sullen. A man and a woman taking part in a ceremony not blatantly happy but prudently furtive, and left trapped in a marriage filled with guilt and resentment.

For the first time she'd fully understood the import of that damning word, 'entrapment'. But she'd been too young and cowardly to set Clint free and had justified the union by saying that she loved him too much to lose him. Now she knew that if she'd really loved him enough she'd have let him go.

From his position near the altar, Clint stared at her unwaveringly. She tried again to tear herself free. Once again, he refused to release her.

Not normally given to paranoid fantasies, Clint couldn't escape the feeling that the words being directed at Alan and Margot were really intended for him.

'Wilt thou have this woman . . . love her, comfort her, honour, and keep her in sickness and in health . . . ?'

What a pitiful failure he'd been at that, too busy being furious at himself for his irresponsible bachelor's ways two months earlier, instead of focusing on his husbandly obligations now. Sharon had been plagued by morning sickness, and he'd been glad to get away from the house for days at a time, because the sight of her pale little face left him feeling like a brute. So much for looking after her 'in sickness and in health'.

As for comforting her . . . She'd miscarried in the apartment that he'd rented in a house a few streets removed from his aunts' place. He hadn't been there at the time, of course, and by the time he got back to town he'd found her paler and more fragile than ever. And more unreachable.

'To my wedded wife, to have and to hold from this day forward...'

Much later that night, when he'd thought she was asleep, her voice had come out of the darkness, full of pain and sadness.

'There's no reason for us to stay married now, is there?'

'I suppose not,' he'd said, and assumed that it was his own sense of loss that made the prospect of freedom seem less thrilling than he'd expected.

'What will you do?'

'Pick up where I had to leave off, I guess. What about you?'

'Go on with my apprenticeship,' she'd said. 'It doesn't start until the beginning of the year, so I haven't missed anything.'

She was just a schoolgirl, he'd thought, and he'd hurtled her into womanhood in the most painful way possible. 'Will you be all right? About losing the baby, I mean.'

Her voice had been full of a grief he hadn't wanted to hear. 'It's probably for the best. Neither of us has been happy these last few weeks.'

But it hadn't been for the best, because they'd both been haunted by what they'd lost, not just in terms of their child, but in the snuffing out of a relationship that, given proper time to grow, might have withstood the worst that life had to throw at it.

She was remembering, too. Across the aisle, her eyes shone greener than water, full of tears. Wounded. By him. To his horror, his own vision blurred and he had to look away.

CHAPTER SIX

THE reception was a nightmare. It seemed to take forever before the speeches were over and the dancing finally began. By the time Clint led Fern on to the floor, the strain of seeing him once again thrown into such proximity with his own daughter threatened to unhinge Sharon.

Allowing a barely decent interval to elapse, she made the move to put an end to her misery. 'May I cut in?'

'You want to dance with me?' Clint's raised eyebrows betrayed his astonishment at her request.

Not really, she felt like replying, but I've had enough of standing helplessly by and leaving my daughter at the mercy of your not so harmless questions.

Fern had walked down the aisle on her father's arm after the ceremony, both of them looking absurdly pleased with the arrangement. She and Clint had posed side by side for the photographer, thereby fixing in perpetuity a similarity in their smiles that Sharon had never before noticed but which now seemed glaringly apparent. Fern had sat next to Clint at the endless seven-course dinner. And throughout, the best Sharon had been able to do was try to lip-read from a distance and pray Fern wasn't indicting her mother by exposing a minefield of information to Clint's scrutiny.

So, 'I'd love to dance with you,' she said, 'if you don't mind, honey.'

'Not a bit,' Clint said.

'I wasn't asking you,' Sharon snapped. 'I was asking Fern.'

'Mommy wouldn't call you "honey".' Fern giggled. 'She doesn't know you enough.'

'You're absolutely right, sweet pea,' Clint agreed, the smile he bestowed Sharon's way reminiscent of a hungry barracuda on the prowl. 'Mommy doesn't know me nearly as well as she thinks she does. Shall we dance, Sharon?'

'I won't be long,' Sharon told Fern, and submitted to having Clint loop his arm around her waist as though they were on the best and most familiar of terms.

Fern examined the sight with frank approval. 'Be long,' she recommended. 'I'll be all right. I'll dance by myself and make my dress spin out like this, see?' And she executed a pirouette to demonstrate.

'It might be better if you found a less crowded spot to do that,' Sharon suggested. 'You'll crash into someone otherwise.'

'And end up flat on your bum.' Clint widened his eyes and made a face to great comic effect, sending Fern into paroxysms of mirth.

'Mommy doesn't let me say "bum",' she squeaked, taking immediate advantage of the chance to do just that. 'She says it's not a word ladies use.'

Sharon tried to keep a straight face. 'Especially not in polite society.'

'Then I guess I owe you and Mommy an apology.' But Clint didn't look sorry, and Sharon could feel the laughter shaking him. 'Why don't you practise your pirouettes outside while I dance with her and try to make amends?'

'But stay close to the clubhouse, where I can see you,' Sharon cautioned her.

The minute they were alone, Clint's arm snaked more resolutely around her waist and drew her a good deal closer than Emily Post would have considered proper. It felt divine.

'It was a lovely wedding service, wasn't it?' Sharon asked brightly, hoping to disguise the giddy discombobulation he invoked.

'Take that phoney smile off your face,' he growled back. 'It doesn't suit you or the occasion. And no, it was a lousy wedding service, at least as far as you and I were concerned. So lousy, in fact, that you cried.'

Trust him to have noticed! And what did he mean— 'It doesn't suit the occasion'? What had he discovered? 'Women always cry at weddings,' she said guardedly, her smile evaporating.

'But not for the reasons that your eyes were swimming, dear heart,' he replied, sweeping her into a reverse turn, then bending her backwards in a Clark Gable dip that demonstrated a superb mastery of dance techniques, regardless of what he'd once told Fern. 'They weren't tears of happiness. They were brought on by the unhappy memory of our own less than glamorous nuptials.'

She clutched the silk lapel of his jacket with her free hand and stifled a squeak. 'As if I still care!' she gasped, as much in relief that they were on a safe topic as the fact that he'd almost literally swept her off her feet.

He straightened her up again without missing a beat. 'Stop playing cute games, Sharon. You'd have to be some sort of saint not to resent that shabby little ceremony we called a wedding. As I recall, you didn't have even a bouquet, let alone a long white gown or a veil. You wore a pale green dress and your grandmother's pearls. And your parents were very disapproving.'

'You wore grey trousers with a navy blazer,' she said soberly, surprised that he should have remembered. 'And while my parents looked positively stony-faced, your aunts smiled and cried at the same time. Afterwards we went back to their house and they served us a lunch of cold salmon and a wedding-cake that they'd made themselves and decorated with fresh flowers from the garden.'

'But your family didn't join us.'

'No,' she said, long since resigned to the alienation from her parents that had never fully healed. 'They had to rush back to catch a flight to Florida, where my father was playing in a golf tournament.'

Clint's voice was almost tender. 'You didn't have much to make the day special, did you?'

I had you, she wanted to tell him, and you were all I ever wanted. Not even her mother's outrage or her father's disappointment had been enough to make her doubt that. 'There wasn't time for anything more elaborate, and it wouldn't have been appropriate, given the circumstances.'

He held her slightly away from him so that he could search her face. 'What circumstances are those?'

As if he couldn't guess! Once her parents had learned of her condition, all their plans for a society wedding on their home turf had been abandoned. 'I absolutely could not face people,' her mother had exclaimed, wrinkling her aristocratic nose in distaste. 'I suppose we should be grateful that you've retained enough decency to get this charade of a wedding out of the way before you start to show.'

'I was the pregnant bride of an unwilling bridegroom,' Sharon said baldly, meeting Clint's gaze without flinching. 'Hardly what you'd call cause for celebration.'

'Did you feel terribly cheated, Sharon?' he asked, and although his expression remained the same there was a world of sadness in his voice.

'If I did,' she said carefully, touched more than she cared to admit, 'I got over it when I became Jason's wife. At least he wasn't coerced into marrying me.'

'I wasn't exactly dragged to the altar kicking and screaming the whole way, you know.'

'You realise, of course,' her mother had declared with daunting certainty, 'that the only reason that man is doing the right thing by you is the fact that your father would horse-whip him if he refused?'

'You weren't exactly over the moon about it, either,' Sharon said, snuffing out her mother's unpleasant contention. 'And afterwards there was so much unspoken resentment that it was like a wall between us. You were very unhappy with me, Clint.'

'I was unhappy with *me*,' he said. 'I blamed myself for the mess we were in.'

She didn't want to get started on the topic of blame. It opened too many doors she had to keep closed. 'Why don't we just forget it? It all happened a long time ago.'

He manoeuvred them to a corner of the dance-floor that was less crowded. 'Don't try to palm me off with platitudes like that, for Pete's sake! It's bothered me ever since we separated that I didn't see the hazards soon enough to steer us around them. There might have been magic between us, Sharon, if things had started out differently. Instead, we wound up in a union held together by guilt and baling wire. If ever a couple came into marriage for all the wrong reasons, we did. We ended up blaming each other, and looking for excuses to walk away from it all.'

'We both made mistakes,' she said, 'and we can't change them at this late date, any more than we can turn back the clock. Too much has happened since for that to be possible.'

'I didn't go to the trouble of tracking you down with the expectation that we could,' he assured her deflatingly. 'All I hoped was that time and distance would give us the perspective to talk things over without recrimination, that we might somehow absolve each other for our sins of omission and commission and, in the full realisation that there's never any way of going back, at least lay the past to rest and find some peace.'

But the past and the present had become so hopelessly intertwined since he'd walked back into her life that Sharon didn't know if her conscience would ever allow her another day's real peace. 'At the risk of annoying you with yet another platitude,' she said, the hope that he might agree feeble, to say the least, 'sometimes it's better to let sleeping dogs lie.'

'A week ago, I'd have said that was certainly a possibility,' he said, 'but then I saw you again and some very strange things started to happen, Sharon—and please don't insult my intelligence by pretending you don't know what I'm talking about.'

Alarm shot through her because she *didn't* know for sure; that was the whole problem. Had Fern let drop some piece of information that had set in motion a dangerous curiosity on his part? Or was he referring to other kinds of feelings—the sexual sort that flared between a man and a woman, torching the atmosphere with electricity? The sort that Sharon was finding increasingly disturbing and hard to ignore.

She risked a peek at his face and decided that if he had the slightest suspicion that Fern was his daughter his primary response would be one of rage rather than regret. His words would be flaying her alive, not sweeping over her in sensual waves.

'It's just nostalgia,' she said, with false airiness. 'It happens all the time at weddings. You see a couple as happy as Margot and Alan and you can't help making comparisons and wishing the same for your own life. Silly, isn't it, when the feelings just aren't there any more?'

He pulled her closer and wrapped his arm more tightly around her waist. Without releasing hers, he brought his other hand up and with his forefinger raised her chin, then bent his head so that they were dancing almost nose to nose. 'Aren't they?' he asked, his sexy, husky voice sending her heart into a series of pixilated cartwheels. 'Are you sure?'

'What . . . ?'

'I kissed you last night,' he said, dipping his head further under the wide brim of her hat, so that his lips were close enough to graze hers, 'half expecting to get my face slapped for it. But you kissed me back.'

'I did not!' She floundered to bring her coping strategies into play, to appear coolly amused instead of indignantly juvenile. 'My lips were in the way, and you took advantage of them.'

She felt the laughter rumble through his chest. His hand stroked up her spine to the back of her neck. 'This is a lovely bit of nonsense you're wearing,' he countered, dancing her on to the long covered veranda of the clubhouse, 'but it has to go.'

And before she could guess his intent or prevent him, he plucked the straw hat from her head and sent it, Devon violets and all, sailing into the flowerbed in the garden below. 'That's better,' he said complacently. 'Now

I can see the lies in your eyes before your mouth gets around to uttering them.'

'What I meant to say,' she amended, stumbling over the words, 'was that you took me by surprise, that's all. If I'd had the slightest inkling of what you had in mind, I *would* have slapped your face.'

'That still doesn't explain why you responded as you did, with a fervour that revived ten-year-old feelings and made them seem fresh as yesterday. I've kissed a lot of women since you and I were a couple, dear heart——'

'Oh, please!' she exclaimed, happy to find herself on solid ground at last. 'Spare me an account of your conquests. I'm really not interested, nor are they any of my business.'

'And not one of them,' he continued, unperturbed by her outburst, 'affected me quite like that little exchange of last night.'

'It's just as well. The sort of liberties you were taking—in a public place, no less—could have landed you in jail.'

'You have that sort of impact on me,' he replied drily. 'I tend to forget all about propriety when I get close to you. Take now, for example. I'm intensely conscious of your lovely body next to me, Sharon. I can feel your breasts, the movement of your hips, the brush of your thighs against mine, and, while I'm somewhat abashed at the results all this proximity is having on me, you ought to be gratified.'

'You're indecent...!' she objected, but faintly, because the truth was that propinquity was unleashing devastation on her, too.

'Not to mention despicable,' he agreed, with unruffled good humour, given his previous admission.

'You ought to be ashamed,' she said.

'No, *you* ought to be, because at least I'm honest enough to admit to how I feel, whereas you . . .' He gave her a little shake, but his voice caressed her. 'You, dear heart, pretend you are unmoved when, in fact, you're terrified. The question is, of whom? Me?' He slipped both arms around her waist and drew her snugly against him from chest to knee with potent effect. 'Or of yourself? Which is it, and why, my darling ex-wife?'

Sharon's heart swelled. He made confession sound so easy, and she wished that it were. She ached to be rid of all the deceit, to tell him, 'Fern's your daughter,' but it wasn't the right time. It never *would* be the right time for her and Clint.

He was watching her closely, but she was rescued from having to answer by a high-pitched scream floating up from the gardens. 'Mommy, Mommy!'

Fear washed over Sharon, momentarily paralysing her. 'That's Fern!'

'Good God, what's the matter with her?' Clint gripped her shoulders almost painfully.

Inside the clubhouse the music played on, punctuated by laughter and the clink of crystal on crystal.

'Mommy!' The shriek came again, galvanising both of them to action.

Racing to the waist-high parapet, Sharon leaned over, unmindful of her own safety. 'I'm coming, sweetheart. Where are you?'

Sobbing screams greeted her, electrifying in their distress. Spurred by the knowledge that her child was in terror or pain, and without thought for her own safety, Sharon grabbed at one of the slender stone columns supporting the veranda roof and tried to hurl herself over the parapet, intent only on reaching Fern's side.

She'd made but minor headway before panic seemed to turn her limbs leaden with fear. She lost her impetus and found herself immobilised, with both feet swinging wildly in the air. She could feel nothing but a constriction around her ribs and waist. She could hear nothing but Fern's desperate cries, carried to her in waves as the blood rushed and receded in her ears.

And then, suddenly, sharply, a hand wrenched her head around and Clint's face swam into bleary focus. 'It's a ten-foot drop to the garden, Sharon. Breaking your own neck isn't going to save Fern's,' he said, his voice as firm as his arm hauling her back to the slate floor of the veranda.

'I have to go to her!'

'Of course you do,' he said, 'but not that way.' And, taking her by the hand, he ran with her along the veranda to the steps that led to the grounds below.

Someone else had already found Fern. One of the waiters was crossing the stretch of lawn towards them, carrying her in his arms. An older woman—a guest whom Sharon didn't know—hurried along at his side. By then, Fern's screams had subsided to wheezing sobs.

'She'll be all right, ma'am,' the waiter said to Sharon.

'I came outside to admire the roses, and suddenly heard her scream and saw her struggling on the grass near the flowers over there, so I called for help,' the woman panted. 'I don't know what happened to her.'

Clint studied clusters of angry red lumps on Fern's arms and neck, then rolled back the hem of her dress to inspect her legs. 'I do,' he said, 'and she's not all right at all.'

Fern, her eyes huge and glassy, sought and found Sharon's face. 'Mommy, I hurt,' she whispered on a fractured breath. 'I don't have any air.'

'Should we call an ambulance, do you think?' the woman enquired nervously.

'Yes, please,' Sharon whispered, stroking the hair away from Fern's forehead. Her skin felt clammy and her breathing was frighteningly shallow. 'Fern, darling, what happened?'

'She's been stung by wasps or bees,' Clint said tersely, gesturing for the waiter to hand her over to him, then striding towards the car park on the far side of the club- house. 'A whole nest of them, from the looks of it. Forget calling an ambulance; there isn't time.'

Cursing her high, impractical heels, Sharon stumbled to keep pace with him. 'How do you know?'

'I just do,' he said. 'Trust me.'

He was Fern's father, but he didn't know that. He was, to all intents and purposes, a man who'd come back to free himself once and for all from the last vestiges of a marriage that had been a disaster from the first; the same man who'd walked away from her once before when she needed him terribly. There was no reason in the world for her to trust him now, and a week ago she'd have laughed at the very idea. Yet she trusted him anyway. There was no one else she wanted by her side at that moment.

'I do,' she said, 'but Clint, I'm frightened. Why is she breathing like that?'

'Shock.' He shifted Fern to his left arm, and jutted out his right hip. 'My car keys are in here somewhere, Sharon.'

She fumbled in his jacket pocket. 'Yes, I've got them.'

'Open the doors and get in the back seat. Do you know anything about CPR?'

She scrambled inside the car, panic skittering up her spine. 'You mean artificial respiration?'

'Call it whatever you like, as long as you know how to use it.'

'Why?' She heard the shrill edge of hysteria in her voice, fought its gathering momentum.

He loaded Fern on to the back seat and rested her pale little face in Sharon's lap. 'Because this is an emergency. You have to keep a really close eye on her. Check her pulse, her breathing.'

'Her breathing?' Fear surged in Sharon's throat, bitter to the taste. This couldn't be happening! A child—*her child*—did not go from robust good health to deadly danger in the space of a few minutes, not from a bee-sting.

Clint heard the underlying terror. 'Get a grip, Sharon. This is no time to fall apart. Your daughter's life depends on your staying calm.'

'I will.' She struggled for control, drew in a massive, shaking breath. 'I will. Tell me what I should do.'

'Watch her, and be ready to resuscitate her if you have to.'

At that, the panic tore free. 'My God, Clint——!'

'*Watch her*, I said! Keep her airway clear.' Slamming closed the back door, he flung himself into the driver's seat and fired up the engine. 'You can collapse later.'

The car surged forward, spitting gravel from under its tyres and screaming around the curve of the driveway. When they reached the road Clint leaned on the horn and didn't let up until the flashing red light of the Emergency entrance to the Crescent Creek Cottage Hospital reflected off the windscreen.

The noise had alerted the staff. Within seconds Fern was hustled inside on a stretcher. A team of doctors ran beside her, monitoring her vital signs. Clint stayed close, relaying information in concise and logical order.

Sharon crawled out of the car and sagged against the open door. She would have berated herself for the weakness that allowed her to let him take her place at her daughter's side, but she was too busy offering prayers for Fern's recovery to worry about so trivial a point of order.

'Your husband asked me to come and get you. Would you like a wheelchair?' A woman in a pink flowered smock appeared at her side, concern and understanding evident in her soft brown eyes. 'You look a little faint, you know.'

'I'll be fine.' Though it was all Sharon could do to stand upright, the shock was wearing off, displaced by a burning anxiety that focused with sharper cruelty on the reality of what had happened in the course of the last fifteen minutes. 'I just need to be with my daughter, that's all.'

'Yes, of course.' A sympathetic hand slipped around her elbow and guided her inside the building. 'But first you have to give the admissions clerk some information about your little girl. The more we know about her, the better we can help her.'

It took forever. Sharon's patience was in rags long before the last item of personal history had been collated. When she was finally free, Clint was beside her, his expression drawn.

The mere act of voicing the question assaulted her like a physical blow. 'How is she?'

'It's as I thought,' he said, walking her to a couch in an alcove and pressing her into it. 'She disturbed a wasps' nest and got stung about fifteen times.'

Sharon looked at him, searching to find the answer she most needed to hear but was afraid to ask for. Instead she skirted around the subject. 'You talked about resuscitating her, Clint. You didn't want to wait for an ambulance.'

'I know,' he said. 'When I saw that she was having trouble breathing, I realised she could be suffering anaphylactic shock. There——'

'*Anafill-what*?' She'd never before heard the word, couldn't so much as repeat it properly, let alone begin to spell it, but the sound of it struck new terror in her heart. 'What's that?'

'I'm not a doctor, Sharon; I'm just guessing. You're better off to wait and get the facts from someone qualified to explain it all to you.'

But hearing from the experts in no way mitigated the gravity of Fern's condition. Sharon had only to look at Clint to know that. The blue of his eyes looked almost bruised, as though he hated having to share his fears with her.

The inevitable question hammered inside her head, refusing to go unanswered. 'Is she going to die, Clint?'

The minute she'd asked, she'd have done anything to unsay the words. Giving them voice allowed them too much power and did terrible things to her faith. What would she do without Fern? How would she ever go on?

Everything she felt must have been written on her face, because Clint squatted down on his heels in front of her and held her, sustaining her with his strength and sanity. His warm, husky voice washed over her with more kindness than she had any right to expect from him. 'No, she isn't! I won't let anything happen to your baby, dear heart; you can count on that.'

The irony of his softly spoken words completely undid her. She collapsed against him and burst into tears that she thought would never end.

CHAPTER SEVEN

CLINT had wanted her to lower her guard, but not like this, to the point of utter devastation. The way she felt in his arms—like a crushed flower that someone had trampled carelessly underfoot—filled him with the profound urge to kill anything that threatened her.

'Sweetheart,' he begged, over and over, all the time pressing her face to his shoulder and stroking the crown of her head. 'Sweetheart, it's going to be all right.'

'Please don't let her die,' she sobbed, her voice muffled against his neck.

'I won't,' he promised, and vowed that he'd go toe to toe with God Himself on that pledge if need be. He hadn't been able to prevent her losing her first child, but he'd rearrange the heavens before he'd let the same thing happen to her second. That little girl in there was going to recover. He would allow no other settlement.

He slewed his gaze over to where the curtain drawn hastily across the cubicle where Fern was being examined had snagged at one corner against a chair. It permitted him just enough of a view to see the intravenous solution dripping into her arm, the tube feeding oxygen through her nostrils. She looked pale, but she was breathing on her own, and that, as he well knew, was a good sign.

Only then did he become aware of the hard lump of tension easing in his own chest. What a lovely child she was! If only Sharon would let him, he could love both mother and daughter so easily.

Perplexed, dismayed, he backed away from that thought. How the hell had those two momentous little words, 'If only', slipped by his guard, not to mention the implications that came with them? His mission was to find freedom for his heart, not fetter it more securely in captivity. Compassion he could afford, but love?

'Mr McClure? I'm Barbara Palliser, the attending physician for your daughter.'

Clint looked up at the woman who came to a stop beside them. 'I'm not the husband,' he said, battered by another wave of shock at the realisation that he hated the fact that Sharon no longer bore his name. 'I'm just a friend of the family.' He indicated Sharon. 'This is Fern's mother.'

The sound of a stranger's voice penetrated Sharon's distress. She raised her head. Her lovely green eyes were dazed with grief and worry. 'Fern . . . ?' she breathed on a creaky whisper, as though her throat were raw.

'She's responding well to medication, Mrs McClure.'

'But is she out of danger?' Clint asked, aware that such reassurance was the only thing that would temper Sharon's anguish and make it bearable.

The semi-evasive reply enraged him. 'She's suffering a very severe allergic reaction to wasp venom,' the good doctor hedged.

If she adds that the patient's doing as well as can be expected, Clint thought savagely, I'm going to lose it and say something socially unacceptable that will probably get me booted out of here and do Sharon no damn good at all!

Either Barbara Palliser was a mother herself or she possessed telepathic powers, because she went on to offer a much more satisfactory prognosis. 'But yes, she's out of danger and we have every reason to expect she'll make a full recovery, Mrs McClure. We'd like to keep her overnight for observation, though.'

'But other people's children get stung all the time, and they don't have to be hospitalised,' Sharon protested, shaking her head in the same bewildered way that people caught in the middle of a battle zone were apt to do. Disbelieving; almost catatonic.

'When they respond as your daughter did, they certainly do,' Dr Palliser assured her. 'I gather this is the first time she's been stung, or you'd already know that. Hers isn't the usual localised painful swelling that most people suffer with an insect bite, but a systemic reaction that is extremely dangerous—what we call anaphylactic shock. It can be fatal, Mrs McClure, and you'll have to make sure she carries an anti-venom kit with her all the time from now on, in case she gets stung again.'

It was too much for her to take in, coming so soon after that nightmare drive to get here. Clint thought Sharon was going to keel over. Her face turned ashen and, if her eyes had been huge before, they seemed to double in size, dwarfing her face.

'You were right,' she said, turning her horrified gaze on him. 'You saved her life, Clint.'

The doctor nodded. 'Yes, he did.'

'And now I'm going to save yours,' he said, pulling Sharon to her feet. 'I'm taking you home. You're exhausted.'

'Good.' The doctor offered a brief, sympathetic smile. 'We don't have too many emergency booths in a hospital this size, and you do look about ready to collapse, Mrs McClure. Check with us in the morning and we'll let you know when you can come and get your daughter.'

'I want to see Fern *now*,' Sharon announced. 'I want to see for myself that she's going to be all right.'

'Of course.' Dr Palliser nodded. 'But just for a couple of minutes. Come with me.'

Clint wasn't sure if the permission extended to him, too, but Sharon clutched his hand so tightly that he had little choice but to accompany her to Fern's bedside.

Sensing their presence, the child opened her eyes and offered a sweet, sleepy smile that almost tore his heart out. Who wouldn't love her?

Her mother bent over her, crooning softly. He watched for a little while, until Fern drifted back to sleep, then touched Sharon on the shoulder. 'Time for you to get some rest, too, Sharon.'

She straightened and turned to face him, the tears shimmering. 'I'm staying here,' she quavered—predictably enough, Clint supposed, given her almost obsessive concern for Fern even when the child was well.

But if she didn't recognise how close to breakdown she was, he did, and he'd had enough medical emergencies for one night. 'No, you're not,' he informed her, with the sort of autocratic determination he'd used when airlifting shell-shocked refugees to safety, and led her firmly out of the cubicle. 'I'm quite prepared to carry you out of here if I have to, but I will not let you spend the night on a vinyl couch in a hospital waiting-room, not when you've got a perfectly good bed back at the Dunns'.'

She opened her mouth to argue, but he stopped her by raising his hand point-duty-officer-fashion. 'That's the way it's going to be, Sharon, so save the objections.'

And just to demonstrate that he was quite willing to back up the threat with action, he swung her off her feet and into his arms.

She sagged against him, most of the fight going out of her. 'I don't want to go to the Dunns',' she said in a surprisingly meek voice.

'Why not?'

'Mrs Dunn will never forgive me for stealing the limelight on Margot's wedding-day.'

'The reception's only half over. Vera Dunn is still holding court at the country club and probably not even aware of our little drama.'

'I still don't want to go back to her house. Sooner or later, someone is sure to tell her that Fern's had an accident, and I'm not up to being reproached for having allowed a minor player to upstage the bride.'

'You're overreacting. Margot would never look at it that way.'

'Margot wouldn't—but her mother would.'

Clint couldn't suppress a grin. Sharon was right; Vera Dunn could be a real piece of work when she put her mind to it. 'She is about as irritating as a buzz-saw at times,' he agreed, 'so I can't say I blame you for wanting to avoid her. The question is, though, where would you like to stay instead? With all the people staying in town for the wedding, I imagine the hotel is full.'

To his astonishment, Sharon linked both arms around his neck in the first spontaneous gesture of trust she'd shown him thus far. 'I don't want to be alone, Clint. Tonight I need to be with someone who understands.'

Don't read more into that than she intends, Bodine, he warned himself. The woman's at the end of her rope and is looking for a little brotherly comfort. Raging hormones have no place in this little scenario. 'No problem,' he said, with a good deal more equanimity than he felt. 'The aunts have rooms to spare. You can stay with us.'

*   *   *

The house was just as she remembered it, with down-cushioned window-seats and sofas so soft that a person could sink into them and almost disappear. A huge bouquet of fresh flowers filled the empty hearth in the parlour; bowls of home-made pot-pourri sat on the antique tables. Old photographs of Clint, some going as far back as his babyhood, covered the walls and the top of the spinet piano. The air smelt of lavender and beeswax, and lace curtains hung at the polished panes of the windows.

There was none of the formal splendour of the Dunns' country estate to be found here, nor any of the chic art nouveau elegance of her own parents' city villa, but there was a warmth and comfort that made it a home, right down to the basset hound that ogled her out of amorous, bloodshot eyes. Too large to be a cottage and too small to qualify as a mansion, the aunts' house rambled much like the roses climbing around the covered porch, wandering off into quiet nooks and landings furnished with fat chintz armchairs and reading lamps—quiet places where a person could escape into her own thoughts and be alone without feeling lonely.

It had embraced Sharon ten years ago and it didn't disappoint her now. The minute she walked in the door, she felt the horror of the last two hours begin to recede.

'How about a brandy?' Clint stood in the entrance to the parlour and watched her as she wandered about the room, touching familiar things and renewing herself.

'Actually,' she said, chafing the goose-flesh that crawled over her bare arms, 'what I'd really like to do is get out of these clothes and into something warmer.'

Seed pearls and aquamarine shantung were a fine combination for a wedding, but they didn't lend themselves well to the aftermath of trauma. What she needed was one of Aunt Celeste's hand-quilted robes to erase the chill that had nothing to do with the weather.

Clint was of a similar mind. 'Go soak in a hot bath, then wrap yourself in one of those dressing-gown things that are always kept in the guest-room wardrobe,' he said, waving a hand toward the broad spiral stairway, 'and, while you're gone, I'll fix us a snack. You'll feel better once you eat something.'

'I'm not hungry, and I don't know how you could be, either.'

'Stress gives me an appetite.' He slapped at his flat stomach, as if she needed a reminder that he was as lean and hard today as he had been a decade ago. 'Go on— scoot! Use the blue room; it's got its own bathroom. You remember where it is—to the right of the first landing?'

How could she forget the blue room? It was where she'd spent her wedding night. 'The honeymoon suite', the aunts had called it, clucking and smiling and trying terribly hard to be discreet when she and Clint had finally gone to bed. How were they to guess the bride and groom weren't deliriously happy, or that they made love with the desperation of a couple seeking an escape from disaster?

'I remember,' she said.

Nothing had changed. The same four-poster bed, its rich cherrywood finish gleaming, stood in the middle of the room, covered with the same puffy blue quilt. The heirloom rocking-chair, the mahogany chiffonier, the narrow cheval mirror, each was in exactly the same spot it had occupied ten summers ago.

The bath-tub was the old-fashioned cast-iron kind, with claw feet and huge brass taps. Deep enough for a person to be able to immerse herself up to the chin, it had been designed by someone who understood the therapeutic powers of warm, scented water.

Clint was mistaken on one point, however. There weren't any quilted robes hanging in the wardrobe, when she went looking, but there was a smocked white cotton nightdress, ornately embroidered with pale blue forget-me-nots and so thoroughly Victorian in style that nothing but her hands and feet showed when Sharon slipped it on.

Pulling aside the curtains, she opened the little bedroom window tucked under the gables and leaned on the ledge, surprised to find that only a pale orange glow remained of the sunset. Enough of the day's heat lingered, though, to perfume the evening with night-scented stock and honeysuckle, just as it had on her wedding night. Tucking her feet under her, she sank down into the rocking-chair, and breathed in the fragrance. And the memories came flooding back...

What had prompted her mother to give her a négligé as a trousseau gift? Some last-minute pang of guilt or regret, perhaps, that she hadn't made more of an effort to provide her only child with the traditional trappings a bride might expect? Or some misguided hope that, if the package were glamorised a little, the groom might be tempted to overlook the fact that he'd been rail-roaded into marriage? Whatever the reason, Sharon had felt ridiculous in the ruffled Hollywood creation, and hadn't worn it. Hers had not been a champagne and roses sort of honeymoon; it had been a 'let's make the best of it' period of adjustment and re-evaluation.

The day after the wedding, they'd moved a few blocks away to the lower floor of a house that had been converted into two apartments. The day after that, Clint had packed a bag with enough clothes to last him a week and had gone out with the local land surveyor, who'd hired him as his assistant to subdivide recreational lake-front property in the mountains a hundred and fifty miles north of town. 'I've got to make a living somehow,' he'd said brusquely, when she'd voiced her dismay at his proposed five-day absences.

She'd had three rooms to clean and more hours than she cared to count in which to dwell on her misery. On the other hand, the couple in the upstairs apartment, who were also newly-weds, were true honeymooners. Their bed had creaked and groaned every night in testimony of their wedded bliss, while she lay lonely in hers and cried into her pillow.

In some ways, the weekends were even worse. She'd been hopelessly in love with Clint, and it had hurt her terribly to see the desolation in his eyes when he came home each Friday, and to know that she was the reason for it. He hadn't taken the job in order to be able to pay the rent, as he'd claimed. He had a degree in political science and could have found more lucrative employment closer to home. No, he'd taken the job to leave himself too physically spent to care about the ambitions he'd had to abandon when he'd done the honourable thing and married her.

Despite his exhaustion, though, she knew he'd often lain awake beside her at night, staring at the darkened ceiling, and she'd felt his remoteness. Sometimes he'd reach for her and they'd make love silently and economically. But although he'd occasionally share his body, he never shared his soul, and she had known better than to ask him for his heart.

He was separate from her, even when they were physically joined. She'd never felt that she was able to touch him, except in the most superficial sense.

After a couple of weeks she'd decided that she had to keep herself occupied or she'd go mad, so during the days she'd started to garden. There were whole beds of neglected roses and lilacs, delphiniums and phlox, which needed weeding and pruning, and a patch of lawn to be trimmed. In the evenings she'd painted the rooms and tried to make the apartment a cheerful, welcoming place that he'd be glad to come home to.

And then, one night, she'd woken up and found she'd started bleeding. By the time Clint had come home three days later, it was all over—or so she'd thought—and too late to save their baby or their marriage. They'd been left with nothing but recriminations that had them hurling damaging, hurtful accusations at each other across an abyss of sadness.

'Why couldn't you have waited for me to help you with the damned garden?'

'Because you're not interested in helping me. You're never here when I need you. It's your fault I lost the baby.'

'Always assuming you were pregnant to begin with! How do I know that wasn't just another one of your ploys to get me to marry you?'

There'd been nothing left after that except the sudden opening of doors that they thought had been shut forever. She'd sensed his impatience to be free of the legalities that still tied him to her, and for the first time was able to offer him something that really mattered: his freedom.

She had agreed to a speedy divorce. Within a week he had left Canada.

He might have dropped off the edge of the earth for all she'd heard from him after that. If she'd had the slightest inkling that he'd come looking for her one day, she might have made a different decision that day in the doctor's office, about six weeks after he disappeared. But he'd sent no messages, no letters, and her sorrow had eroded to bitter resentment.

She had decided she hated him. It had been so much less painful than admitting she loved him. And when she'd learned that she'd conceived fraternal twins and lost only one of them, she'd hoarded the knowledge and told herself that the surviving baby was better off with no father at all than with one who'd been so reluctant to accept the role in the first place. And in the years that followed, life had slowly regained a measure of sweetness.

Music drifted up the stairs, something calm and restful by Debussy. The notes fell like small round pebbles into a quiet pond, so gentle that they scarcely caused a ripple.

Sharon leaned back in the rocking-chair and closed her eyes, thinking about that other child. It wasn't something she often did—ten years was a long time to keep such a tenuous memory alive—but every once in a while she found herself wondering: had it been a boy or a girl? Would it have resembled her, as Fern did, or would it have looked like Clint?

At first he paid no attention to the fact that she was taking so long. He changed from the formal rented suit to a blue shirt and denim jeans as soft and comfortable as a pair of old slippers, then called the hospital to check on Fern and left the aunts' phone number in case some change in her condition occurred. He sliced tomatoes and carved wafer-thin slices of honey-cured ham. His aunts weren't great imbibers of alcohol, but Jubilee made a mean apricot brandy that went very well with coffee,

and there was half a damson pie in the refrigerator just
begging to be served up with a dollop of ice-cream.

When he glanced at the schoolhouse clock on the
kitchen wall, saw that an hour had passed, and realised
that if Sharon was still upstairs she was awfully quiet,
he decided to go looking for her. He didn't like the disappointment that washed over him at the idea that she
might have skipped out on him.

There was no light showing under the guest-room door,
no sound of running water to indicate that she might
still be in the bath-tub. Very quietly, he turned the knob
and inched the door ajar.

He saw her at once, huddled in the rocking-chair with
the folds of her gown spilling around her ankles and
trailing to the floor. Her face was bathed in faint star-
light, just enough for him to see tear tracks silvering her
cheeks and the fact that she was crying in her sleep.

Perhaps a floorboard creaked under his feet. More
likely, though, he let out a groan at the sight of her,
because her pain or grief immediately became his, too.

Why was that? Had the habit of shouldering responsibility for others become too much a part of his
life for him to react any other way? Or was it simply an
extension of the guilt he'd nursed for so long—the auto-
matic assumption that if she was suffering it was his
fault?

No matter. Something disturbed her. She awoke with
a jolt, sat upright in the old rocker, and swung her head
blindly to where he stood in the doorway, haloed by the
light in the hall behind him. 'What...?'

'Sorry,' he said. 'I didn't mean to startle you. I came
to make sure you were OK, that's all. You were gone
rather a long time.'

The alarm drained out of her. 'I was dreaming,' she said, pressing her fingertips to her temples.

'It must have been a nightmare.' He stepped cautiously over the threshold, unsure of his welcome. 'You were crying.'

'So I was.' She wiped absently at her cheeks.

'Were you dreaming about Fern? I checked with the hospital a few minutes ago and she's doing just fine.'

'No,' Sharon said. 'I was dreaming about her——'

The words choked off abruptly, smothered by the hand she clapped to her mouth. She turned huge, horrified eyes towards him.

It happened again then, that slamming pain in his midriff, so much stronger this time that he felt driven to act on it. Unable to stop himself, he plucked her bodily from the chair so that he could sit in it himself and snuggle her on his lap.

'Dreaming about what, darling?' he crooned softly. 'Why don't you tell me? Talking often helps, and I'm a good listener.'

She froze in his arms, appalled at what she'd almost confessed. Would he have been as anxious to comfort her if she'd finished what she'd started to say—that she'd been dreaming about Fern's twin? She wished she had the courage to find out.

'Your being here helps,' she said, and in a way it was true. It felt right to be close to him like this. The secret of Fern's paternity lay between them like a land-mine primed to explode, but not even that could blind her to the knowledge that the more time she spent with him, the easier it became to understand why she'd fallen headlong in love with him in the first place.

Was that what prompted the insidious notion that, given more favourable circumstances, those early feelings could mature into something more substantial than so much adolescent stardust? 'Talk to me instead,' she begged, squashing the thought before it incurred fresh disaster and heartache. 'Tell me what you did after the divorce.'

'Why dredge up the unhappy past when the present is so much more relevant?' he asked, running a warm, dry palm down her arm until he found her hand.

'Because I'm missing a whole piece of your life and I can't help being curious about what you did with it. You aren't the same man I once knew, and I want to know what changed you.'

Time had mellowed Clint. The wicked sense of fun that had first attracted her to him had re-established itself as a permanent part of his personality, in charming contrast to his strong and sober sense of purpose. He'd matured into a man at last in control of every facet of his life, and perhaps this afforded him a more indulgent outlook on the rest of the world, but during the few short weeks of their marriage he'd shown little tolerance, either for himself or for others. He'd been like a caged animal, searching for an avenue of escape. His frustration at not finding one had simmered so close to the surface that she'd been almost afraid of him at times.

'Are you disappointed at what I've become? Is that it?' he asked her now.

Would that she were! How much easier it would be to resist him then. 'No. I'm just curious.' She wriggled more snugly against his shoulder and allowed her fingers to curl around his. 'Where did you go when you left this country?'

He laughed. 'You're a bit old for bedtime stories, dear heart, but I'll humour you, just this once. My first stop was India.'

She'd always seen him as some sort of modern-day crusader, fighting other people's wars for the thrill of it and covering himself with glory in the process, yet India didn't seem a very likely place for such adventures. 'What did you do there?'

'Drove an old mail truck back and forth across the country, collecting waifs and orphans and delivering them to hostels, where they were taken care of until such time as better arrangements could be made for them.'

'You must have found that very satisfying.'

'I suppose I did, to begin with, but I soon became frustrated by the limitations I faced every day. Speed makes all the difference when it comes to saving lives, and that old truck was always breaking down. I had to find a quicker, more efficient method of getting around, so I learned to fly fixed-wing aircraft, then joined forces with an Australian guy who flew helicopters. Between us we covered a lot more territory and had some pretty hair-raising experiences along the way.'

'How long did you stay?'

'A couple of years. Eventually there were enough people involved for the project to win government backing, so we moved on to fresh adventures.'

His voice reminded her of velvet drawn repeatedly over silk, slightly rough without being at all ungentle, and pleasurably hypnotic. His thumb stroked absently past the elastic hem of her sleeve to trace circles over her inner wrist. The night could have been forty hours long and she would not have tired of listening to him or being touched by him. 'Where did you go next?'

'Africa—Ethiopia and Nigeria—then South America. Paraguay, Bolivia, Brazil.' His tone changed, grew darker and more distant. 'And it was the same thing every-where. Men killing each other, people starving, children dying. And fools like me who deluded themselves into thinking they could make a difference.'

'Don't say that,' she protested. 'What you did helped.'

'It didn't amount to a row of beans. People continued to starve and children continued to die, sometimes violently and always tragically. Those children...' His voice was suddenly raw with anguish. 'I sometimes think the faces of those children will follow me to my grave.'

It was her turn to offer comfort, and it took only a very small movement for her to lift her head and press her lips to his cheek. 'Their lives were made better for having known you, Clint.'

'Was yours?' he asked in a low voice, turning his face so that his mouth was close to hers.

He was looking at her. She could see the faint gleam of the stars reflecting in his eyes. She felt the intensity of his gaze, heard the plea in his words, and for once it was easy to be honest with him. 'Yes,' she whispered. 'Oh, yes...' *You taught me how to love!*

Her answer died on a sigh that became hopelessly tangled against his lips. She didn't know who initiated the kiss, nor did she care at first. She was far too occupied returning in full measure the demands his mouth was making on hers. Her arms tightened around his neck, her head fell back against his shoulder, and if the rocking-chair wasn't meant for two it wasn't designed for secrets, either. She knew very well the impact of that kiss on him.

'What were we talking about?' he whispered, necklacing kisses from one corner of her mouth to the other like so many pearls on a string.

Keep your wits about you and watch what you say, she told herself sternly, but her brain ignored her and joined forces with her racing heart. 'How much better my life has been because of you,' she said, the words exacting a terrible outlay of energy as they stumbled from her mouth.

'I fail to see how,' Clint murmured, untying the ribbons at her throat.

She ought to distract him, find some way to stop him. She'd already allowed him too much latitude, and if she let him touch her more intimately she'd be lost and have no one but herself to blame for the outcome. To indulge the craving for him that she'd suffered almost from the moment she'd set eyes on him again was pure madness.

She sat up and pushed away his hands. 'You haven't mentioned anything about other women in your life,' she said bluntly, seizing on the one topic guaranteed to sour the intimacy of the moment.

He grew very still. 'Ah, so it's the women I've known that you really want to hear about,' he said softly, a slow smile glimmering over his mouth.

'Well, unless you spent the last ten years in a monastery, you must have known some,' she said, wishing she hadn't brought up the subject, because, far from defusing her aching desire, she'd merely fuelled it with jealousy.

'Do you mean in the biblical sense, dear heart?' he enquired mischievously.

She twisted the ribbons of her gown between her fingers and tried to look blasé. 'Naturally,' she said, sounding commendably bored.

He leaned his head against the high back of the rocker and rested his hands along its arms. 'Well, let me see, there were Fatima and Salome in Egypt...and then was Carmen in Argentina, and after her came Sche-

herazade in Arabia.' He rolled his eyes until the whites
gleamed in the dark. 'Scheherazade,' he murmured,
practically licking his lips, 'was quite fantastic.'

'I'm sure she was,' Sharon said waspishly, 'but I really
don't want a list of names and addresses of your many
conquests.'

He sat up straight, setting the chair to a wild rocking.
'What do you want, then? To hear that I remained
faithful to you, even though you upped and married
another man before the sheets were cold from my
sleeping in them?'

'I was just wondering in general because it seemed
time to change the subject,' she said, shrivelling under
his attack. 'Did you—er—did you really know a
Scheherazade?'

'No.' He sighed with a trace of his old impatience.
'Nor did I know a Fatima or Carmen or Salome. But
there were other women.'

'Oh,' she said in a small voice, and wished he didn't
always feel compelled to be so damned forthright with
his answers.

'If you didn't want to know, you shouldn't have
asked,' he chided. 'If, on the other hand, what you're
really asking is if they had any lasting significance in my
life, then the answer is no.'

'But you made love to them,' she said, deciding that
when it came to self-flagellation she deserved first prize.

'In certain situations,' Clint said, with strained for-
bearance. 'For example, in extreme danger—the sort
where you can't be at all sure you won't wake up dead
the next morning—people tend to turn to each other. On
occasion, there were women, Sharon, to whom I turned.
You might choose to interpret that as my having used

them. I saw it as a mutual and generous exchange of comfort.'

She had no warning of what her next words would be. They popped out before she had the chance to silence them. 'Did you ever think of me when you were with them?'

'Frequently. Are you satisfied, or are there more crazy questions where that one came from?'

'No more questions,' she said.

He cupped her cheek in his hand and turned her mouth to his. 'Then I have a question for you.'

'And what's that?' she asked nervously.

'Why do you care?'

When she needed it the most, her ability to prevaricate deserted her. 'I don't know,' she whispered.

He tilted up her chin. 'I do,' he said, kissing her throat. 'It's because you don't want anyone else to come between us, especially not now. It's because you want it to be just the two of us, here and now, on that bed over there. Not because we're surrounded by danger or threats from outside, but because that old magic is working for us again, whether you want to admit it or not.'

CHAPTER EIGHT

CLINT'S mouth singed where it touched, the flame spreading down into her lungs and parching as it went. 'Am I right?' he murmured.

'What...?'

'You heard me.'

She swallowed twice. 'I—er—I...'

'A simple yes or no will do.' He lifted his head and trailed the fingers of each hand down the sides of her neck until they formed a V at the open ribbons of her nightgown. 'But you do have to answer me, Sharon, and you do have to tell the truth.'

If ever a lie was justified, it was then, but she couldn't voice it. His eyes held hers and compelled her to honesty. 'Yes,' she said, on the merest whisper of a breath.

He nodded and expelled a long sigh. 'Yes,' he echoed and, carrying her to the bed, laid her against the pillows and looked down at her face for a long time without touching her. 'Oh, yes!'

Very deliberately then, he bent and kissed the corner of her mouth, pushed aside the ribbons of her gown, and touched his lips to the spot where her pulse quivered with the frantic, uneven flutter of a captured butterfly.

Behind him, the lamp at the top of the stairs spilled a beam of light across the wall, a plea for discretion before they sank into bewitchment. 'The door...' she protested, jerking her head towards it. 'What if your aunts...?'

Lifting his head, Clint glanced over his shoulder and cursed softly. 'That would never do,' he agreed, reluctantly leaving her side to remedy the situation.

To her relief, closing the door plunged the room into near-darkness. She was just able to discern him moving to the foot of the bed. She heard the tell-tale clink of a belt buckle, the soft hiss of a zip. His clothes hit the floor with a quiet thud, and then he moved away, towards the high chiffonier. For one insane moment Sharon wondered if, overcome by uncharacteristic modesty, he was looking for pyjamas or something.

The scrape and flare of a match disabused her of any such notion. Yellow candlelight chased the shadows to the corners of the room and showed him silhouetted against the wall. He was not wearing pyjamas. He was not wearing anything. He was stalking back to the bed, stark naked.

Sharon promptly shut her eyes, overcome by a tidal wave of shyness. Making love in the semi-dark was one thing; clearly seeing and being seen was quite another.

'Open your eyes, dear heart,' he said, his raspy, sexy voice seeming to reach out to stroke over her as the mattress sank under his weight.

Reluctantly she did. He loomed above her, large, powerful, intimidating. 'That's better,' he said.

With excruciating delicacy his fingers skimmed from her throat to her feet and grasped the hem of her gown. Then they began the journey back, but slowly this time, pleating the fabric as they went.

He uncovered her ankles, lifted them, and dipped his head to bestow a long, slow kiss on each instep. The reverberations shot the length of her, shaking her to the roots of the hair on her head.

He bared her calves and traced their curve with his tongue. Her knees fell apart, slack with invitation, but he was bent on a more leisurely seduction. Declining to accept, he pressed them together and fanned his breath over her thigh to that demure sweep of skin that really did nothing more than join a woman's leg to the rest of her body. Not a secret place, to be kept hidden from all but a lover's eyes, but one she exposed without shame when she wore a swimsuit. Yet when Clint found it and stopped to test its resilience with quick, light flicks of his tongue, it shed all pretence of innocence and responded with a volatile humming that elicited a moan of startled pleasure from Sharon.

He pushed the gown higher, followed it with his mouth. He looped her waist with kisses, counted each rib with his tongue, swirled his mouth over the slope of her breasts. The flame leapt more fiercely.

'Give me your hand,' he commanded, his voice rustling over her like dry leaves.

She obeyed, completely at his mercy. He pulled the sleeve of her gown free, then followed suit with the other. Last, he lifted the garment clear of her head and left her fully uncovered, then let his eyes roam over her in a ritual of renewal that left her trembling.

Her nineteen-year-old body had been the lure that had tempted and trapped him before. Would it betray her now? She was almost thirty, and the signs were there for anyone who chose to look for them: the breasts not quite as firm and high, the hips a little rounder, the waist never again as slender as it had been before childbirth. Would he notice? Would he compare? And if he saw the changes, would he still want her?

She squirmed, afraid to look him in the eye, afraid that uncompromising honesty of his would not allow him to dissemble at what he saw.

'Be still,' he growled, and to ensure that she obeyed he took her wrists and held them above her head. Pinned beneath him, she had no choice but to submit as he set about a scrupulous examination of discovery. He did not miss an inch and he would not be hurried. She felt stripped to the soul and mortally vulnerable under that fine and lingering scrutiny.

When at last he spoke, it was merely to repeat that same, gravelly 'Yes!', but it told her volumes, as did his heavy-lidded gaze. Whatever else he might be feeling, it wasn't disappointment.

The knowledge sparked a tiny courage in her that freed her to return the favour. She dared to look—at his shoulders, his arms, his chest—and discovered that he was as powerfully lean and beautiful at thirty-eight as he had been in his twenties.

Growing braver, she allowed her gaze to slide down the tapering line of his torso, past the flat plane of his stomach to his neat and narrow waist. And then she threw all caution to the windless night, dipped her eyes lower still, and saw that he was not nearly as reconciled to patient seduction as she'd first thought, but was waging a terrible battle to hold himself in check.

It gave her confidence an enormous boost. Very gently she slipped her wrist free of his hold and pressed her hand to his skull, imprisoning him against her.

Desire hammered at him, an exquisite, unrelenting torture screaming for an appeasement he would not grant. In the past it seemed he had always made love to her hastily, in the dark, either because instant gratifi-

cation had seemed crucial to survival, or because night
hid the quiet desperation he knew lurked in her eyes.

But if he retained no clear memory of how she'd
looked at nineteen, he knew he would never forget the
woman lying beneath him now, with the light from the
candle painting her in translucent colour.

Had his bride been as lovely as this exquisite stranger
with skin as warm as sun-kissed peaches and as silky as
cream? She had *felt* different then, that much he did
know. She'd been a girl, lovely in the way that early
spring was lovely, on the brink of unfolding, fresh and
untouched. But she was all woman now, her early
promise of beauty in full bloom and spiced with mystery
and allure.

He wanted to taste every inch of her and kiss every
curve. He wanted to know her, really know her, to delve
below her elegant surface to the complex grace of her
soul. And most of all, he wanted the thrill of discovery
to last beyond the moment.

He settled his mouth again on her breast and found
her nipple ripe and ready for him. A distant tremor seized
her, like the far-off warning of an earthquake, fire beneath the cool ice of her reserve.

Her breath fluttered light and rapid in her throat.
Blindly she reached for him. 'Let me touch you,' she
begged, pushing persuasively at his chest. He rolled on
to his back, intrigued and delighted by her sudden
aggression.

But the intrigue soon died and the delight thickened
to a painful intensity. Her fingers were nimble as
humming-birds, their erotic promise devising tortures
he'd never imagined. When she lifted her head and closed
her mouth on his bare chest, his heart gave a great

thudding heave, then seemed to stop. Its dying echo left him too stunned to prepare himself for her next attack.

She nibbled at his shoulder, stroked her tongue up his throat, then lifted her head and smiled into his eyes. 'That's better,' she said.

He'd sadly underestimated the opposition! 'Better for whom?' he croaked, deciding that immediate retaliatory action was called for if he seriously wanted to prolong the pleasure of the moment. Cupping the back of her head, he brought her mouth down hard on his, seeking to disarm her with a kiss entirely dedicated to imitating the act of love.

It was a fine idea except that it backfired. Her lips opened in welcome, deluding him into believing that he was in control and she merely complying with his demands. But honey had never tasted sweeter, and sampling it once wasn't enough. He probed deeper, and never noticed that the doors to escape had closed behind him until it was too late and she was wreaking a devastation of her own beside which his meagre attack paled.

In the full knowledge that he was completely distracted and unable to defend himself elsewhere, she set about enslaving him completely. Her hands, cool and soft as a breeze, shaped his waist and smoothed down his hips, turned hot, possessive vixen, and closed over him. And if that weren't penalty enough to teach any man a lesson, she laughed low in her throat, a sound so utterly female and full of promise that, if she'd asked him for the moon in exchange for making love with him, he'd have used the stars as stepping-stones to get it for her.

Only one thing saved him: the knowledge that if he didn't wrest control away from her the pleasure would end too soon. With an agility that cost him dearly and took her completely by surprise, he rolled her over until she was lying beside him.

'My turn,' he whispered hoarsely, and set about teaching her a lesson he didn't intend she would soon forget.

He kissed her, then he kissed her again. He slid both arms around her and pinned her beneath him, and kissed her a third time, a long, warm, open-mouthed, delicious kiss. And all the time his hands shaped her, coaxing, tormenting, cajoling.

He was more daring than she. Where his hands went, his mouth followed, leaving in their wake an involuntary trembling she could not subdue.

She sighed his name, and she whimpered for him to stop, and she very charmingly begged him not to. And when she melted, helpless to prevent her throbbing capitulation to his attack, he tried to smile in victory and found he couldn't. Her eyes, limpid and unfocused, were utterly defenceless, killing any pretence of laughter in him and evoking instead a feeling dangerously close to love.

There was no more delaying. He wasn't made of stone, after all. Bracing himself on his forearms, he held her face between his hands, nudged apart her thighs, and sank into her. Her hips melted against his, begging outrageously. She was all satin acceptance, tight and welcoming, and she almost destroyed him. For one brief, terrible moment, desire clutched at him so relentlessly that he thought it would all be over before he could begin to give her one tenth of the pleasure she had already afforded him.

He froze, buried his face in her hair, and recited the days of the week in a litany of devout concentration, drawing in a great gasp of gratitude when the delaying tactic took some effect.

After perhaps thirty seconds, he moved very cautiously. She responded, the lovely aching rhythm meshing as though they'd rehearsed together for years. She looked up at him, and her gaze was clear and unafraid. For the first time they were truly united with no secrets between them.

Inevitably, the tempo increased. Passion shimmered, expectant, tantalising. Again he sought to delay. If it had been in his power, he would never have let it end.

'I want you to know,' he murmured, looking deep into her beautiful eyes, 'that those other women...' He paused, dragged a breath from deep down in his lungs to fortify himself against the grabbing hunger. 'They meant nothing, Sharon.'

'Please...' she whispered, her fingers digging into the flesh of his shoulder.

He thought she was trying to silence him, but he had to go on; he had to tell her that this time was like no other. He couldn't let her believe that for him it was just another release. 'They were substitutes for the real thing, dear heart.'

He heard his voice from a growing distance, wavering, wrestling, losing the battle. It might have been the first time since the last time he'd held her. It *was* the first time he'd made love in ten years.

'This,' he whispered hoarsely, 'is for all those nights when I let you lie lonely beside me.'

He felt her tighten around him. 'Oh, please,' she begged, hopelessness swimming in her voice, 'please don't make me love you again.'

So help him, he couldn't resist the lure of her sweet, soft lips or the words they were uttering. Dropping his mouth hard on hers, he set about releasing all the fire simmering within her.

She gasped, convulsed around him. Melted and convulsed, over and over. And he was lost, his control shot to hell and his determination to make this moment last fragmented by that old, relentless hunger that he'd tried for so long to ignore. It didn't matter how many women he'd kissed since the divorce, or how many had shared his bed, his nights.

It didn't matter and it didn't help. Covering her with unplanned, frantic kisses that missed as often as they found their mark, he dissolved into a brilliant, blinding shaking apart—a dissolution of the man he'd become into something eternal and beautiful because he was with her. 'Why can't I make you love me again, my darling?' he whispered, between heaving, jagged breaths. '*You've* bewitched *me* again.'

It had never been this way with Jason, Sharon thought dimly, fighting to snatch oxygen from the place where her lungs used to be. Never such complete surrender, never such astounding passion, never such brutal release as she found with Clint.

It did no good to tell herself that he spelled danger, that that pagan sensuality of his was coupled with an intellect so acute that he would never allow a romantic interlude to cloud his judgement. It didn't seem to matter that tomorrow, when the cool head of reason again prevailed, the ramifications of tonight's events would turn the rest of her life into a shambles.

What mattered was that Clint's arms were around her, holding her safe until the shattered parts of her reassembled themselves. What mattered was that, just once, he had made love to her, instead of having sex. She would not reproach herself for her weakness, or fret at how different things might have been had Fern been conceived in such a manner. She would allow nothing else to intrude until she had crystallised this night in her memory so that it would remain clear and strong for the rest of her life.

He wasn't there when she awoke the next morning, but Aunt Celeste was. She shuffled to the bedside with a tea tray in her hands. 'Darling girl...' She beamed when Sharon opened sleepy eyes. 'How lovely it is to see you back in our home again!'

Sharon shrank under the covers, mortified by the nightgown lying in a heap on the floor. Her lips felt crushed, her face rosy with whisker burn. Her body ached pleasurably. She might as well have worn a placard around her neck, advertising the events of last night.

'How did you know I was here?' she mumbled, then wondered if there were any other dopey questions where that one came from.

'Clinton told us at breakfast.'

'You've had breakfast already? I wish you'd woken me. I need to phone the hospital about Fern.'

'Clinton already did, and she's just fine. You can pick her up any time you're ready, but he left strict instructions that you weren't to be disturbed before ten—said you underwent quite an ordeal last night, you poor thing, and that you'd earned your rest.'

The rat! They'd made love until the sun came up, snatching sleep in each other's arms until the breathtaking hunger brought them together again. Small wonder she felt limp as a rag doll.

Aunt Celeste patted her cheek lovingly. 'I brewed you raspberry tea, darling. So restorative, I always find, when a person's had a hard night of it. Come down as soon as you're dressed. Jubilee has made you waffles for breakfast.'

Immediately she was alone, Sharon leapt from the bed and raced to the mirror. What she saw staring back at her was every bit as bad as she'd feared: the face of a woman half dazed with love. Starry-eyed, sultry, sated. She had to erase the look, and quickly.

Within ten minutes she had showered and scrambled into her clothes. Fully dressed, she felt much more in command of herself.

Jubilee Bodine might have been harder of hearing than her sister, but she compensated by being much more observant. 'My gracious, child,' she declared, snapping closed the lid of the waffle iron and turning a shrewd eye her way as Sharon slid on to the chair in the breakfast nook of the big kitchen, 'you look no more rested than Our Boy this morning. What's the matter—couldn't the pair of you sleep?'

Sharon choked on the orange juice Celeste had poured for her. 'I... Yes—um—very well... We...' She sputtered, coughed, and proceeded to reduce herself to total absurdity. 'We—had—a wonderful—er...'

'Night,' Aunt Jubilee finished for her. 'Yes, I can tell. Slap her on the back, Celeste, before she has a heart attack.'

Sharon mopped her eyes with her serviette and decided that this was definitely a case of least said, soonest mended. Wily Aunt Jubilee *knew*, which meant that before long she'd apprise Celeste of the situation, too. Afraid to look either of them in the eye, Sharon stared out of the window.

'Cat got your tongue?' Aunt Jubilee enquired archly, setting peach syrup and fresh cream on the table.

Sharon searched for some scintillating reply. 'I was admiring the pink rose in the garden,' she offered weakly. 'See how lovely it looks with the dew still on it?'

'You sound like something out of a child's first reader,' Jubilee pronounced. '"Oh, oh, see Spot run! See Sharon run! See Sharon pretend she doesn't want to know where Clinton is!"' She cackled with malicious delight. 'Pour the girl some coffee, Celeste. It might restore her wits.'

'Don't tease her, Jubilee!' Celeste scolded, slip-slopping in her large, comfortable slippers across the kitchen floor. 'Her little daughter's in the hospital and she's worried.'

'I know that.' Jubilee deposited a plate heaped with golden waffles in front of Sharon. 'One of the joys of passing eighty is being able to say what you please without getting rapped on the knuckles for it, so save your breath, Sister. Sharon ought to know by now that I've always loved her.' She fixed Sharon in another piercing gaze and smiled slyly. 'Eat, child, before you wilt. You need to replenish your energy.'

'How was the rest of the wedding?' Sharon asked, determined to steer the conversation to less suggestive channels. 'I'm afraid we missed quite a lot of it.'

'Lovely,' Aunt Celeste sighed. 'Simply lovely!'

'Ostentatious,' Jubilee said, 'although I have to say, your gowns were quite beautiful, Sharon. Margot did look exquisite—but then so did you.'

Celeste nodded. 'And little Fern. What a shame the day was spoiled for her.'

'What a blessing Clinton was there,' Jubilee said.

'Yes.' Sharon leapt at the chance to steer the conversation to a mutually acceptable topic. 'I was so impressed at the way he took charge. He guessed right away what had happened and seemed to know exactly what to do.'

'Well, of course he did!' Jubilee exclaimed. 'He's had enough practice, after all.'

'He's allergic to bee-stings, too,' Celeste added, seeing Sharon's puzzled frown. 'He always had to carry a little anti-venom kit with him when he was a boy.'

'Still does,' Jubilee said. 'Especially with him spending so much time in foreign places where they have all sorts of biting insects no right-minded man would want to associate with.'

The waffles were delicious, the coffee strong and flavourful. Sharon had been on the verge of relaxing until this last little titbit of information was dropped in her lap. She could almost feel herself turn pale. 'Clint is allergic to bee-stings?' she repeated. 'I didn't know that.'

'You would have if you'd been around him when he was little, dear girl,' Celeste said, refilling her coffee-cup. 'Children seem to have a talent for stumbling on nests in the most unlikely places.'

'Fern's never been stung before,' Sharon said.

'That's because she's a little city girl,' Celeste replied comfortably. 'They don't go climbing trees and exploring in the bushes the way little boys in the country do. Why, it seems to me that hardly a day went by when Clint was young that he didn't stumble on a nest of one kind or another. We got very used to coping with emergencies.' She stirred her coffee meditatively. 'It's quite a coincidence, when you stop to think about it, that Fern should suffer from the same sort of reaction.'

Mindless panic took hold of Sharon. It was the only way she could explain the utter idiocy of her next remark. 'It's not hereditary,' she blurted out, and managed to up-end her cup into its saucer.

Jubilee was looking at her strangely. 'My gracious, Sharon, no one suggested it is.'

'Of course not.' She dabbed agitatedly at a spot of coffee on the embroidered cloth, babbling the whole time. 'It's just that...well, what I meant is that *I'm* not allergic, nor was Jason. I didn't mean...didn't mean...'

Jubilee responded very uncharacteristically to that outpouring of excuses. She patted Sharon's hand. 'No need to explain, dear child,' she remarked gently. 'I understand exactly what you meant.'

Sharon was afraid she did, only too well.

Celeste rose and went over to the china cupboard. 'Let me get you a fresh cup, dear.'

'No, thank you!' Plopping her serviette on the table, Sharon pushed back her chair and tried not to appear too suddenly anxious to be gone. 'It's getting late and I really would like to go back to the Dunns' and change out of this outfit before I pick up Fern.'

'You are dressed rather formally for the morning,' Jubilee acknowledged, with that same enigmatic expression still on her face, 'but if you wait a few more minutes Clinton should be back. He's gone into Harperville to return his rented suit, but I'm sure he'd be only too glad to drive you to the hospital when he gets back.'

That was the last thing Sharon wanted. If Jubilee hadn't already put two and two together and come up with four, she was coming awfully close. The sooner Sharon put some distance—a lot of distance! —between herself and the Bodines, the less chance of her opening her mouth and letting something even more incriminating fall out.

'I couldn't possibly put him to all that trouble,' she said firmly.

'But he'll be disappointed at having missed you,' Celeste objected. 'Jubilee, persuade her to wait for Clinton.'

'The girl's in a tearing hurry, Sister, as you'd be able to see if you stopped flapping around long enough to take a look. Nevertheless . . .' Jubilee fastened a severe gaze on Sharon ' . . . he is going to wonder what drove you away so quickly.'

Let him draw whatever conclusions he pleased, Sharon thought. She'd behaved like a complete fool, on a number of counts. As if that defensive gaffe about heredity weren't enough, she'd actually been entertaining romantic fantasies about her and Clint somehow managing to find a happy ending together, when she knew that was something that could never happen. Her deception stood between them. It always would.

She was furious with herself; furious and disgusted. She was no more in touch with reality now than she had been at nineteen if she'd reached the point of deluding herself into believing that she could tell him the truth, then expect that, dazzled by one magical night of love, he'd forgive her.

Not likely, not with the Clint Bodine she knew!

'I have other things that I'd planned to do today as soon as I've picked up Fern,' she told the aunts.

Like catch the noon flight back to Vancouver. She couldn't afford to spend another day—or night—in Crescent Creek.

CHAPTER NINE

VANCOUVER was hot, humid and too crowded after the rural peace of Crescent Creek. Even the penthouse seemed claustrophobic, and Sharon found none of the tranquillity there that usually awaited her after time spent elsewhere. She also knew why. She missed Clint. Desperately.

To make matters worse, Fern talked about him incessantly. He'd become her favourite topic of conversation, and she was disappointed—disturbingly so—at having been whisked back to town before she could say goodbye to him. It was all Sharon could do not to snap back that life would have been a lot simpler if he'd never said hello, either.

Another change of scene seemed like an excellent diversion, both for mother and daughter—something as far removed from reminders of Clint as it was possible to find. 'How would you like to visit Disneyland?' she suggested, two days after they had fled Crescent Creek.

'Disneyland?' Fern's eyes were like saucers. 'Mommy, yes!'

'Then spend the rest of the summer driving up the California coast? We could start in San Diego, take a tour of Hollywood, go to San Francisco, and visit all the mission towns along the way. It's really beautiful down there, sweetheart, and I think you'd have fun.'

'I'd love it, I know I would.'

'We'd get back a few days before school starts, and by then...' Sharon let the words dribble into silence.

She could hardly finish what she'd been thinking—that by then she'd have her priorities firmly in place again—without inviting questions she didn't want to answer from her sometimes too perceptive daughter.

But Fern's smile faded a little anyway. 'What's the matter, Mommy? Are you feeling sad again?'

Giving herself a mental shake, Sharon vowed to leave Clint in Crescent Creek, where he belonged, and forge ahead with new places and new experiences. 'Absolutely not.'

But Fern was wise beyond her years. 'Then why are we going away when we only just got home? When you came to get me from the hospital, you said you wanted to get back to Vancouver as fast as you could, and now you want to leave again.'

'You didn't have much of a birthday party this year,' Sharon replied, thinking fast on her feet for a change. 'What with all the work involved in Margot's wedding, your special day got sort of swept under the carpet, so consider this trip a belated celebration. We'll have a wonderful time, I promise.'

And they did. They came back to Vancouver late one afternoon towards the end of the first week of September to find that the enervating heat of summer had passed. Across the Strait, the mountains on the distant islands loomed dusky purple against a sky of clear, cool green, splashed with gold where the sun had gone down. Indian summer had arrived—that marvellous month-long reprieve of crisp mornings, mild, sunny afternoons and cool evenings. Before the cold rains of winter set in, Clint Bodine would be no more than a distant memory. Sharon was convinced of all those things, especially the last.

'As soon as we've unpacked, we'll phone and order in pizza,' she told Fern, drawing up the blinds and flinging open the terrace doors to the cool ocean breeze. 'Then, while you put your room into half-decent order, I'll take a shower, and tomorrow we'll go shopping for your school supplies.'

'Back to normal, right, Mommy?'

'Exactly,' Sharon said, and heaved a sigh of relief. There were no recorded phone messages from Clint, no letters among the mail that had piled up during her absence.

The madness, thank God, had passed.

He knew which day she was due back. The seven weeks he'd spent camping out in a hotel across the street from her prestigious address had allowed him plenty of time to get to know the doorman in her apartment. Extracting snippets of information from the man was a piece of cake for someone with his investigative skills.

He'd spent that particular day reading in the park next door, choosing a spot that gave him a perfect view of the front entrance to her building. He saw the taxi draw up, saw her and Fern get out, and gave her exactly one hour to get herself organised. Then he made his move: twenty yards down the street to the florist's, twenty yards back, and the most boyishly winsome smile he could drum up for the concierge.

'The McClure residence, Charles, please.'

'I'll have to phone up first, sir. I can't let you in otherwise.'

Clint brandished the huge bouquets of roses he carried in each hand. 'I was hoping to surprise the ladies.'

Charles hesitated long enough for Clint to slip him a twenty-dollar bill—no mean feat, considering he was snowed under with flowers. 'Be a good guy and bend the rules just this once. I promise you won't be held responsible if they throw me out on my ear!'

'Very well, Mr Bodine. It's the penthouse lift, at the far end of the lobby.'

It was a very luxurious lobby and a very luxurious lift, so he wasn't unprepared for the quiet elegance of the private foyer when he reached the fortieth floor. Sharon had indeed done very well for herself.

The soft Westminster chimes of the bell had barely faded before Fern opened the door. He couldn't hide the pleasure he felt as her face broke into a dazzling smile of recognition.

'Mr Bodine! I thought you were the pizza man!'

'I hope you're not disappointed,' he teased. 'How are you, Miss McClure?'

'Actually,' she confided, gesturing for him to step inside the apartment with adorable ersatz sophistication, 'I'm supposed to be cleaning my room, which is rather boring, but now that you're here I feel a whole lot better.'

'No more bee-stings to make life exciting?'

She made a face. 'No.'

'Glad to hear it, but I wish you hadn't skipped town so quickly after your last attack. I was going to bring flowers to your bedside, to help you recuperate. However...' he presented the bouquet of yellow roses with a flourish '...better late than never.'

The sparkle in her eyes would have put emeralds to shame. 'No one ever gave me flowers before!'

He wanted to hug the kid, he really did. That smile of hers touched the most extraordinary soft spot in him, as though he'd known it all his life. 'That's a terrible oversight on someone's part,' he said gravely, and indicated the pink roses he still held. 'These are for your mom. Is she here?'

'Yes, but you can't see her—at least, not right now.'

For the first time, it occurred to him that Sharon might have slipped out by a rear entrance. 'Why not?'

'She's in the shower.'

He ought to have known better than to think for a minute that Sharon would leave Fern alone to fend for herself. Nevertheless, relief left him slightly giddy. 'And I don't suppose she'd like it if I visited her in there, would she?'

The child erupted into an infectious stream of giggles. 'No. She's bare naked!'

Clint's throat ran suddenly dry at the delectability of that mental picture.

'But you can wait till she's dressed,' Fern assured him.

He swallowed. 'I'd like that, if you'll keep me company.'

She looked dubious. 'Well, you'd have to wait till I've finished cleaning my room.'

'Let me help. You'll be finished twice as fast then.'

'I'm supposed to do it by myself—but you could put my suitcases on the top shelf in my closet, if you like,' she decided, her face clearing. 'It's too high for me to reach. Even Mommy has to stand on a chair.'

As she spoke, she led the way down a long hall. The walls were hung with paintings that, unless he missed his mark, were originals, and the marble-tiled floor was covered with a silk carpet runner. Once again, it occurred to him that Sharon had made a tremendous success of her fashion career, if what he had seen of her home so far was anything to go by. He felt better, knowing that. At least not all her ambitions had fallen short of the mark.

'In here,' Fern said, showing him through an open door to a charmingly feminine room.

Peripherally, he noticed the ruffles, the authentic Victorian wicker furniture, but the photograph was what struck him most forcibly. It sat in a silver frame on her bedside table, and he found his eyes drawn to it the minute he set foot over the threshold. It was a typical happy family portrait with Sharon holding Fern on her lap and the late and saintly Jason standing tall and proud behind them.

He'd been a good-looking man, dark-haired and serious, Clint noted sourly. Reliable, stable, all the things he hadn't been when it had been his turn to call her his wife. It was all he could do not to take the damn picture and turn it face down on the glass-topped table.

'That's my daddy.' He hadn't heard Fern approach. She stood beside him, with an armload of T-shirts and socks in danger of spilling over on to the floor, and looked solemnly at the portrait. 'He's dead now.'

'Yes,' Clint said gently, ashamed of himself. 'I know. Your mommy told me. You must miss him very much.'

'I miss having a daddy,' she said pragmatically, 'but I've sort of forgotten what he looked like. I only remember when I look at his picture.'

'I don't remember my father at all, or my mother. They died when I was a baby.'

She regarded him out of large, sympathetic eyes. 'Who changed your diapers, then?'

'My aunts,' he said, laughing. 'You met them at the wedding. They adopted me. Actually, they were my father's aunts, which technically makes them my great-aunts.'

'Oh, I don't have any of those,' Fern informed him, dumping the clothes into an open drawer, 'but I have a grandma and grandpa. They're my mommy's parents.'

'Ah, yes!' Clint leaned against the edge of her desk and folded his arms. 'The worthy Maxine and George Carstairs.'

'How do you know their names?'

'I think your mother mentioned them,' he improvised hastily, and decided he'd have to be more careful of what he let slip, or Sharon would have his head.

'They're my guardians, so they'd probably have to adopt me if something bad happened to Mommy,' Fern volunteered matter-of-factly. 'Grandfather wouldn't mind, but I don't think Grandmother would like it much.'

'Well, not that anything bad's going to happen to your mommy, but why do you think Grandmother wouldn't like it?'

'She says she's always left holding the baby and having to explain it to her friends.'

Clint hid a smile. 'That's just an expression, Fern. It isn't meant to be taken literally.'

'I don't know what "lit…"' —what that word means.'

'Well, it means it doesn't really mean what it says.' Then, seeing that his explanation was merely adding to her confusion, he scratched his head and tried again. 'Let me give you another example: if it's pouring with rain, you might say, "it's raining cats and dogs", but you don't actually see cats and dogs falling out of the sky.'

'Don't you like cats and dogs?'

'Yes,' he said, wondering how the conversation had veered so far off the track.

He soon found out that it hadn't. 'Then I still don't know what that word means.' Fern furrowed her brow. 'Because Grandma doesn't like me. She says I'm Mommy's "perpestual reminder", and *that* means I'm a pest.'

And Maxine was obviously still a bitch who hadn't approved of Sharon's second husband any more than she had her first. 'No, it doesn't, sweet pea,' Clint said. 'It means you're an ongoing source of joy and pleasure to your mom and all your friends.'

'You're nice.' Fern's smile was pure sunshine. 'Would you like to see my scrap-book?' she offered, scooping up a large album from her desk and handing it to him. 'I saved every card I ever got, for Christmas and my birthdays and Easter and everything, ever since I was a baby, and pasted them in here—except for these.' She indicated about a dozen loose cards tucked inside the front cover. 'They're the ones I got for my birthday this year, but I haven't got around to putting them in yet. We had to go to Margot's wedding right after my party, and then we went to California.'

Some irregularity in that item of information triggered an objection at the back of his mind—something to do with the timing of her birthday—but before he could bring the anomaly into sharper focus she was dragging her empty suitcase over the floor to the closet.

Stuffing her album under his arm, he went to help. 'As soon as I've stowed this for you, I'd love to look through your scrap-book,' he said, filing the nagging question for later reference. And if he ever ran into Maxine Carstairs again, he'd wring her scrawny neck!

Once the suitcase was stacked away Fern led him into a truly beautiful living-room decorated in shades of celadon and cream and furnished in mahogany. 'You can sit in here; it's more comfortable,' she said, once again the perfect hostess. 'And I'll tell Mommy that you're here.'

'Don't do that.' He settled on a couch and spread the scrap-book before him on a long, marble-topped coffee-table. As he did so, the loose cards that she hadn't had time to paste in place slid out and scattered over the rug at his feet. 'Just tell her she's got company,' he said, bending to retrieve them. 'I want to surprise her.'

Fern giggled conspiratorially. 'I love surprises!'

It took him a few moments to reply. The anomaly was back, distracting him with its insistent demand for attention. 'Don't we all?' he finally murmured, staring at the cards in his hand. Something here definitely didn't add up, and this time the expression meant exactly what it said.

When Fern knocked on her bedroom door and said there was someone to see her, Sharon's first thought was that the pizza delivery boy had arrived early. She wrapped her hair in a towel, turban fashion, belted her terrycloth robe securely, and went down the hall to pay him. But the front door was closed, and the voices—mainly Fern's—were coming from the living-room.

'Please not Mother!' Sharon prayed, moving barefoot across the cool marble tiles. She wasn't in the mood for a lecture on the ill-advisability of pampering a child with extended holidays and junk food.

She was practically across the threshold to the living-room before she realised who her visitor was, and she thought her heart would stop. How often she had dreamed about him in recent weeks; how often she'd woken lonely in the night! But dreams and memories didn't hold a candle to the reality of his presence.

He sat in her pristine living-room, carved like some fallen angel brooding over the loss of paradise in his black shirt and close-fitting black jeans, with his dark gold skin and pale gold hair. She wished she could run into his arms and that the tears suddenly welling in her eyes were inspired by joy instead of grief. Because, of course, no matter what the reason that had brought him to her, she had to send him away again.

'Mommy's here,' Fern said, practically bursting with excitement, and any thoughts Sharon might have entertained about slipping away and declaring herself indisposed for company evaporated as Clint rose from the couch and slowly turned to look at her.

He didn't say a word, just watched her across the width of the room, his eyes veiled, his mouth unsmiling. Fern looked from him to Sharon and back again, that acute radar peculiar to children alerting her to the charged atmosphere. 'Mommy?' she asked uncertainly. 'Aren't you happy that Mr Bodine came to see us?'

Sharon blinked back the tears, 'Yes, sweetheart.' But the answer had a hollow ring, even to her ears, and the air almost crackled as the spool of tension between her and Clint gradually tautened. 'Why don't you go downstairs and visit Jenna now, and leave us by ourselves for a while?'

Jenna was Fern's best friend and lived in the apartment directly below the penthouse. Normally the two girls jumped at the chance to be together, but this time Fern hesitated.

'I thought it would be all right to let him in, Mommy. He's our friend. We know him.'

Clint spoke then, but although the words were directed at Fern his gaze didn't waver from Sharon's face.

'It *was* all right, sweet pea. Your mom just wasn't expecting me, that's all.'

'So I'm not in trouble?'

His face seemed bleached with shock. His eyes, though, glowed like blue coals. 'Not you, honey,' he said, and fired a thin smile Sharon's way. It was the deadliest and most subtle of threats.

Panic skittered over her, leaving her skin clammy and her pulse erratic. Without warning, he moved towards her. She held herself very still, an invisible mist of fear creeping around her ankles and laying icy claim to the blood in her veins.

Clint came to a stop less than a foot away. From a great distance, she heard the front door close behind Fern.

'I've waited seven weeks for this moment,' he said, in a curiously soft, flat voice. 'I think such patience deserves a proper welcome, don't you?'

His hands were cold around her neck. Chillingly so. He stepped closer, tilted up her chin with his thumbs. Her neck snapped back so abruptly that her towel turban came all unravelled and fell to the floor. She went to twist away from him, but he threaded unyielding fingers through the wet tangle of her hair and immobilised her. Before she could object, he brought his mouth down on hers, and his lips were cold, too.

She tried to breathe and couldn't. Tried to swallow, to relieve some of the aching tension in her throat, and couldn't. Tried to close her eyes, and dared not, because his remained open, staring soullessly down at her throughout that interminable, horrible kiss.

'Have you missed me, dear heart?' he whispered, at last releasing her hair and running his mouth over her cheek to her ear.

'Yes.' She was too terrified to lie.

'Then why did you run away from me? After our night together, I thought we were well on the way to a fresh start. Was I wrong?'

'Yes,' she said faintly.

He looked down at her reproachfully and traced the outline of her throat with an icy fingertip. 'Do I take that to mean it was nothing more than a one-night stand for you?'

'No,' she mumbled. She could control nothing—not her brain, not her body. Every part of her, from her voice to her limbs, was shaking. His touch unnerved her completely, left her feeling as though she might disintegrate into a thousand tiny pieces at his feet. 'Please,' she pleaded, 'let me go. I think I'm feeling faint.'

But he was not disposed to show mercy. 'Faint? Oh, I don't think so. I think "frightened" is closer to the truth.' He appraised her face with chilling detachment. 'Why don't we sit down and discuss what it is that has you so petrified of me all of a sudden? Except that...' he backed up to the sofa, leaned against it, and pulled her firmly closer, so that she could feel every well-honed, steely inch of him pressed against her, and he could feel her trembling fear '...it really isn't sudden at all, is it, my darling? You've been afraid of me ever since the day you walked into my arms in the middle of the Dunns' driveway, the week before the wedding. Don't you think it's time you told me why?'

It was the worst kind of nightmare come true, the one where a person could not run from an unseen and oppressive danger. She could not control the shivering apprehension that possessed her. 'I'm cold,' she complained, and that much at least was the truth. But he was burning, she realised, for all that his kiss had chilled her, and although she was moulded against his warmth it couldn't touch her.

'Cold?' His concern was patently phoney. 'Yes, I'd say you're cold. Cold and hard. What other way is there to describe a woman who plays fast and loose with a man's heart, then walks away from him without a word?'

Over his shoulder she saw the roses, at least three dozen lying on the coffee-table on the other side of the sofa, nestled in a bed of maidenhair ferns and tied with satin ribbon. She'd have noticed them sooner if he hadn't blocked her view. 'Is that what this visit is all about, Clint?' she asked, a tiny hope springing to life inside her. 'The fact that we made unplanned love but, this time, I didn't use it as a means of trying to hold you to account?'

'What if I wanted to be held accountable?' he shot back.

If she didn't exactly begin to relax, at least she experienced a slight lessening of the awful tension that had gripped her ever since she'd walked into the room and looked into his eyes. 'I'm sorry if I hurt your feelings,' she said. 'That wasn't my intention.'

'Then let's talk about what you did intend.'

'I'd rather not.' This time when she tried to pull away, he let her go, and she escaped to the piano, because it allowed her to put about as much distance as possible between him and her.

'I'd rather,' he returned inflexibly, 'and, what's more, I think you owe me some sort of explanation. I've come a long way and waited a long time to sort this out, my darling, and I don't intend to be blown off by that sort of excuse.'

He'd never called her 'my darling' in the old days, and the way he kept repeating the words now, with that cutting edge in his husky voice, slashed fine lines through her nerves without leaving a scar.

'So,' he went on, 'why don't you do the socially acceptable thing and offer me a drink? Then we'll sit down together like the nice civilised adults we pride ourselves on being, and you can start at the beginning and tell me exactly what you had in mind when you hopped into the sack with me.'

'That's a degrading and vulgar description, even for you, Clint,' she said, stung.

'I'm a vulgar and degrading man when my pride's on the line,' he replied flatly.

So that was it! She might have known it wasn't his heart that had been hurt.

'Well? Are you going to offer me that drink, or do I pour my own?'

She complied in the sincere hope that, because she did, he'd have the good grace to cut his unannounced visit short. Much more of this cat-and-mouse game he was playing with her emotions, and she'd crack up completely. 'What would you like?'

'Whisky,' he said, his husky voice as unforgiving as an Arctic wind stripping the trees bare, 'and you might as well pour one for yourself while you're at it.'

The fear crawled over her again. 'I never touch hard liquor,' she said righteously, almost tottering to the antique victrola which did duty as a bar.

He stalked her relentlessly. 'Well, believe me when I tell you that, before this night is over, you'll wish you did,' he said, in that same ruthlessly controlled tone. 'Before you and I have finished our little talk, you're going to wish you could swill down anything that will dull your sensibilities as speedily as possible.' He closed in on her until she could feel his breath scorching the back of her neck. 'And after it's over, your life is going to seem like one long, miserable hangover!'

There was a rage in him such as she'd never seen before. It doubled the terror she was struggling so hard to suppress until it threatened to choke her. She had to swallow twice before she managed to articulate a reply. 'You're obviously extremely upset, Clint, but that hardly justifies your ungentlemanly threats. We're talking about only one night, after all, and I'd have thought you'd be glad that, this time, I'm not falling all over you and protesting my undying love.'

His hand reached past her and removed the crystal glass from her grasp. 'You're shaking again,' he observed dispassionately. 'You never used to be so nervous around men.'

'I'm not used to being harassed this way,' she retorted. 'Jason would never have dreamed of treating me like this.'

'Ah, yes, Jason.' Clint raised his drink in a mocking salute. 'Tell me something, dear heart...' He paused, sipped his whisky reflectively, then turned the full force of his chilling blue gaze on her face. 'Did he mind very much taking on a daughter when he married you?'

The blood seemed to ice in her veins. He'd found out! She didn't know how, or when; she just knew. And the only question was what he planned to do with the information. But because a tiny part of her brain held out the hope that she was wrong, that he didn't know or, at worst, only suspected, she had to bluff it out. 'What are you talking about, Clint?'

'The fact that you already had a child when you married Mr Jason McClure.'

'Oh, that!' Agitation left her too light-headed to consider the wisdom of what she said next. 'Your Aunt Jubilee voiced her suspicions to you,' she babbled, 'but that's all they were—suspicions. I'm afraid you've both jumped to the wrong conclusions.'

'Please leave my aunts out of this,' Clint said flatly, sauntering back to the sofa, and retrieving something from the coffee-table. 'And for God's sweet sake, spare me any more of your lies.'

She saw then what lay half concealed by the bouquet of roses: Fern's scrap-book, filled with mementoes of anniversaries, some of which pre-dated Jason's entry into their lives. Clint extracted a card from the heap lying loose on the table, and Sharon recognised it at once. How could she not? She'd given it to Fern herself, an ornate, lace-edged Victorian reproduction of a golden-haired child on a swing under an arbour of flowers. The inscription across the bottom leapt out to indict her: 'Happy Ninth Birthday to a Special Daughter'.

The numbed realisation that the charade had finally played to its conclusion paralysed Sharon and reduced everything to half-speed in somewhat the same way that the truly frightening part of a horror movie slowed down for greater impact. It took the utmost courage for her to raise her eyes and meet the condemnation she knew she'd find in Clint's.

CHAPTER TEN

THE heavy throbbing of Sharon's heart deafened her, battered at her ribs. She clutched at the victrola and felt a fingernail rip down to the quick, but it might have happened to someone else for all that the pain impinged on her. She tried to speak, but although she opened her mouth no sound came out. She simply stood there, stretching her lips like some grotesque gargoyle, while her blood seeped down to her ankles and took every facet of her neatly ordered life with it.

'Don't tell me you haven't got a nice, tidy rebuttal ready,' Clint said. If he had held a knife to her throat with the murderous blade pricking at her skin just enough to draw a pinpoint of blood in a foretaste of what was still to come, she could not have been more terrified.

'I don't—I don't...don't know...' Oh, God, how could she have prepared for this moment? How could she have suspected the pain of trying to explain her convoluted and monstrous deceit?

'You never did lose my baby, did you?' he enquired with deadly composure. 'You just told me that to punish me because I wasn't lavishing you with the sort of attention you'd been used to all your life.'

'I did...lose the baby,' she whimpered.

The ring of Baccarat crystal smashing against mahogany shattered the atmosphere with musical violence. 'What sort of imbecile do you think I am?' Clint raged, contempt blazing in his eyes. 'I can count, Mrs McClure.

146

That's my little girl who sleeps in the room down the hall, and I want to know how.'

He looked lethal. Attila the Hun on a rampage was a pussycat compared to Clint at that moment.

'There were two babies,' she cried on a dry sob. 'I lost one, and Fern . . . Fern was the twin that survived.'

Her pronouncement effected a miraculous change. His fury died as suddenly as it had flared, replaced by a stunned acceptance of a truth too bizarre to be fabrication. 'You conceived twins?' he asked hollowly.

'Yes,' she said, adding idiotically, 'two of them. Fraternal. I didn't know . . . not until after you and I . . .'

He paced around her with about as much trust as a man inspecting a wild cat. 'Why didn't you let me know?'

'I didn't know where you were,' she said, and flinched at the pathetic weakness of such an excuse.

'My aunts could have told you. They always knew where I could be reached.' He lifted a hank of hair from behind and settled a parody of a kiss at the nape of her neck. 'But you didn't want me to know, did you, Sharon?'

She cringed at his touch. 'I didn't . . .'

He ran stealthy fingers inside the collar of her terry-cloth robe, leaving behind a trail of goose-flesh. 'Imagine that,' he said conversationally. 'My oh, so anxious little bride didn't want me to know that I had fathered two children. She didn't want to share any more.'

Suddenly Sharon had had enough. 'How do you know what I did and didn't want, Clint?' she cried, spinning away from him. 'You were no more interested in how I felt then than you are now.'

'Don't you try to turn this around and pin the blame on me,' he shot back.

She ran a distracted hand through her hair. 'I'm not. I'm just trying to make you understand how I felt. I was only nineteen, Clint. A child, divorced and alone. The choices facing me then didn't seem as clean-cut and simple as they might appear now, and if you think any of them were easy you couldn't be more wrong.'

'I'm overcome with pity,' he sneered. 'You poor, misunderstood little thing, having to live with the consequences of your actions!'

'You're not the only one who's suffered, Clint,' she said wearily. 'I know all about loneliness and regret and heartache.'

'You don't know diddly-squat!'

She couldn't look at him, not if she wanted to pursue her own defence. It hurt her too much to see how wounded he was. 'You don't have to forgive me,' she said, her voice catching. 'You don't even have to understand me, but you owe me the chance to explain how——'

'I don't owe you a damned thing, Sharon.' He swung back to the bar and snatched up another glass. She heard the liquor splash over the polished surface of the victrola, heard the decanter crash down on the silver tray, heard his breath heaving in his lungs.

'Even a criminal's entitled to a hearing before he's convicted,' she said. 'Can't you at least allow me that much?'

He tipped back his head and tossed the whisky down his throat in one gulp. Although he stood with his back to her, she could tell from his ramrod-straight spine that he held on to his control by a very precarious thread.

The silence spun out, unbroken, for a good thirty seconds. When he made no move to end it, she took it to mean he was prepared to hear what she had to say. 'You made it very clear,' she began, the truth coming easily at last, 'that you couldn't wait to be free of me. The tragedy of losing our baby was tempered for you by the chance it gave you to get out of a relationship that had never, even at its best, been what you really wanted.'

'I married you,' he cut in rawly. 'That counted for something.'

'Something?' She sighed. 'It counted for everything with me, Clint; that's the whole point.'

'No,' he contradicted. 'If it had, you would have found a way to let me know. You would have wanted that baby to know its father.'

'I did!' she cried passionately. 'I wanted that almost as much as I wanted you to love me.'

'You expect me to swallow that?' His eyes condemned her. 'You gave my daughter to another man, Sharon, gave her another man's name.'

'I didn't marry Jason until over two years after you left,' she said. 'By then I had reconciled myself to never seeing you again.'

'*Two years*? It was more like two months the last time you ran this story by me.' His anger rolled over her like soft thunder. 'Yet not once, in all that time, did it once occur to you that I had a right to know I'd fathered a second child.'

'Why would it?' she flared back. 'You weren't all that thrilled to hear the news the first time around.'

'No, I wasn't, but that doesn't mean I didn't mourn the baby we lost, and you had no right—*no right*, do you hear?—to keep the knowledge of Fern's birth from me. My God...!' He paced to the glass doors leading to the terrace, pounded his fist against the wooden frame and set the panes to rattling, and swung back to point an accusing finger at her. 'You spout off about being entitled to a hearing before I find you guilty, but when did you grant me the same concession, Sharon? Or did you think it was no more than I deserved to wander the face of the earth, trying to exonerate myself for having screwed up your life and, incidentally, my own as well?'

'I didn't think you'd care,' she whispered.

'You didn't *want* to think. It was more comfortable to forget I ever existed. I might as well have been dead.'

'Yes!' She swiped at the tears splashing down her face. 'I told myself you were, because it was easier to get on with my life that way, but I never forgot you, though heaven knows I wish I could have.'

'Well, of course you didn't, dear heart. You had a little reminder in Fern. I can't believe...' he shook his head '...can't believe how stupid I've been. The signs were all there from the start, if I'd chosen to see them. I wonder if, at some gut level, I haven't known all along and just didn't want to believe you'd sink to cheating me like this.' His face was haggard. 'I hope you've found it all very entertaining.'

'I'd hardly call being nineteen and alone and pregnant by a man who disappeared "entertaining".'

'You weren't alone. You had your parents, who were no doubt over the moon that I'd shown myself to be every bit as reprehensible as they'd always thought me to be.'

His assessment wasn't too far off the mark. 'Of course we'll stand by you,' her mother had said, pasting on her martyred air. 'When the time comes, you can count on us to be there.' But when, in the throes of her worst contraction, Sharon had cried out for Clint, her mother had said scornfully, 'Save your energy for what's still to come, Sharon. Clint Bodine isn't going to bring you one iota of comfort or relief, and the sooner you accept that fact, the sooner all this will be over.'

All this... Fern. Love and loneliness. Triumph and sorrow. Victory and loss. Because, despite the joys of motherhood, the success of her career and, eventually, Jason, a tiny piece of Sharon's heart had remained a wilderness—parched, arid, starved. There hadn't been a man alive who could bring it back to life, except Clint. And he had fallen off the edge of the earth.

'Clint...' She appealed to him with outstretched hands.

He shrugged her off. 'Who else knows about this? The whole damned town?'

'Only Margot and my parents—and Jason, of course.'

'I never was quite good enough for the Carstairs' gently reared daughter, was I? Tell me, was Jason more their type? More conservative? More docile?'

'No. He didn't particularly like my mother.'

'Your *father* doesn't particularly like your mother!'

'This isn't about my parents, Clint. It's about us—and Fern.'

'On that, at least, we agree.' He inspected his neatly trimmed fingernails as though it were of the utmost importance that they be flawlessly clean. When he looked at her again, he no longer hid behind anger or cruelty to mask his pain. 'Why couldn't you just have come to me? Or was I too low a life-form, after everything that had happened between us?'

'No!'

He ignored her denial. 'Did I make just one mistake too many—was that it?' He shook his head, his expression mirroring disgust, though for whom she couldn't tell. 'Well, I shouldn't have impregnated you, Sharon. I shouldn't have walked away. I shouldn't have done a lot of things that I did, but you certainly came up with the punishment to fit all my crimes in this lifetime and the next. What I want to know is this: when was it all supposed to stop? If I hadn't come looking for you, would I ever have found out I have a daughter? Or would I have gone to my grave believing I'd ruined your life?'

'Ever since we met again I've wished you knew the truth.'

'Then why didn't you tell me?' The question radiated scorn. 'You had opportunity enough. Our one-night stand would have been the perfect time.'

'No! When you kiss me, touch me, everything else fades away, Clint, even Fern, even the lies. It's always been that way; it always will be. When you make love to me,' she went on, telling him everything now that she had nothing left to lose, 'my whole world becomes you, and nothing else seems to matter. I fall in love with you all over again, so completely that good sense and judgement fly out the window, and all sorts of impossible cravings and improbable dreams fly in.'

He sneered, brushing aside her words with the contempt they no doubt deserved. 'Do you know how long I've blamed myself for our failed marriage? Do you care that there've been other women—*good* women, Sharon, *honest* women—who'd have made excellent wives but who never had the chance because *you* wouldn't vacate the position?'

'You told me none of those women mattered,' she whimpered, aghast all over again at how much it hurt to think of him with someone else. 'And you've never wanted a wife. You're just saying that to punish me.'

'Am I? Haven't you wondered why I showed up here today?'

If she had, she'd long since forgotten. It seemed an
aeon ago that she'd stepped out of the shower and into
this waking nightmare. 'Why did you?'

'I came to ask you to marry me again.' He laughed
with grim amusement. 'I came to ask if you'd let me be
Fern's stepfather. Isn't that rich? Now I don't have to
do either.'

She ignored his last statement, too amazed to consider
its implications. 'Marry me? Why?'

He looked her over as if she were some very good
piece of imitation jewellery when what he'd been looking
for was the genuine article. 'Because I thought I loved
you,' he said hollowly, 'and because I'm such a bloody
fool that I thought you loved me back.'

'I've always loved you,' she cried, consumed by pain.
'I never stopped.'

'You expect me to believe that?'

'No more than I believe you,' she conceded. 'Not once,
in all the times we've been together, did you tell me you
loved me——until now, when it's too late to matter.
Perhaps, if you had, I'd have found the courage to tell
you what I should have told you nine years ago. Perhaps
there wouldn't have been any need to keep Fern a secret
to begin with.' She sank on to the nearest chair, dull
exhaustion seeping through her. 'Where do we go from
here, Clint? It seems there's no repairing the damage.'

'Oh, it hasn't all been a complete waste of energy,' he
said. 'I didn't get what I came for, but I'm not exactly
leaving empty-handed.' He placed his glass on the man-
telpiece. 'I came here a lovesick bachelor and I'm leaving
a heart-whole father. Not a bad exchange, I'd say. The
only problem is...' his voice faltered, just for a second
'...my daughter calls me Mr Bodine, like the well-
mannered little girl you've brought her up to be.'

'I never meant it to be this way,' Sharon cried, in a pitiful attempt to exonerate actions grown hideous in the last few minutes.

'You meant to punish me,' he said. 'You meant to make me pay, and God knows I have. Well, now it's your turn.'

A new kind of horror crept over Sharon. 'You can't tell Fern!'

'I can do a lot more than that, my darling. I can sue for visitation rights. I want to get married again, whether or not you're the lucky bride, and I want to make a home. How do you suppose Fern will take to the idea of a stepmother?'

Some other woman supplanting her in her daughter's life? Over her dead body! 'You can take your wife-elect and go to you know where!' she spat.

'To hell, you mean? Oh, I don't think so. I've already spent enough time there to last me the rest of my life. I think I deserve a little bit of heaven for a change. Too bad you won't be the one to share it with me.'

'If you so much as try to drag Fern into a court battle, Clint, I'll make sure you never see her again.'

'Don't adopt that snotty attitude with me, Sharon,' he returned witheringly. 'I won't stand for it.'

'I don't take orders from you, Clint Bodine.'

'As of now, you do. As of now, I'm the one calling the shots.'

Of all the consequences she'd ever imagined, having Fern end up in the middle of a custody battle was the last thing Sharon had ever envisaged. She could think of nothing more disastrous to her daughter's well-being. 'Clint, please! If you have any feelings for Fern at all, don't use her to punish me.'

He surveyed her for a long, long time, his expression unreadable. Then his shoulders slumped and he turned away from her and wandered over to the piano, where there was a photograph of Jason that had been taken just before he died. Sharon kept it there for Fern's sake, because no little girl should have to lose two fathers so early on in her life. 'You really do hold all the cards, don't you, dear heart,' Clint said, 'even to forcing me to play second fiddle to a dead man? Oh, God; oh, God!'

His voice broke and a great shuddering sigh swept over him. When he swung back to face her, she saw there were tears in his blue eyes. She'd never seen him cry. She'd never heard a heart break. She saw and heard both in him at that moment, and nothing she'd ever known hurt her as much as that. She thought the pain might kill her. And wished it would.

'I love you so much.' She took a step towards him, let her whole heart show in her eyes. 'It doesn't have to end this way, Clint.'

He fended her off as if she were poison, and she knew she was about to lose him yet again. 'Stay away from me,' he said hoarsely.

Despair lent her courage. She kept on coming until she could run her hands over his beautiful face and touched her lips to his beautiful mouth. She kissed him, interweaving tenderness with erotic sensuality, employing all the finesse she could muster. It wasn't a role to which she was accustomed, but she couldn't bear to watch him walk out of her life a second time without one last desperate attempt to hold him.

Just for an instant he weakened. For one brief and lovely moment his arms slipped to her waist and his mouth softened in response, before he thrust her roughly away.

'The attraction's still there for us, Clint,' she whispered entreatingly. 'It will always be there.'

'Yes, it's still there,' he acknowledged, 'and it's damned near fatal.'

'You almost kissed me just now.'

'Yes, I did.' His rage was gone, his grief was under control, and he spoke to her kindly, the way a person might speak to an indulged, not very bright child.

Despair withered her heart. 'You cared enough to come here and ask me to marry you. What can I do to make things right for us again?'

He sighed patiently. 'I don't have to explain to you that it takes more than sex to make a marriage work, Sharon. It takes respect and it takes trust. How am I supposed to respect a woman who doesn't trust me enough to let me deal with the truth on my own terms? Tell me that and I might be able to come up with an answer to your question. But in the meantime there's nothing you can do to set things right. I'm afraid this time we really are washed up.'

He was walking towards, the door, out of her life, out of Fern's life. She was ready to grovel, plead, beg... bargain with her life, if she had to. 'Will we hear from you again?'

He misunderstood what she was asking. 'No,' he said, turning to look at her one last time. His eyes were as barren as a wasteland. 'I won't expose your secret—not because I want to spare you, but because of Fern. Because I won't destroy her memories of the only father she's ever known, and I won't show up her mother for the liar that she really is.'

'That wasn't what I meant. I——'

'But in return, there is one thing I do insist on. In the unlikely event that you should find yourself needing financial help—with her education, perhaps, or something like that—I want it to be me you come to, not your parents.'

'I won't know where to find you,' she said dully, a worn-out theme on a broken-down old record.

His lips curled in disgust. 'Try Crescent Creek. My roving days are over, and I'm settling down in my home town. I never got around to telling you that I made a small fortune helping rich families relocate to safe countries. I'm worth rather a lot of money these days—enough to buy the local airport for my private use, and the quarter section next to it. I'm going to become a rancher—inhale the scents and sounds of nature, get back to basics, connect with the environment, and all that sort of wholesome stuff.'

He flung a contemptuous glance around her living-room, at the baby grand piano, the Persian rugs, the silk upholstery, and shrugged his broad, magnificent shoulders. A rueful smile touched his lips. 'Come to think of it, you probably wouldn't have accepted my marriage proposal once you knew it would mean living in the boonies, even if you did have a private jet at your disposal to get you to wherever you needed to go for your business. I'm afraid Crescent Creek isn't quite up to your impeccable standards.'

She would live with him in a mud hut in the middle of the jungle, but he'd never believe her now. 'Is that all?' she asked, more defeated than she'd ever been in her life.

'Not quite. You can strike your mother as Fern's legal guardian in the event that something should happen to you. I'll take responsibility for my daughter, and, from all accounts, that's one thing Maxine will thank me for.'

He opened the front door, walked into the foyer, pressed the button to summon the lift.

He took her heart with him. She could feel it tear loose and follow him, and the only miracle was that it left behind no visible scar. 'Clint...!' His name strangled on a sob. 'What can I do to prove how much I love you?'

'There's nothing you can do,' he said, stepping inside the lift, 'except stay the hell out of my life.'

The doors whispered shut with their usual well-bred caution, cutting off her last image of him a little bit at a time. And then he was gone and her life was almost the same as it had been two hours before.

Almost, but not quite. Because the burden of deceit had at last been lifted from her shoulders. And because before she only thought she knew what a broken heart felt like, whereas now she knew.

Somehow she got through the next month and a half. School began for Fern, and Sharon worked long hours preparing to show her fall collection, which turned out to be her most successful ever. But the victory was empty and the future bleak. The world of fashion had lost its charm and no longer absorbed her as it once had.

Then, one day towards the end of October, Fern brought matters to a head. 'I heard you crying in bed last night, Mommy.'

'Oh, that! It——' Sharon fumbled for an explanation, but Fern cut her off.

'You cry almost every night, and your eyes are all pink and fat when you get up for breakfast.'

Well, that description certainly fitted! She'd looked like hell in the morning lately, and felt even worse.

'Ever since we got home from California,' Fern went on relentlessly. 'And you get up in the night, too, and make hot milk.'

'I sometimes have trouble sleeping, sweetheart.'

Her daughter regarded her with wise green eyes. 'Then you ought to do something abut it.'

And just like that, Sharon knew that Clint had been wrong. There *was* something she could do to prove how much she loved him. It would take time and it would take courage, and if it backfired it would cost her dearly, but there was something she could do.

'There's something I have to tell you, Fern, and I'm a little afraid,' she said, hoping her daughter's heart would be big enough to forgive the lies and accept the truth. 'It's a secret that I've kept for years, but I think it's time now to share it with you, because it's something you have a right to know.'

CHAPTER ELEVEN

SOME time in the night of December the twenty-third a howling blizzard swept down from the Arctic and blanketed the country around Crescent Creek under almost two feet of snow. Clint stood at the top of the porch steps and looked out at a Christmas-card world, with the trees all draped in white and half the landmarks obliterated. The patches of sky showing between the clouds were the brilliant, intense blue that, this far north of the equator, heralded the onset of a cold snap the likes of which he'd almost forgotten existed. His first Christmas at home in years had dressed itself up royally for the occasion.

They were playing Christmas music on the radio, schmaltzy songs about chestnuts roasting and lovers rolling around in the snow while sleigh bells rang. For some reason it made the ache of missing Sharon worse than usual, a damnable weakness which he deplored but seemed helpless to prevent. He'd tried a thousand times to devise a way back to her, but came up against the same obstacle every time: she hadn't trusted him enough and she hadn't loved him enough. And even having reached that same conclusion every time, still he missed her.

He couldn't rid himself of the memory of that last embrace. The untutored desperation of her kiss had dealt him a fatal blow, but he'd had his sights so firmly set on revenge that she'd slipped past his guard without his noticing it until the damage had been done. He'd been haunted day and night ever since.

They said, those nameless know-it-alls who decreed such lore, that keeping busy helped, so he'd tried keeping busy. He'd built his aunts a smart new bungalow to spare Celeste's arthritic knees and hips. He'd started a thoroughbred horse-breeding ranch on his hundred and sixty acres of rolling land.

He'd also looked for a wife, without success. Not that there weren't willing candidates, even in a town as small as Crescent Creek. As one of the major landowners in the area, plus the fact that he was single and under forty, he was considered extremely eligible. Even Vera Dunn had condescended to invite him to her pre-Christmas soirée last weekend, an event at which he'd been the flattering focus of attention by the cream of Crescent Creek's unmarried ladies. He had tried very hard to drum up some enthusiasm for their regard. Instead he'd been left empty and indifferent.

He ought to have known better. He'd run all over the world for the better part of a decade, trying with a conspicuous lack of success to forget Sharon. She was in his blood, worse than some damned tropical disease, and he might just as well learn to live with the fact.

Behind him, the aunts' old house—his house now—was decked out in winking coloured lights and holly wreaths, in keeping with the spirit of the season. Ever since they'd moved to their new place his aunts had made a habit of sneaking back when he wasn't around and doing things for him, from baking pies to bottling preserves and filling his freezer with three-course dinners that required nothing from him but a quick zap in the microwave oven.

'Because you have no wife,' they'd always say when he asked them why they spent their limited energies on a man perfectly capable of looking after himself. No doubt this latest display of yule-tide excess had been installed for the same reason, and, instead of a winter cruise to the Bahamas, he wished his Christmas gift to them could be the presentation of some suitable woman for their approval as a niece-in-law.

He glanced up at the sky. It was going to snow again. The clouds were thickening into a solid pale grey ceiling, and the temperature had surely dropped another five degrees since he'd first come out of the house. He'd better get a move on if he was to accomplish everything he had planned for the day and be back in time to meet the aunts at the country club for Christmas Eve dinner. There was a stack of paperwork waiting for his attention at the airfield, and before the light faded he wanted to get out to the ranch to check on his prize mare, My Girl. His chief hand had phoned earlier to tell him she'd probably foal before the day was over.

The four-wheel-drive truck slithered briefly on the driveway before cutting a swath through the snow. Across the street a family of boys raced around, pelting each other with snowballs, while their sisters lay on their backs on the ground and flailed their arms up and down to make snow angels.

Clint couldn't help himself. He looked at those carefree kids and, even though he knew the pang would linger all day, he allowed his thoughts to dwell on Fern. What was she doing at this moment? Was she too old to hang up a stocking?

Not that she needed one for the gift he'd be giving to her. The trust fund he'd established in her name would remain his secret, because she was too smart not to

wonder why a near-stranger would want to give her the
sort of money he intended setting aside for her, and also
because he couldn't stomach the thought of receiving a
dutiful note of gratitude that began, 'Dear Mr Bodine...'
For now, the satisfaction of knowing he was con-
tributing something to her future was thanks enough.
He couldn't help but hope, though, that the card he'd
sent her would end up another cherished souvenir in her
scrap-book.

It was hard to believe that a mild drizzle had been falling
in Vancouver and that they were only an hour's flight
away from home when they stepped out of the new
airport at Harperville shortly after noon on Christmas
Eve.

Fern was enchanted. 'I didn't know it would be
snowing. It's like Switzerland, Mommy!'

The man in charge of the car rental desk was of a
similar, though less enthusiastic opinion. 'Driving thirty
miles to Crescent Creek in this, lady? You'd be better
to wait out the storm here and go tomorrow. You'll still
be in plenty of time for the turkey dinner, and you're
more likely to get there in one piece.'

But Sharon was nervous enough at what lay before
her. She didn't think she could wait another day to go
through with what she had planned. 'I'm an experienced
driver,' she assured the man, whose concern was well-
meant, 'and surely the ploughs are out already?'

'Probably,' he agreed, 'but at the rate this stuff is
coming down the roads'll be clogged again before you
know it. However, if you're that determined to go...'
He scanned the row of keys hanging on a board behind
him and selected one. 'You'd better take something with
dual airbags and a good set of winter tyres. I'll get

someone to start the engine and warm up the car while you sign the lease.'

It was mid-afternoon before they reached the out-skirts of Crescent Creek, but, despite having made slow progress, Sharon didn't experience any real difficulty until she tried to negotiate the long, slow hill that curved up the last half-mile to the aunts' house. The car, which had behaved with exemplary decorum up to that point, balked at the steepness of the grade and slid gracefully backwards, coming to rest with its elegant nose in the air in a drift on the side of the road. Nothing Sharon could do would coax it to move again.

'We'll have to walk the rest of the way,' she told Fern. 'Button up, sweetheart, and put on your mittens. It's snowing again and there's a horrible wind blowing.'

But it was worse than horrible; it was vicious—a freezing gale that numbed their faces and blasted them with snow until they could barely see. Sharon clutched Fern by the hand, knowing that the effort of battling the cold and the deep snow was draining her daughter's strength at an even more alarming rate than it sapped her own.

They weren't dressed for this kind of weather. The gale cut through their clothes as cleanly as a knife through butter, and the final four hundred yards was pure agony. When at last the lights from the house showed through the gloom, Sharon's apprehension at soon seeing Clint again was tempered by huge relief that she and Fern would shortly be warming themselves by a roaring fire.

'Well, we're here,' she panted, pulling Fern into the lee of the garage and out of the worst of the storm. 'Are you sure that you're still up to what comes next?'

Fern swallowed, all her certainty in happy endings apparently swept away in the blizzard. 'What if he doesn't care any more, Mommy?'

'Oh, he cares, sweetheart. No matter how he behaves when he sees me, you can be sure he'll be glad to see you.'

'He has to be glad to see both of us,' Fern insisted.

'I hope he is,' Sharon said, with heartfelt sincerity, 'but even if he isn't I hope you'll still be able to do what we planned.'

Fern looked across at the house. The coloured lights strung along the porch and around the windows twinkled through the gloom in welcome, but Sharon could see that her daughter felt very unsure of herself. 'What if he wants me to stay but he tells you to go away, Mommy?'

'I've booked us a room at the hotel until after Christmas. I'll go there.'

'I don't want to stay here by myself.'

She wasn't nearly as grown-up as she sometimes seemed, and Sharon wondered, not for the first time, if she was asking too much of her daughter. Maybe she'd asked too much ever since that moment in October when she'd decided to try to prove to Clint that she was capable of honesty and deserving of respect, but it was too late to backtrack now. 'The aunts will be there, too. Remember how much you liked them when we came out for the wedding?'

'Yes.' Fern tugged the hood of her jacket more securely around her ears and offered a wan smile. 'Let's go. And don't worry, Mommy. It'll all be OK, you'll see.'

They trudged the last few yards up the path to the steps, with the snow so deep in places that it trickled down inside their boots. Even over so short a distance, the wind slashed at their faces and drew tears from their eyes before they reached the sanctuary of the porch.

'We'd better do something about this, or he'll think we're sorry to see him, instead of the other way around.' Sharon fished through her bag for tissues and stifled the urge to giggle hysterically. She was wound up tighter than a spring, and it wouldn't take much to tip her control over the edge. 'That's better,' she said, mopping at their tears before they froze on their cheeks. 'Ring the bell, sweetheart, and let's get this over with.'

Fern reached for the old-fashioned iron bell and pulled on the handle. They could hear its clanging chimes echoing through the house, but they were the only two who did.

'No one's home.' Sharon sagged with disappointment and fatigue. So much effort, so much anticipation and anxiety, and for what?

'Well, they haven't gone far,' Fern said, rubbing at the frosted window-panes with her mittened hand and pressing her face to the glass. 'They've got lights on down the hall and I can see a Christmas tree in the corner of one of the rooms.'

Her teeth were chattering with the cold, and her face had taken on a pinched, white look that alarmed Sharon. 'We can't hang around out here in weather like this, and it's too far to fight our way back to the car, even if we could get it to go anywhere,' she decided, and groped for the door-handle, half hidden by an enormous be-ribboned holly wreath.

As was the custom in a town where everyone knew everyone else, the door wasn't locked. It swung open, the tail-ends of the scarlet satin ribbons wafting in the current of warm pine-scented air that streamed out to greet the visitors. 'Come on, Fern,' she urged. 'We'll wait inside and at least be warm.'

There was a fire all set and ready to go in the hearth in the living-room. In the kitchen a tray of freshly baked mince tarts sat cooling on the scrubbed-pine table and a pot of something that smelled like Jubilee's home-made lentil soup simmered on the stove.

Sharon took peripheral note of it all as she knelt and touched a match to the kindling in the fireplace, then turned her attention to stripping off Fern's sodden outer clothing. The child was practically swaying on her feet, and submitted with unusual docility to being undressed like a baby. The cold had eaten through to her bones, and she seemed on the verge of hyperthermia. It was going to take more than the still meagre warmth of the fire to restore her body heat. A hot bath and a bowl of Jubilee's soup were in order.

By the time the grandfather clock in the hall struck four Fern was sound asleep on the living-room sofa, snuggled under one of Celeste's hand-made quilts, and Sharon was left with nothing to do but pace the floor and wait for the aunts to come home and tell her where she could find Clint. But every time she peered through the window it seemed that a bit more of the driveway had been obliterated by the snow, and it occurred to her that perhaps the old dears were stranded and wouldn't make it home that night at all.

By five o'clock her nerves were stretched to breaking-point. She'd waited nearly three months to try to set things right with Clint. She didn't think she could endure waiting another day.

For all her anxiety, however, she didn't hear the sound of an engine or see the lights of a vehicle creeping up the snow-clogged driveway. She was busy feeding the fire,

and had no idea that anyone was home until she felt a
breath of icy air from the outside weaving around her
legs, followed by the sound of snow being stamped from
boots too heavy to belong to a woman's foot.

Rising silently from the hearth, Sharon stole out to
the hall, half knowing and half dreading that it was Clint
who had finally shown up.

He didn't notice her. He slapped the snow from his
leather gloves, shouldered the door closed, and leaned
against it in a gesture of exhaustion. But if his face was
drawn with fatigue, there was an elation in his eyes that
more than compensated for it. He was thinner, and he
looked not happy exactly, but satisfied and content. Until
his glance fell on the two pairs of boots—hers and
Fern's—and stared down at them, perplexed and suddenly wary.

It was time to announce herself. 'I wasn't expecting
you,' she said, stepping out of the shadows.

He pushed away from the door and flicked on the
lamp set on a table near the wall. 'I think that's supposed to be my line,' he said, holding himself very still
and wiping his face clean of all emotion. She had no
idea whether he was angry, surprised, or shocked. 'How
did you get in here, Sharon?'

'The door wasn't locked, and it was so cold outside——'

He rolled his eyes. 'The aunts were here!' he said, as
if that explained everything.

'Yes,' Sharon said. 'That's who I was waiting for, but
you're not them.'

'No, I'm not,' he agreed. 'My aunts are shorter and
fatter. And older.'

'And they're not men.' Oh, lord, Sharon! Better to
keep your mouth shut if this is the best you can do!

'To the best of my knowledge, no,' he said, still with that same inscrutable expression. 'Now why don't we stop this silly bantering and you just come right out and tell me what you're doing in my house?'

'*Your* house? But your aunts——?'

'Don't live here any more. They have a new place closer to the centre of town.'

'I had no idea.'

'Why should you? It's hardly any of your concern.' He shrugged out of his shearling-lined jacket and slung it over the newel post at the foot of the spiral staircase. Then he flexed his shoulders and rolled his head in a tight circle to relieve the cramped muscles in the back of his neck. 'What do you want, Sharon? It's been a long day.'

'I can see it has,' she said softly, feasting her eyes on the sight of him. He looked tough and capable, strong, determined and utterly beautiful, but she couldn't tell him so. She couldn't tell him anything of the feelings he aroused in her—how she ached to smooth away the grooves of tension at each side of his mouth, how she longed to go to him and put her arms around him and hold him.

But he must have read all of it on her face, because he turned away and fiddled with the collar of his jacket, as though he couldn't stand to look at her a moment longer. 'My Girl went into labour this morning,' he said, tossing the words over his shoulder like a challenge. 'It's her first, and I feel as if I've been up since dawn. I need something to wake me up, so I'm going to make a pot of coffee. You can join me, if you want, and tell me what it is that's brought you up here in such foul weather.'

She barely heard him. The aunts' absence and the freshly baked mince tarts, the home-made soup, in a house decked out for Christmas with no one home to enjoy any of it, suddenly made a ghastly sort of sense. He was married. His wife—someone else, not her, someone young and fresh and innocent—was about to give birth to his child!

The floor seemed to rock under her, shifting the whole scenario into a new and cruel focus. The chances she'd taken, telling Fern the truth, the hopes she'd nurtured, had all been for nothing. She'd always known they might amount to too little, but she'd never expected they'd come too late. 'Oh, God!'

He jerked around at the sound of that strangled moan, his fear that he might succumb to the grinding need to touch her eclipsed by a more insidious dread. 'Sharon, what's the matter? Is it Fern?'

'Fern?' She looked shattered, her eyes wide and staring, her sudden pallor alarming. 'No,' she said brokenly, 'it's not Fern.'

He reached for her then, afraid she might collapse. 'Tell me,' he begged urgently, and took her hands. They were colder than his, colder than ice. 'What is it? Why are you here?'

The tears gushed from her eyes at that, fountains of them splashing down her face from some deep inner well. She looked small and fragile and beautiful, and he couldn't stand it. It was time to stop fooling himself. His arms, his heart, his whole life, were empty without her.

He curled his hand around her fine narrow waist and drew her to him as naturally as the sun shone on June brides . . . and wondered how in hell he'd ever let her go the first time. 'Sharon,' he whispered hoarsely, 'tell me what's wrong and, whatever it is, we'll deal with it together.'

It was the wrong thing to say, though he couldn't fathom why. One minute she was leaning against him as if he were the last solid thing left on earth, the next springing away from him as if he'd stabbed her.

'She might not like that,' she said, her voice bleak behind the tears. 'I wouldn't, in her place.'

'Who?' he asked, mystified. 'Fern?'

'Your...wife.'

She had such difficulty getting the word out that it took him a moment to comprehend what she'd said. Even after he'd figured it out, it still didn't make any sense. 'What wife?' he asked, reaching for her again. 'I'm not married.'

'*Her*, then!' she spat, shying away from him. 'Your pregnant lady or whatever you want to call her.'

Light dawned. He smiled, almost obscenely gratified at the conclusions she'd reached and the reactions they'd provoked. 'You mean My Girl?'

She let out a muffled groan and backed away.

He stalked her. 'My Girl delivered this afternoon, dear heart——'

'Don't call me that! Don't *ever* call me that again!'

'A fine black colt.' He trapped her in the corner, next to the grandfather clock. 'Cute as a bug. You'll love him, dear heart.'

She was all ready to fire another missile of rage when his words sank home and left her speechless. He took immediate advantage and dipped his head to kiss her full on the mouth. She tasted like heaven, and he wondered why he'd been such a stubborn fool that he'd resisted so long something that felt so completely right. 'Merry Christmas, dear heart,' he murmured.

She wrenched her mouth free. 'A horse?' she practically shrieked. 'We're talking about a horse, not a wife?'

'We'd better be,' he said, sliding his hands up her shoulders and imprisoning her face so that he could kiss her again. 'I only met My Girl five months ago, which means she was six months pregnant when I bought her.'

Sharon flushed. 'I've made a fool of myself again.'

'I'm afraid you have,' he said. 'You're always expecting the worst from me, and I can see it's going to take a lifetime to teach you differently.'

Outside the snow batted softly at the windows, insistent as ever, but the frozen look in Sharon's eyes was melting a little. 'A lifetime?' she echoed. 'But you said the last time I saw you that you were going to find some other woman.'

'Some other woman won't do, I'm afraid. A man wants someone who makes him feel like a thirty-year-old lover even when he's eighty-nine and ready to meet his Maker. He wants more than a woman; he wants a wife. A mother for his children. I had both of those things in you, and was foolish enough to let them go. Now I want them back again.'

She looked at him, a trace of doubt in her expression. 'But what about what I did? What about——?'

'No.' He laid a finger over her lips. 'No more raking over the past. What's done is done, and the miracle is that none of it changes the one thing that really matters.'

Her voice trembled, and so did her mouth under his finger. 'What's that?'

'That life with you is better than life without you, and that nothing should keep us apart any longer. I love you,' he said. 'I've always loved you. I always will.'

'Does that mean we have a truce?' she asked.

He reached for her again, threaded gentle fingers through her hair, brought her up hard against him. 'I think "surrender" is more like it.'

'I did that a long time ago, Clint.'

'So did I, dear heart, but I'm only just getting around to admitting it.'

'Are you going to kiss her again?' an interested voice enquired from the shadows of the living-room.

He almost yelped in shock. 'Yes,' he finally managed. 'Merry Christmas, sweet pea.'

'Merry Christmas, Daddy.'

It took a full minute before her answer struck home. It took an answer like that to distract him from the woman quivering in his arms. Not quite daring to believe, he turned to face his daughter. She sat perched on the arm of the sofa like one of Santa's elves, draped in a quilt. The only thing missing was the pointed cap. 'What did you call me?'

'Daddy,' she repeated. 'I hope you don't mind.'

He turned dazed eyes back to Sharon. 'She knows?'

'Yes.'

'You told her?'

'Yes.'

'Why?'

'Because I wanted to give you something special, not just for Christmas but for the rest of your life. Something that I should have given you a long time ago. Something to prove how much I've learned to trust you, and how deeply I've always loved you. I told her everything, Clint, right from the beginning.'

He struggled to find his voice, lodged somewhere at the back of a throat grown thick with emotions he could barely control. 'You didn't have to do that,' he said.

And he meant it. Taking from her wasn't the issue; it was what he had to give that counted. That was what love was really all about.

'Are you going to marry her?' Fern wanted to know, head cocked inquisitively to one side.

'Definitely. I won't take no for an answer.'

'Oh, good! I'll get to be a bridesmaid again.'

'Not so fast, sweet pea,' Clint said. 'This time I have some serious courting to do before the wedding. And there's something you have to do even sooner than that. Before midnight tonight, in fact.'

The first person they saw when they walked through the doors of the country club was Vera Dunn.

'Why, Clinton Bodine, you sly thing!' She intercepted his passage, pouncing on him with the eagerness of a starving coyote. 'I've been looking for you all over the place. I want you to meet my niece, Cassandra.'

'And I want you to meet my fiancée, Sharon,' he replied, drawing them both close to him, 'and my daughter, Fern.'

It was almost worth all the wasted years to see the socially adept Vera Dunn outmanoeuvred on her own turf. She paled visibly and retreated a step. 'You can't possibly mean that,' she declared faintly.

'I was never more serious in my life. Compliments of the season to you all.'

'You enjoyed that!' Sharon accused him, as he swept them towards the dining-room.

He grinned and slid a possessive arm around her waist. 'I did.'

The aunts didn't see Clint and his guests sneak up on them. They were seated with their backs to the room, at a corner table next to the fireplace. Against the window an enormous Noble fir reached to the twelve-foot ceiling, its branches pricked with pinpoints of light.

'If Clinton doesn't get here in the next five minutes,' Jubilee boomed, 'I'm going to order another sherry. Will you join me, Sister?'

'Two sherries before dinner?' Celeste sounded scandalised. 'Oh, I don't think so, Jubilee. Why, I might get tipsy and do something foolish like invite the waiter to dance a two-step!'

'Then pray abstain,' Jubilee replied tartly. 'With your feet, you'd look like a duck trying to stamp out a forest fire.'

Fern started to giggle helplessly at that. Shaking a warning finger her way, Clint stepped forward and kissed his aunts on the cheek. 'Make it champagne instead,' he said, 'and we'll join you. This is a special occasion. Merry Christmas, Aunt Jubilee, Aunt Celeste.'

'What sort of special occasion?' Jubilee asked.

Celeste beamed and hugged him. 'Merry Christmas, dear boy.'

'And who's "we"?' Jubilee wanted to know, unmollified. 'I'm not in the mood for guessing games, Clinton. You've kept me waiting too long for my dinner.'

'I have found the perfect Christmas gift for you,' he said.

'Rubbish,' Jubilee declared. 'What you've done is gone out and spent a fortune on things we don't need, when the one thing we'd most like wouldn't cost you a penny.'

'We know you're tired of hearing it, but all we want is to see you get married, dear boy,' Celeste put in.

'I am,' Clint said.

'We're not getting any younger, after all, and it would be nice for us to know that you had a little family of your own before...'

'We're pushing up daisies,' Jubilee finished for her. 'Mercy, Celeste; I sometimes think you can't wait to have me nailed down in my casket, and at this rate it might happen sooner rather than later. Sit down, for pity's sake, Clinton, and read the menu. I'm near starving to death. The gift, whatever it is, can wait until we've eaten.'

Fern started to giggle again, and no number of glares from Sharon could silence her. Neither of the aunts noticed.

Clint sighed and rolled his eyes. 'I said I'm getting married. I'm giving you a niece-in-law for Christmas, one who comes with an extra bonus.'

'I do believe he's serious, Jubilee,' Celeste declared, dropping the menu in her lap.

'There's only ever been one woman for you, Clinton,' Jubilee warned.

'I know,' he said.

Celeste looked behind her then, saw Sharon and Fern, and struggled out of her chair, squealing with well-bred delight. 'Clinton! Oh, my dear, dear boy!'

But Jubilee's head didn't move. She just smiled, a wise, eighty-two-year-old smile. 'So you finally sorted it all out, Clinton, and about time too,' she said, on a satisfied breath, and held a hand over her shoulder. 'Come and give me a kiss, Sharon, and bring my great-great-niece with you. I've waited a long time for this day to come.'

THE WEDDING EFFECT
SOPHIE WESTON

Born in London, **Sophie Weston** is a traveler by nature who started writing when she was five. She wrote her first romance recovering from illness, thinking her traveling was over. She was wrong, but she enjoyed it so much that she carried on. These days she lives in the heart of the city with two demanding cats and a cherry tree—and travels the world looking for settings for her stories.

CHAPTER ONE

IT WAS raining hard as Penny Dane sprinted across the tarmac to the double doors marked 'Hospital Administration'. She could feel the rain dripping off the feathery curls that had escaped from under her headscarf. They ran unpleasantly down her neck as she ran down the corridor.

Another breathless day, she thought ruefully. Another day of trying to do sixteen hours' work in eight, of making a thousand pounds do the work of double that figure. Another day when she would have no time to paint. *Again*.

The telephones were already ringing in her office. She picked up the nearest, shrugging one arm out of her wet anorak as she did so.

'St Anne's Hospital Administration.'

'Mrs Dane?'

It was Karen Harris, secretary to the hospital's most irascible consultant. Penny knew from experience that this would be a string of complaints. Too lengthy to deal with yet, she decided, so she said briskly, 'I'll have to call you back, Karen. The other phone is going.'

She broke the call and picked up the next line.

'St Anne's...'

This time it was a fellow administrator in another hospital in the district. She noted his problem and promised to call him back too. He did not want to spend any longer on the phone than she did.

'Last one,' she said to herself, easing the other arm out of her anorak. It fell squashily on to her chair and a strong aroma of damp mackintosh arose.

Penny wrinkled her nose. 'St Anne——'

'Penny. Darling, at last. That beastly phone has been ringing for *hours*.'

For thirty years the throaty voice had brought strong men out in a cold sweat all round the world. It had the same effect on Penny, though for different reasons. She braced herself for resistance.

'Hello, Mother! Nice to hear you. But unexpected.'

'Don't tell me I shouldn't ring you at work,' said Laura Brinkman, a laugh in the world-famous voice.

Even down the telephone on a wet Monday, when the audience was no one any more interesting than her eldest daughter, the charm was palpable, Penny thought despairingly. It was only too easy to see how Laura Brinkman had got her own way all her life. And her daughter was no more immune to the charm than anyone else. 'I've tried and tried to get you at home and all I get is your horrible answering-machine.'

'You could leave a message,' Penny pointed out. 'That's the object of the thing.'

Laura dismissed the suggestion. 'You know I hate them. Besides, I want to talk to you, darling.'

Penny's heart sank further, her suspicions confirmed. That meant her mother wanted her to do something and didn't want to run the risk of being refused. If she had left a message on the answering-machine then Penny would have had time to marshal her defences.

'I'm terribly busy, Mother,' she said warningly.

Laura laughed. 'I'd gathered that, darling. We never seem to see you these days.'

It was not a new complaint. What was more, if she could ever bring herself to admit it, Laura knew why.

Laura, an eternal optimist, lived in a world of constant sunshine where everyone loved everyone else, her daughters were beautiful, and their husbands adored them. It was not just that her mother never referred to bad experiences, Penny thought, it was that she did not allow them to have happened. Whenever anything bad happened to anyone she loved, Laura Brinkman rewrote history—gaily and thoroughly.

Penny loved her mother, but too much time spent in her sweetly scatty company made her feel that she would never get in touch with the real world again. Normally she did not brood too much on her past. But after a long weekend in Shropshire she would find herself driving back to London grimly reciting the events of the dreadful course of her marriage in case she started to live in Laura's fantasy universe as well. It made family reunions a strain.

And that, of course, was what Laura would want. Her youngest daughter was getting married and in Laura's dramatic hands the wedding was turning into a production of royal proportions. In the frenzy of happy activity, Laura would want all her daughters about her. In particular what she would want, Penny was fairly sure, was something between a jobbing gardener and an international personal assistant. A conveniently unattached eldest daughter without pressing domestic duties, however, would do.

'Mother, I'm up to my ears here. I can't take any time off.'

'The hospital will understand,' Laura assured her with the happy conviction of someone whose only office work, back in her glamorous teens, had been fitted round kindly friends of the family saying that of *course* she must go to Ascot if she had been invited. 'Tell them your mother needs you.'

Penny considered screaming, thought better of it, and shut her eyes. She took a long calming breath and reminded herself that it did no good to reason with Laura. Stay pleasant, stay firm and don't get pulled into an argument, she adjured herself.

'Celia's wedding—Celia helps you,' she said firmly.

The trouble was Celia, a model with gorgeous eyes and skin and the sweetest of temperaments, could not be trusted to find a shop without losing herself. Organising a society wedding, even her own, was way out of her reach.

'Celia's going to Jamaica,' said Laura, not without relief, Penny thought. 'On a shoot. She couldn't help me even if she wanted to.'

So it *was* the wedding arrangements. Laura wanted help and didn't see any reason why her eldest daughter shouldn't provide it. Penny winced.

The light on her telephone began to blink again.

'What exactly is it that you want, Mother? I'm on my own and there's someone else queuing on the line,' Penny said. 'Make it quick.'

Laura recognised the urgency of true feeling when she heard it. 'I need you home the week before the wedding,' she said with a briskness worthy of Penny herself. 'Things are piling up and I'll be on my own. Your father,' she added in a neutral tone, 'won't be back till the night before.'

There was a range of complicated messages there. Penny did not want to think about them at the moment.

The door opened and Sister Casualty put her head round the door. Penny beckoned her in. Sister Flynn perched on the corner of a desk and began to remove her wilting cap.

'Not the whole week,' she said, scanning the wall-chart of absences that she kept pinned on the wall. 'I can manage a long weekend the weekend before, though. We can get a lot done in four days,' she added bracingly.

It was even true. In the last five painful years she had acquired a practical efficiency that she would never have believed possible in her dreamy teens, Penny thought with amusement.

Laura said suddenly, 'Darling, is this wedding difficult for you?'

Penny flinched. But she said steadily enough, 'Only where it hits my diary.'

'I know it must *remind* you,' Laura said.

Penny's fingers were hovering over the control buttons of the telephone. 'Mother, I've *got* to go,' she said desperately.

'Just one other thing, darling.' Laura sounded distracted. But that could, thought Penny as she listened in gathering wrath, be a guilty conscience. 'Michael's old tutor. He'll be arriving on the Friday some time. Of course the girls and I will all be out with Celia and the bridesmaids and dear Michael will still be in London. So you'll have to collect the professor and look after him. Well, I mustn't keep you, darling. I know how busy you are.'

She rang off. So, by that time, had the other caller.

Penny put the receiver down slowly, tipped her head back and gave a small, ladylike scream.

Sue Flynn grinned. 'Do I detect a mother in action?'

Penny shook her head despairingly. 'See a lot of post-mother trauma in Casualty, Sue?'

She stood up and started to shake out the squashed anorak. Sue got off her desk and took it from her, smoothing it out with practised fingers. She had three rugby-playing sons and she knew about battered clothes.

'See a lot of it everywhere,' she said serenely. 'What does she want? Half your life, by the sound of it.'

Penny took the anorak and hung it on the peg behind the door.

'No, it's not as bad as that, thank God. Though it was once——' She stopped, annoyed at having said so much. She gave herself a little shake and gave a lop-sided grin. 'Don't listen to me, Sue. I just got up too late to finish a sketch and I'm mad with frustration as a result. Mother's not unreasonable. I'm just making a fuss about nothing.'

She ran her hand through the untidy blonde curls, grimacing at the dampness against her neck.

Sue looked at her shrewdly. 'Making a fuss isn't one of your outstanding qualities,' she observed. 'What's wrong? Is it this society wedding?' Sue knew more about Penny than most people.

Penny pulled a face. 'Oh, partly, I think. Partly it's my father. It sounds as if he's not being very co-operative.'

'The wedding effect,' Sue said sagely.

Penny was riffling through the papers in her in-tray. 'The what?'

'The wedding effect,' Sue repeated obligingly. She shook her head. 'They're supposed to such wonderful things. But in my experience all they do is make people fight. They seem to bring everything that's wrong in everyone's life bubbling to the surface.'

Struck, Penny stopped fiddling with the papers and thought about it.

'Contrast, I suppose. The happy couple gets a fairytale. Everyone else has the same old frustrations they're stuck with,' she said drily.

A drip trickled off the end of a curl and splashed on to a letter. Immediately the ink signature began to blur.

'Damn,' said Penny, recoiling. She wrung out a particularly sodden hank of hair and said, 'I know it's too early but I want a coffee. Do you?'

Sue widened her eyes. 'For me it's late, not early. I thought you'd never ask. I'll get it.'

There was a machine at the end of the corridor. By the time Sue came back with two black sugarless coffees, Penny had got her desk in some sort of order, fielded another phone call and switched on her computer. She was looking at her dairy page on the screen. She had still not sat down.

'Tough day?' asked Sue, peering over her shoulder. She passed the plastic cup over carefully.

'Thanks. No worse than usual.' Penny sipped and gave a long sigh of appreciation. 'Thank God for whoever it was who discovered coffee.' She looked at her notepad and pulled a face. 'Correction—it is worse than usual. Karen rang. Mr Perry must be on the warpath again. That man missed his vocation when he became a doctor. He would have made someone a wonderful housekeeper.'

Sue chuckled. 'Being a bit fussy, is he?'

Penny glared at the notepad. 'Some consultants want body-scanners. Mr Perry wants more carpet-sweepers. Last time he summoned me up there he wanted the conference-room curtains washed.'

Sue looked amused. 'Probably just an excuse to get you up to his room alone.'

Penny took that calmly. 'Much more likely he thought I ought to take them home and wash them myself.'

'That's your job?'

Penny was shaken with a laugh. 'The consultants think my job is to keep them happy. And everyone else seems to think that I'm the only person who can deal with Mr Perry—including him. So I'm the target every time he thinks his status isn't being recognised sufficiently.'

'That's because you're not afraid of him,' Sue said. She sipped her coffee and thought about it. 'And you don't go weak at the knees when he smiles at you either.' She looked at her friend thoughtfully. 'As a matter of interest, why don't you? Most of the nursing staff do.'

'You don't,' Penny objected.

'I'm an old married woman with flat feet. You're a green-eyed blonde. Gorgeous, independent, unentangled. Excellent melting knee material. So why do you stay solid as an iceberg? It's against Nature.'

Penny shrugged. 'That must depend on your nature, surely.'

Sue sent her an incredulous look. 'Are you telling me you're a dedicated spinster?'

Penny flushed, looking away.

'I don't believe you,' Sue said positively.

In spite of herself, Penny laughed at her friend's conviction.

'Why not?'

'Well, you married once,' Sue pointed out.

'Maybe that's why,' Penny suggested quietly.

Sue was staring at her as if she had never seen her before. She said slowly, 'When you first came here the hospital grapevine had you paired up with every bachelor in the place. They've given up now, of course. But we've all asked ourselves why. Is she immune? And, if so, why?'

This was getting on to dangerous ground. Penny swirled her coffee round and round in the plastic mug. A strange little smile played around her mouth.

'Why is an old married woman immune?' she countered at last.

'Too many men in my life,' Sue said promptly. 'Too many rugby shirts to wash. Too many cooked breakfasts when I'm out on my feet. I know the price.'

Penny's smile slipped a little. 'Maybe I do too.'

Sue's eyebrows rose. 'Your ex was a protein-heavy rugby player?'

Penny had never tried to hide the fact that she was divorced. She had removed her ring and called herself Ms but there had been no point in changing her name. Too many people knew her by it. Too many people knew about Alan. Not all about Alan, of course. At the thought Penny shuddered involuntarily.

No one at the hospital had ever met him. It was after the maelstrom that she had taken her first job at St Anne's. It had been a deliberate choice to go somewhere completely new, where nobody knew her. Her family had been furious at her giving up her career but she had had to get away from the art college where they knew altogether too much about Alan—where they could guess far too much about the wretchedness that had been her marriage.

Now she said carefully, 'Not exactly. But living with him taught me that marriage and me was not a good combination.'

Sue's eyebrows stayed up. 'No marriage, mmm? And no marriage means no man?' She considered Penny, her kindly eyes shrewd. 'Isn't that a rather old-fashioned idea?'

Penny kept her cool and met the sharp eyes. She laughed with gentle mockery. 'Are you telling me you're the last of the red-hot swingers, Sue?'

Sister Flynn grinned. She had been married for eighteen years. 'I can dream,' she retorted. 'And you could do more than dream if you wanted to.'

Penny's amusement died abruptly. 'I don't,' she said shortly.

Sue was not offended. She swigged her coffee.

'Is that why you're feeling harassed about this wedding?' she asked, her expression innocent.

Penny stiffened. 'Who says I'm harassed?'

Sue smiled. 'Aren't you?'

'Why should I be?'

'No reason.' Sue crunched up her plastic cup and lobbed it inaccurately at the wastepaper basket. 'Only it's another part of the wedding effect,' she said, watching her friend from under her lashes. 'Friends and relatives come round and ask, "You next?"'

Penny looked appalled. 'They wouldn't.'

Sue shrugged.

'They *wouldn't*. I mean, it's not as if I'm going to be a bridesmaid or anything.'

'You know your own family best,' Sue said in a tone that disclaimed all responsibility.

Penny pushed a harassed hand through her hair. 'Yes, but—— Do you really think they'd——? I'm not a girl any more, for heaven's sake. They must have stopped matchmaking for me years ago.'

'Mothers,' said Sue with authority, 'never stop matchmaking until the match is made. And stuck,' she added as an afterthought.

Penny sat down slowly on her chair. She looked, thought Sue in some amusement, as if she had received a body-blow.

'Divorce is no deterrent?' she asked in a hopeless tone.

'Just the reverse.'

'I don't understand.'

'Well, the old guard look on it as a challenge. By the old guard,' Sue explained painstakingly, 'I mean mothers and godmothers and assorted aunts—maybe even the odd grandmother. The old guard like to prove that they can find a better man for you than you did yourself.'

Penny closed her eyes. 'More suitable,' she murmured.

Sue was entertained. 'Exactly. From their point of view there is no reason you shouldn't try again. There may even,' she added wickedly, 'already be a man picked out for you. That's the way they do it in my family, anyway. If he escorts you to the church or sits next to you at dinner then find out if he's married. If he isn't, they plan that he soon will be. To you.'

Penny opened her eyes. 'You're joking.' It sounded like a plea.

'Seen it done,' said Sue cheerfully.

Penny glared at her. 'Do you like spreading gloom and despondency? Is it some sort of revenge on the world for your unsocial hours?'

Sue shook her head, chuckling. 'Only telling the truth—cross my heart,' she said virtuously.

'I wasn't looking forward to this wedding to begin with,' Penny said involuntarily.

Sue raised her eyebrows at this betraying exclamation. But she said nothing and Penny did not notice, too engrossed in her own thoughts to register her friend's look of speculation.

'Now I'll never be able to relax for a moment,' she was saying, half to herself. 'Every man who walks in, I'll be wondering whether he's married.'

Sue laughed aloud. 'That will make a nice change,' she said firmly.

'What?'

'Instead of every man who walks in wondering the same about you.'

'*What*?'

'You just don't see it, do you?' Sue shook her head in mock exasperation. 'It's so damn wasteful. If I didn't like you so much I could scratch your eyes out.'

Penny looked blank.

Sue gave a sigh and said with exaggerated patience, 'There aren't a lot of green-eyed blondes around. Especially not those who look like you do. Men tend to notice. And you don't notice them noticing. It's enough to make you weep.'

Penny looked uncomfortable. 'I—don't want another relationship, Sue. Even if I could. I'm not cut out for it.'

It was obvious that she meant it. There was nothing of mock anger, mock horror in the quiet voice. This was not teasing. This was serious stuff. Sue stared at her, honestly puzzled.

Penny's mouth twisted. 'I know what I'm talking about, Sue. Believe me.' She shook her head suddenly. 'I only hope my mother does,' she added ruefully.

Sue was relieved by this return to her normal tone.

'Well, don't waste your energy fighting her,' she advised. 'Mothers come armour-plated. And they bounce back.'

'But——'

'Ignore your mother. Freeze out the candidate,' she advised briskly. 'After all, she can't handcuff you together. Just look down that aristocratic nose at him and the poor chap will stagger off and drown himself in champagne. Or find himself a spare bridesmaid,' she added with a chuckle.

Penny laughed. If there was a slightly hectic note to the laughter, they both ignored it.

'You should see the bridesmaids,' she said practically. 'They're all models who work with Celia. There isn't one of them who has ever been spare in her life. Anyone who matched up to their specifications wouldn't be available for Mother to make a match with for me.'

Sue clicked her tongue. 'Stop denigrating yourself. I've told you—you're gorgeous. Or you are when your hair isn't in rats' tails and you aren't wearing a smelly anorak,' she added fairly. 'Maybe the candidate likes his ladies intelligent as well as beautiful.'

'I don't care how he likes his ladies,' Penny said firmly. 'I'm not going to be one of them.' She glared at her friend. 'Stop laughing. You're no help at all. In fact, I suspect you made all this up just to come and worry me because you've had a boring night.'

Sue chuckled, not denying it. Penny screwed up her cup and threw it at her.

'Oh, go home and cook some breakfasts and stop keeping honest women from their work.' The phone rang again. She put out a hand to it, grimacing. 'I hope this wedding effect of yours doesn't get any worse. My work schedule won't take it.'

She remembered that exchange ruefully six weeks later. She was sitting on a windy rural station waiting for the last train of the day which would decant Professor Guard. It was raining again, though less hard.

Her work schedule had certainly taken a pounding these last weeks, thought Penny. Since she worked in London her mother saw no reason not to phone her with requests to collect whatever essentials were not available in Shropshire. As a result Penny had spent an uncomfortable number of the last weeks' lunch hours flying around the West End on wedding errands.

She had done no painting at all, Penny thought. She had been too tired, too much involved in her mother's activities. And too on edge, she admitted to herself now. Oh, well, it would soon be over.

She looked at her watch. The train was late. That was standard. It did not even matter as there was no dinner to rush back for. There was a casserole in the Aga for when she returned with the professor.

'Darling, throw a stew at the man,' Laura had said lightly. 'You do wonderful stews.'

'You hate stew,' Penny had said, torn between amusement and exasperation. Laura had presented her with the news that she was to meet the man and give him dinner the moment she walked in through the studded front door.

'Yes, but he may not,' her mother said reasonably. She added with a touch of elegant malice, 'These impoverished academics are usually glad of a square meal.'

'Even stew,' murmured Penny.

'Darling, don't be touchy,' Laura said. 'Are you going to change?'

'To cook?' Penny asked sarcastically.

Laura gave the tiniest of shrugs. 'Well, you are going out to the station.'

'I think the commuters will survive the sight of my trousers,' Penny said.

Laura had hesitated, then shrugged again. She knew there was not much point in trying to persuade Penny to do anything against her will. She contented herself with a final pointed stare at Penny's shabby trousers as she and Celia wafted through the kitchen on a cloud of silk and Arpège on their way to the car.

Penny remembered the look now, and laughed. Her mother had conceded defeat on the matter of her clothes; Penny had conceded defeat over the responsibility for the unknown visitor.

She had tried to get out of meeting him. Her mother had countered her every argument. There were no taxis at this rural station. No one else was available.

'I don't even know what he looks like,' Penny had said in desperation. 'Won't you at least come with me?' she asked her sister. 'You could go on to dinner afterwards.'

Celia looked vaguely surprised. 'Mummy would kill me. She's got this whole evening organised to the second. I've been threatened with horrors if I'm even too long in the bath,' she said with feeling. 'Anyway, there'd be no point. I've never met the chap. No one knows what he looks like except Mike. Use your initiative, Pen.'

'How?' asked Penny gloomily, chopping onions and sniffing hard as she did so.

'Oh, look for someone like Albert Einstein, I expect,' Celia said with a giggle. 'He's a philosopher and *frightfully* eminent. He'll be about ninety.'

So here she was, wrapped up against the evening chill with her fingertips smelling slightly of onion, waiting for an elderly genius and looking forward to a heavy evening keeping him amused. Well, thought Penny wryly, it was better than wandering round the garden, torturing herself with bittersweet memories. Or shouting over the noise at the fashionable restaurant Laura had booked for Celia's last night of freedom.

Freedom, thought Penny with a little superstitious shiver. It was precious. She hoped Celia would never regret its loss. Though Mike was different from Alan, of course. And Celia was older and more sensible than Penny had been...

Stop it, she told herself. That's behind you now and Alan is dead. Let it rest. Celia will be happy enough. And if she isn't it's her business. Nothing to do with you. Don't dramatise.

She looked at her watch again and scanned the horizon. Yes, there it was. The train pulled round the curve of track that would bring it to Sanderham. Penny pulled up her jacket collar against the wind and stepped forward.

It was not a busy station but this was the train that brought the few commuters home. Before the train stopped doors were opening and people were jumping out, scurrying for the exit, the car park and their evening meal. It was the start of the weekend, after all.

Penny searched the arrivals for a raincoat and wild grey hair. There were none. She looked again. Even glasses and an air of academic abstraction would have been a help, she thought wryly. None of the descending passengers met that description either.

Einstein he clearly isn't, Penny said to herself, ruefully.

There was nothing for it. She would just have to wait until those with homes to go to had gone and she would pick up the one survivor. Apart from a man in jeans and cowboy boots and another in a railway uniform, any one of the men on the platform could have been a professor of philosophy. She could not guess which of these respectable middle-aged men with briefcases was Michael's old tutor.

She stepped back and propped her shoulder against the station wall. The middle-aged crowd flooded past her. None of them stopped. None of them hesitated. None of them seemed to be expecting to be met. In fact, to a man, they looked tired and harried.

I know how they feel, thought Penny with sympathy. Except the man in cowboy boots. He did not look as if he knew the meaning of the word 'tired'. As he strolled down the platform she saw that he moved with the casual grace of an athlete. Her artist's eye appreciated that classical perfection. He looked as if all his joints and muscles had been oiled to work—lithe and immaculate, at peak performance, Penny thought. Her fingers twitched. If she had had her notebook she would have made one of her lightning sketches.

She gave herself a mental shake. She couldn't hang around on the local station staring at complete strangers, she told herself. Especially at young men. They might not like it and they could get altogether the wrong impression.

But as the stranger came closer she saw that he was not that young. Notwithstanding that air of consummate fitness, there were lines on the handsome face that added several years and a whole world of experience to the picture. Penny found she was staring at him, in spite of herself.

He was very striking. At first sight she had thought his hair was fair. Now she saw that it was pure white. White like the powdered wig of an eighteenth-century rake, she thought, with an odd little shiver. But it did not look powdered at all. It looked soft and springy, as if it would be a delight to run your fingers through. It glinted in the evening sun above a handsome cynical face.

Looking at strongly marked dark brows and the devil-may-care tilt of his head, Penny thought it was an adventurer's face. A face that had seen a lot, done a lot and not cared very much about any of it. Or anyone. And none the less attractive for that.

Compulsively attractive, she realised as one of those dark brows winged up. He had caught her staring at him. For a tiny moment their eyes locked. Penny's throat closed. There was a laughing challenge there that brought all her defence shields crashing into position. Blushing furiously, she turned away.

She ostentatiously scanned the crowd streaming past her. All the time she was conscious of the level, considering gaze as he came closer. Oh, *hell*, she thought, stabbing her hands into her pockets.

Her nerves were suddenly raw with the prospect of embarrassment. He must have thought she was trying to pick him up, she realised. If he approached her then she had no one to blame but herself. She knew she shouldn't have stared. She didn't know why she had done it. She didn't normally.

Penny lifted her chin and looked hard in the opposite direction. The man was still approaching, not hurrying. She swallowed. He wouldn't accost her, she assured herself. People didn't. Not on country railway stations at seven o'clock in the evening.

Think of something else, she told herself. Remember what you're supposed to be doing here, after all. *Concentrate*. With a little start she realised that the platform was almost empty. No one had passed her who appeared remotely uncertain; no one seemed as if they were expecting to be met. It looked as if the professor had missed the train, after all.

Penny sighed, taking her hands out of her pockets. This, she thought, was going to be a nuisance. She might try ringing Mike to find out where the professor had stayed last night but the odds were that Mike was already out on his stag-night party.

That meant she would probably not be able to track the old boy down. She would just have to come back and meet every succeeding train tonight. She could ring the main terminus, she thought, frowning. Maybe they could be persuaded to put up a notice to attract the attention of a foreign visitor changing trains.

'Damn,' she said aloud.

A soft American voice said in her ear, 'Hi, gorgeous, looking for me?'

Penny jumped about a foot in the air and came down breathing hard. Obviously Americans didn't know the conventions prevailing on English country railway stations at seven o'clock in the evening.

She prepared to be glacial.

'I think not.'

'Sure?'

Close to, he was even more attractive. He had a light tan which made his teeth look ice-field-white and his eyes as blue as the Mediterranean on a summer day. In fact they were the bluest eyes she had ever seen, Penny thought. And they were dancing. He did not seem at all put out by her snub. She struggled with a slight feeling of being caught up in a whirlwind.

'Positive,' she said, with more determination than she felt. There was a distinct look of appreciation along with the laughter in those blue eyes.

He shook his head. 'That's a shame.' He looked round the now empty platform. 'Looks like I could use a ride.'

Penny stared at him in outrage. 'What are you suggesting?'

Those worldly eyes were mocking. 'Only a ride, honey, I promise. Unless you——?'

The unfinished question brought deeper colour to her cheeks. It didn't make it any easier to bear that she had invited this insolence by staring at him in the first place.

She said coldly, 'I am afraid I am waiting for someone.'

The dark brows rose and the mouth tilted. It was, Penny saw with a little shudder, a beautiful mouth with a sensual sculpted line that one day she was going to have to draw. From memory, she told herself firmly.

'Waiting for someone? Not me?' he said softly.

'You——' She bit it off before she said something she would regret. 'Definitely not you. Someone old and respectable,' she said with bite. 'Whom I seem to have missed. I must go and see if I can ring my future brother-in-law,' she added, half to herself.

She turned a definite shoulder on him. Yet again he was not disconcerted. He put out a hand and turned her back, quite calmly and with great ease. Penny was speechless.

'Miss Brinkman.'

She stared at him blankly. He had a lazy smile that somehow made him look more raffish than even the jeans and the boots did. The hint of mockery was still there but he had cut down on the blatant appreciation, she saw. A horrible suspicion held her rigid.

'I knew you must be,' he said with a satisfaction which made her wince as if he had insulted her. His hand fell from her shoulder and was held out imperatively. 'Guard. Zoltan Guard.'

Even his hand was beautiful—long-fingered and beautifully kept. It wasn't fair, Penny thought. She felt a great wave of embarrassment close over her head. First she had stared at him openly, virtually inviting him to chat her up. Then she had snubbed him—admittedly not with notable success. Now he was claiming to be the honoured visitor. Cool, competent Penny Dane had never felt so thoroughly flustered in her life.

Penny blinked. 'Professor Guard?' she said weakly.

It couldn't be true. Please God, don't let it be true.

The blue eyes were amused but without compassion. 'That's me.'

It *was* true. He found her hand and shook it purposefully.

His handshake was firm. To her relief he did not hold on to her hand. He would have been quite justified, Penny allowed, after her treating him as if he was trying to pick her up. But he did not.

She curbed her gratitude. This was not a chivalrous refusal to take advantage, she thought, meeting his mocking expression head-on. This was lack of interest. As soon as he let her go Penny eased her crushed fingers, rubbing them with her gloved left hand as the blood returned.

Professor Guard, she found, was looking at her with amused comprehension.

'Not what you'd been led to expect?'

Penny strove for self-possession and achieved it. Years of iron self-control gave you some advantages, she thought grimly.

'Not quite,' she allowed. She was getting her second wind. She gave him a careful smile, not meeting his eyes by means of the useful tactic of fixing her eyes on those black eyebrows. 'I'll have to have a word with my new brother-in-law about the accuracy of his briefing.'

Now the decisive brows rose.

'Mike's briefing is all right. He described you to a whisker,' the unexpected Professor Guard said softly.

Once again Penny thought she detected a touch of tolerant scorn. Of course to a dashing creature like this her serviceable navy-blue trousers and jacket would look very dull. Especially as the trousers still bore smudges of flour from the dusting she had given the meat in the casserole. She stiffened.

To her surprise, she saw him note it. His evident amusement grew.

'I recognised you, didn't I?' he added blandly.

'Just as well,' Penny said with a suggestion of a snap. She looked up the deserted platform. 'Did you leave your luggage in the waiting-room?'

He patted the soft sports bag slung over one shoulder. 'My luggage.'

'Oh,' said Penny.

She wondered briefly if the squashy bag could possibly contain a suit. And—if it didn't—what he would wear to the wedding. And what her mother would say. Her mouth twitched at the thought. Suddenly she felt a lot more cheerful.

'Well, that's easy,' she said, pulling herself together. 'The car's in the car park. Let's go.'

It was her own elderly runabout. She had meant to tidy the interior. In the end she had not had the time. In contrast with the clean, unencumbered lines of the man it suddenly looked like a travelling dustbin. Penny started to apologise for the state of the car and stopped herself. Professor Guard seemed to have an unrivalled ability to get her on the raw, she thought wryly.

He did not comment, merely holding out his hand for the car keys.

Slightly to her own surprise Penny found herself handing them over. But a protest was called for.

'Don't like being driven by a woman, Professor Guard?' she asked sweetly.

He looked at her through narrowed eyes for a moment. Then he flung back his head and laughed.

'Honey, you've got some weird ideas about me,' he told her. He stacked his bag competently in the untidy boot and went round to the driver's door. Unlocking it, he opened it with a flourish and stood back.

Penny felt herself flushing. Wrong-footed again!

'Thank you,' she said arctically, getting in.

He grinned down at her and dropped the keys into her lap before closing the door on her.

'You obviously think I'm a hobo. But I was brought up to be a gentleman,' he drawled.

He went round to the passenger side before she could answer and swung lithely into the car. Penny looked away. She had been right about the muscles—he was an ultra-fit hobo.

She set the car in motion, conscious of him watching her. It took a special effort not to fumble the controls. Now, why? she thought, annoyed.

As they swung out of the car park her companion stretched his long legs in front of him and pushed back his seat as far as it would go.

'Tell me,' he drawled. 'What were you expecting?'

Penny sent him a quick, assessing look from under her lashes and decided to tell him the truth. Maybe that would shake that impossible cool, she thought balefully.

'Albert Einstein,' she told him with satisfaction.

There was a blank silence.

'Einstein?'

'That's what they told me to look for. I was expecting someone vague and elderly and brilliant,' Penny said crisply. 'Possibly with a violin.'

His shoulders began to shake.

'Einstein,' he said again. He seemed delighted. 'If Mike told you that, you're right; his briefing does need some improvement.'

'To be honest, I don't know what Michael said,' Penny admitted. 'I got your description second-hand. From my sister Celia, along with the time of your train.'

'It was good of you to meet me anyhow,' Zoltan Guard said easily. 'And to put me up. I expected to be sleeping on Mike's floor.'

Penny restrained herself from saying that from the look of him he would probably have been more comfortable doing just that. Her mother was not going to take kindly to jeans and cowboy boots at her Victorian-style wedding. But he would find that out soon enough, Penny thought. She did not think her mother's disapproval was going to be much of a problem for him so there was no point in warning him.

Instead she said politely, 'There's rather a houseful, I'm afraid. Family, bridesmaids and so on.'

'Interesting,' he said lazily.

But when she took him into the comfortable farm-house kitchen where the family habitually congregated the emptiness of the house was evident. He stopped and one of those satanic eyebrows rose.

'Houseful? Seems like we're all alone.'

For no reason that she could think of Penny blushed again. She had blushed more in the last hour than she had in the whole of the previous five years, she thought in annoyance.

She said, with an effort at indifference, 'The others have gone out. It's a sort of tradition. Friends of the bride and groom take them out separately the night before they get married.'

He grinned, a lop-sided flash of perfect teeth. 'I've heard of it. Sounds kind of a dangerous tradition to me.'

It was so much what she thought herself that, in spite of herself, Penny gave a small laugh. 'It can be. I don't think Celia or Michael are intending to do anything very riotous, though.'

'Oh, intentions.' Zoltan Guard shrugged. 'Intentions are rarely dangerous, in my experience. It's the outcome you have to worry about.' He surveyed her across the scrubbed ash table. 'Is that why you stayed behind? You're the emergency recovery officer if things go wrong?'

Penny laughed again, more easily this time.

'Not me. I didn't go along because no matter how unriotous the party is it will be too big and noisy for me. My family know that I don't like parties.'

'Interesting,' he said again.

He sat on the corner of the table, swinging one booted foot. He was looking at her as if she were some new species of wildlife, Penny thought, with a return of her former irritation.

'Not particularly,' she said with a shrug. 'Lots of people don't like parties.'

'Oh, sure. But they don't get dumped by their affectionate families because of it.'

'They didn't dump me...'

'Leaving you to meet Albert Einstein while they go out on the town? That's not dumping you?' he queried softly. His eyes were oddly watchful.

Penny's brows knitted in puzzlement.

'That's got nothing to do with it. It was just sensible as I wasn't going with them anyway.'

'Are you telling me you offered?'

Penny opened her mouth to say that she had. But something about the look in the cool blue eyes—or her own innate honesty—stopped her.

'Thought not,' said odious Professor Guard. He crossed one long denim-clad leg over the other and smiled at her lazily. 'Bit of a Cinderella, aren't you, Miss Brinkman?'

'I am not,' said Penny with emphasis, 'a Cinderella. Or anything similarly wimpish. I am a working woman. I go where I please and do what I want.'

The detestable man was laughing openly.

'Excellent,' he drawled. He stood up in a leisurely fashion and came round the table to her.

'And my name is not Brinkman,' she went on, unheeding. 'It's Dane.'

He stopped. 'Married?'

Damn him, he sounded incredulous. Penny would have given anything to say yes. But he would find out the truth soon enough, even if she did.

'Divorced,' she spat, hating him.

He resumed his stroll towards her. 'Surprise me,' he murmured.

'You are the rudest man I've ever met,' Penny told him, outraged.

That gave him pause. 'Am I? You must have led a very sheltered life.'

She glared. 'I'm administrator of a substantial London hospital. Believe me, that's not a sheltered life.'

'One wouldn't have thought so,' he agreed. 'So how come you've never met anyone as rude as I am?' He sounded genuinely puzzled. 'Do you frighten off all the candidates?'

The tranquil tone did not disguise the fact that this was another attempt to put her down, Penny thought. She tilted her chin. He might be a guest in her mother's house but he was not going to browbeat her into accepting implied insults without fighting her corner. She had learned to stand up for herself in the last five years. And, in the last analysis, she had learned to discard the ladylike behaviour her mother prized so much as well.

'Candidates for what?' Penny said contemptuously.

The blue eyes glinted as if he had scored an unexpected victory.

'This,' said Professor Zoltan Guard quite gently.

CHAPTER TWO

IT WAS not a passionate kiss. Over the distance of years Penny remembered passion with shuddering clarity. This had nothing in common with what she remembered.

Instead it was a slow, reflective exploration of her lips. It felt as if he was kissing her to see if he liked the taste, Penny realised.

It was a disconcerting thought, and not an altogether flattering one. She flinched in his arms.

'What are you *doing*?' she said in muffled protest.

The arms were strong. Well, she might have guessed that from the ease with which he had detained her on the platform. Penny, knowing far too much about the physical strength with which a man could overwhelm a woman, went very still.

He did not release her. But the unpredictable guest raised his head and looked at her. Meeting the blue eyes, Penny realised with indignation that he was enjoying himself hugely.

'It's called kissing,' he said helpfully.

Penny let out a little breath of exasperation. To her relief, though she did not let him see it, the incipient panic began to subside.

'I know what it's called,' she retorted.

She put her arm across his chest and pushed hard to lever herself away from him. She was fit and was used to thinking herself strong for a woman. If she had been this fit when Alan——

She broke off the thought. With a slight shock she realised that, fit or not, she was making not the slightest impression on him. He was laughing down at her.

'Surprising,' he observed.

Penny's eyes narrowed. She stared up into the amused, determined face and read a challenge.

'What's surprising?' she demanded suspiciously.

'That you know what it's called when you so manifestly don't know how to do it.'

Penny glared at him and shook back her hair out of her eyes.

'Maybe I just don't want to do it,' she pointed out. 'Not just at the moment. And maybe—who knows?—not with you.' The arm was like a steel bar across her shoulderblades. She flicked an ostentatious glance down at the hand grasping her upper arm and pushed against his chest again. With no more success. 'I know what murder's called too,' she added, panting slightly.

The dark brows rose. 'Interesting,' he said for the third time.

This time she did not demand an explanation. She was fairly sure it would be unpalatable and probably insulting.

'Will you let me go, please?' she asked with restraint. 'I would like to breathe again.'

He laughed aloud at that. But the look he gave her was speculative.

'Curiouser and curiouser. Kissing comes in the same category as murder and a man can crush the breath out of you by just putting a friendly arm round your shoulders. Could we have a serious hang-up here?'

There was a little silence. For a moment Penny felt as if he had hit her—one of those frightening, chopping blows she had seen demonstrated in her martial arts classes. Just for a moment she felt as if he had chopped the breath out of her.

She pulled herself together. She was shaking a little. She pushed herself as far back from his chest as she could and tilted her head to meet his mocking eyes full on.

'Don't play psychological games with me,' she said quietly.

The dark brows twitched together. He looked as if he was going to answer but she swept on.

'You're here as a guest at my sister's wedding, not as my psychoanalyst. My hang-ups or the lack of them are none of your business, Professor Guard.'

Just for a moment, unbelievably, his arms seemed to tighten. Penny gasped. All the fear surged up again like a fountain. Eyes dilating, her head went back in protest. But at once he was letting her go.

He stepped away from her. 'Of course they're not,' he said soothingly. He was watching her from under slightly frowning brows. But his voice, when he spoke, was cool. 'I'm sorry if I alarmed you.' He didn't sound sorry at all. Just intrigued.

Penny twitched her shoulders, smoothed her hair and shrugged out of her jacket, ignoring the hint of mockery.

'You did not,' she said with precision, 'alarm me. Do you usually alarm women, Professor Guard?'

He seemed to consider it. 'Only first-year students who haven't bothered with a decent excuse for submitting their papers late,' he said at last, solemnly. 'They're not all women, of course.' He primmed his mouth but she could see that his eyes were laughing again. He put his head on one side and asked blandly, 'Does that make it better or worse?'

Penny put her jacket over the back of a chair and smoothed the shoulders. She eyed him, wary but puzzled.

'Does what make it better or worse?'

'That I terrorise people irrespective of their sex?' he asked solemnly.

Penny knew she was being teased. It was a long time since anyone had teased her. It was annoying but also slightly exhilarating. She could, she knew, give him as good as she got. She smiled at him sweetly.

'You say that as if you enjoy terrorising people, Professor Guard.'

His mouth twitched. 'In a good cause, Miss Brinkman. In a good cause. People have to be shaken up from time to time.'

She heard the private amusement in his voice and did not like it. In a rush she remembered Sue Flynn's theory about unattached men and spare daughters at weddings. She went cold. They couldn't. Could they?

Looking at Professor Zoltan Guard and those wickedly laughing blue eyes, she was not sure.

'And am I a good cause?' she challenged.

His eyes gleamed. 'Good? I don't know. You might be rewarding. I shall have to think about it.'

Her smile became less sweet. 'Don't bother. I don't need shaking up.'

'Ah, but you don't know what you need,' he told her solemnly.

Penny held on to her temper. 'All right. I don't *want* shaking up.'

He was looking at her mouth in a thoughtful way. She became even less sure of her family's innocence in the matter of matchmaking. She was quite sure that Zoltan Guard had never been innocent of any devilment in his life. She pressed her lips together. Seeing it, he smiled.

'Yes, I can see that. It's not the same thing, of course.'

Penny had a sudden image of what he must be like as a teacher—exciting, probably even inspiring and utterly maddening.

'Maybe not,' she said carefully. 'But, either way, you don't need to worry about it, do you? As you're just passing through, I mean.'

Green eyes met blue with an electric clash that almost made Penny retreat a step in pure surprise. Zoltan laughed.

'You may be one hell of an administrator, Miss Brinkman, but I have to tell you that as a psychologist you're nowhere,' he told her softly.

Penny was shaken. Suddenly all desire to challenge him left her.

'Mrs Dane,' she reminded him curtly.

'Of course.' His eyes narrowed, considering her. 'You still use his name,' he mused. 'How does he like having Mrs Dane wandering around when she isn't *his* Mrs Dane any more?'

He was clever, thought Penny, with a little shiver. Alan had hated it. What was his was his forever, he had told her. So she sidestepped the question.

Lifting her chin, she told him, 'My husband is dead.'

That startled him. The mockery fell away like a cloak. He looked shocked. 'I'm sorry.'

Shocked and impossibly sexy, Penny found to her consternation. She averted her eyes and nodded briefly. She was not going to tell him that she had not seen Alan for four years before he finally died in a drunken streetfight in Guayaquil. She was not going to tell Zoltan Guard anything at all.

'You weren't to know,' she said curtly.

He was frowning. 'Mike should have told me.'

She shrugged. 'Why? I thought you were quite satisfied with his briefing.'

Zoltan Guard stared down at her. 'I was wrong. He left out the essentials.'

Penny contemplated demanding an explanation of that. She discarded the idea. She might well not be able to handle any explanation provided by this unpredictable man, she thought wryly.

She said, 'Well, if you've got enough information on my past history then perhaps I can show you your room now,' she said.

He pursed his mouth. 'Enough information for what?'

'Whatever you normally use it for.' A thought occurred to her. She glinted a look up at him every bit as challenging as his own had been. 'Except don't try terrorising me, Professor Guard. It's some time since I was a student but I always handed in my essays on time.'

His eyes swept up and down her in one comprehensive survey—as she would pass a brush of primer over a new canvas. Penny shuddered as if he had touched her. She managed to contain her shocked little gasp. But nothing could prevent her instinctive retreat from him.

His eyes met hers. He smiled slowly. 'Interesting.'

Penny turned away, disturbed. 'I wish you'd stop saying that,' she said, trying to sound irritated. Better to let the man think that he irritated her than to allow him to suspect what that look really did to her pulses. 'It makes me feel like a monkey in a zoo.'

'Monkeys aren't nearly so—intriguing.'

She gave a snort of sudden laughter. 'I'll take that as a compliment. Not every woman would.'

'Not every woman,' said Zoltan Guard imperturbably, 'is more intriguing than a monkey.'

Penny gave up. 'Your room,' she said firmly. 'Come on.' Her responsibilities as hostess suddenly smote her so she added, 'Feel free to rest if you're tired. There's a casserole, but don't feel you have to eat now—or at all if you'd rather not.'

'You're very hospitable.'

There was a dry note in his voice. Penny ignored it. She led the way out of the kitchen and up the dark panelled staircase. 'You're on the top floor, I'm afraid. The first floor is full of bridesmaids.'

He followed her into the low-ceilinged room and dropped his bag on the bed.

'Look out for the beams,' she warned. 'This used to be the servants' quarters when the house was built. They must have been shorter than everyone else. Or they might not have minded decapitating the servants, I suppose.'

'Guess not.' He strolled over to the window and looked across the treetops to the distant hills. 'Fine view. Is that a pool complex I see down there?'

'Yes. My father is mad about fitness.'

'Great,' said the visitor easily. 'I could do with a decent swim. I've had my knees under my chin on airplanes all this week.'

'Oh.' She was taken aback. 'Of course. I'll get the key and take you down...'

He flung up a hand.

'Not yet, honey. First things first. You mentioned food.'

Penny smiled at that, her constraint forgotten. 'In the oven. It's only stew, I'm afraid. Warming, but hardly gourmet fare. I hope you don't mind.'

'Honey,' he said with feeling, 'anything that doesn't smell of plastic and taste of rubber is fine by me.'

'Well, it shouldn't do that,' she said, amused. 'Come down when you're ready.'

He did not keep her waiting long. He strolled into the kitchen as she was squatting in front of the range, peering under the lid of the casserole. He was still wearing the ancient jeans but he had changed into a fresh dark blue shirt and a loose jacket. He looked relaxed—and very sophisticated, Penny saw with misgiving. Not quite Laura's academic grateful for a square meal, she thought wryly. She stood up, feeling embarrassed. She wondered how she could ever have taken him for a hobo as he had quite rightly detected.

He stopped, sniffing appreciatively.

'Now that smells like real home-cooking.'

Penny was wry. 'It ought to. It's the only thing I know how to cook.'

Zolton Guard raised an eyebrow. 'So you cook as well, Cinderella.'

Penny felt her temper flicker and curbed it. 'As well as what?' she asked in an even tone.

'Meeting strange men at railway stations while your sisters are out on the town.' There was a note of laughter as well as challenge in the smooth voice.

Penny brought the pot out of the oven and straightened. It was cast-iron, too heavy to slap down on to the kitchen range with all the force of which she was capable. Though she would have liked to.

'I thought we would eat in here,' she said, ignoring his mischievous expression. 'The dining-room is full of wedding paraphernalia. And it's cold,' she added truthfully.

'Yes, I'd forgotten how cold England could be in May,' he agreed. 'It must be twenty years since I was here at this time of year.' He looked around. 'Can I do anything?'

Penny retrieved vegetables from the warm oven. She shook her head.

'It's all done.' She remembered her mother's parting instructions on hospitality and added conscientiously, 'Unless you'd like some wine with it? You could open a bottle.'

'Sure thing.' He did not need to be told where the wine was, she saw. He inspected the wine rack in the corner of the kitchen. 'Something rich and warming on this dark and stormy night?'

Penny shivered, in spite of the warmth of the kitchen.

'Whatever you like.'

He selected a bottle. He did not need to ask for a corkscrew either. He produced a complicated pen-knife from his pocket, identified the corkscrew attachment and opened the bottle with swift competence. He brought it to the table, restoring the knife to the pocket of his shirt.

She ladled casserole on to a warmed plate and handed it across the table to him.

'Help yourself to vegetables.'

'Surely,' he said again.

But he did not sit down until she had served her own food and seated herself. He held her chair for her while she did so.

Penny was a little taken aback. It was a slightly old-fashioned courtesy and she was not used to it from her brothers-in-law. Or from the men she occasionally fed in her studio flat.

'Thank you,' she said, a little flustered. So flustered, in fact, that she gave him her shyest smile.

His eyebrows twitched together. Just for a second or two he stood there beside her, staring down at her as if he were seeing her for the first time. Then he seemed to give a small shrug before taking his own place.

Penny had that odd sensation of breathlessness again. To disguise it—as much from herself as from him—she pushed the dish of vegetables across the table to him.

'Where did you know Michael, Professor Guard? It can't have been at university if you haven't been to England for twenty years.'

'Zoltan,' he corrected.

Penny acknowledged that with a flicker of her lashes.

'Oh, I've been. Just not in the summer. Or what you English like to think of as the summer. I was teaching a couple of terms as a visiting academic when I first met Mike.' He smiled reminiscently. 'They even called me the Visitor. Made me feel like a little green man from Mars. Come to think of it, I guess that's how some of my colleagues did think of me.'

Penny surveyed the handsome face with its hint of wildness, thought of the comfortably sober academics her father liked to bring home for dinner when he wasn't out on the road, and found she wasn't surprised. She took a mouthful of stew, paused.

'So what were you teaching? Philosophy?'

'Philosophy's a big subject,' he said tolerantly. He reached for the bottle. 'Have some wine. You've been out in the wind and the rain too.'

She accepted silently. She found that was the easiest way. You didn't have to drink it, after all. If you said you didn't want any then people would exclaim and make a fuss and try and push you into it. Five years had taught that the easiest thing was to let them fill your glass and then ignore it.

Zoltan poured wine for her and then filled his own glass.

'Logic, mainly.'

She was intrigued. 'Logic? But—do people learn that at university?'

He forked up some food and tasted it. 'This is good stuff, Cinderella. When you get tired of being a downtrodden cook-chauffeuse you could set up a great fast-food joint.'

'Thank you,' she said coolly. 'Do they really go to university to learn logic?'

'Why shouldn't they learn logic at university?'

'Well—it seems so basic.' Penny floundered. 'I mean, we're all logical, aren't we? Isn't that what modern education is all about?'

He waved his fork at her. 'Basic fallacy. It's what education should be all about. We ought to be explaining to the next generation how we reached our own conclusions and how to do it themselves with new data. Instead we teach our kids to memorise facts. They're no better at working things out from first principles than your average medieval monk was.' He thought about it. 'In fact worse.' He took some more food, chewing enjoyably. 'I gave a paper on the subject in Gothenburg last year.'

'Oh,' said Penny, slightly overwhelmed. 'And that's what you taught Michael?'

He shook his head. 'Logic is what I do to earn my crust. My real interest is the philosophy of war. It's not quite a respectable subject—anyway the historians think it belongs to them—so I stick with the traditional stuff to keep the punters happy. But Mike was doing a thesis on the propaganda of conflict. So we did some work together. Have you read it?'

All Penny knew about her intended brother-in-law was that he was some sort of journalist who looked as if he had been brained by a champion every time Celia walked into the room. She shook her head.

'Pity. It's good. You should. Can I have some more of your concoction, Cinderella?'

Penny gave him her sweetest smile. 'Only if you stop calling me Cinderella.'

He chuckled, unabashed. 'Only if you start calling me Zoltan.'

She blushed faintly. It was ridiculous, she told herself, rising and busying herself at the stove to disguise the hint of colour in her cheeks. She was not a child. She had not blushed for years—and certainly not because a man invited her to use his Christian name. Or rather *told* her to use his Christian name, she corrected mentally.

She could feel him watching her. She strove for the indifferent composure with which she usually treated the numerous strangers she found in her parents' house.

She turned back and gave him his replenished plate.

'Zoltan? What nationality is that?' she asked.

'Hungarian.'

She sat down. He took up his fork again and began to eat with expressions of pleasure.

'And?' she prompted.

He looked up. 'And?'

'How come you've got a Hungarian name?' she said patiently. 'Or half a Hungarian name. You can't get more English than Guard, I suppose.'

He chuckled. 'So I gather. It was easier than listening to your compatriots tie their tongues in knots mangling my real name. It's a whole Hungarian name, I'm afraid.'

Penny stared. 'Hungarian? But—you're American, aren't you? You don't *sound* like a Hungarian.' It came

out like an accusation, to her embarrassment. She
flushed.

The blue eyes twinkled. 'And in Hungary they say I
don't *look* like a Hungarian,' he retorted, mimicking her
tone. 'The fact remains, however.'

'But—what are you doing in England?'

His look of amusement deepened. 'I was invited,' he
reminded her.

Penny realised she was being teased. She glared. He
made a face laughing.

'All right. You want the life story,' he said. 'You shall
have it.' He picked up his wine and leaned back in his
chair, cradling it. 'Born Budapest. A complete mongrel.
One Hungarian grandparent, one Russian, one Austrian,
one French. Early talent for mathematics. Graduated.
Taught. Got bored. Went to Frankfurt to learn computer sciences. Graduated. Taught. Got bored. Went to
Cambridge on a research project. Wormed my way into
the philosophy school. Thesis. Taught.'

'Got bored,' Penny finished drily.

He sipped his wine. 'Yes, eventually. I have a very low
boredom threshold.'

'What did you do when you left Cambridge?'

He looked at her with an odd wariness. 'Mike didn't
say?'

It was too good an opportunity to crunch some of
that impossible confidence. Penny would have been in-
human to pass it up.

'Mike's never mentioned you.'

He was not noticeably crushed. His mouth tilted in
an appreciative smile.

'That's put me in my place,' he murmured.

Penny's eyes sharpened. Too clever indeed.

'It doesn't appear to have,' she pointed out acidly.

One wicked eyebrow flicked up. 'Oh, you like the wounds to show, do you?' He still sounded amused. 'And Mike said you were civilised.' He shook his head mournfully.

Penny regarded him with some dudgeon. 'I think,' she said, 'that I would like to know exactly what my future brother-in-law said about me.'

She met Zoltan's eyes squarely. They were dancing.

'You wouldn't,' he said positively.

Penny stiffened. 'What do you mean?'

'Well, you said you didn't want to be shaken up,' he pointed out in a voice of gentle reason. 'If I gave you a run-down on Mike's briefing you could be seriously shaken up.'

She looked at him in silence for a long time. He looked back. His expression was pleasant but completely unreadable. Then his mouth twitched.

'All right,' she said at last. 'You play poker better than I do.'

'I play poker better than anyone I know,' he said lazily. 'Don't worry about it.'

She sent him a look of deep dislike. The arrogance of the man was truly breathtaking.

'Nothing you could do or say would worry me,' Penny announced.

He pursed his lips. 'I think you underestimate both of us.'

She digested that and decided she didn't like the implications at all.

'I think you've been dealing with students too long, Professor Guard,' she told him. 'You don't terrorise me and you don't worry me.'

He leaned back in his chair and considered her thoughtfully.

'OK. You want to know what Mike said? I'll tell you.'

Penny stirred uneasily. Then sat still. She had invited this, after all. She wished she had realised that she had been inviting that penetrating stare as well.

'He said you were bright. Very bright. And bright enough to hide it—though he didn't know why you wanted to.' He looked at her speculatively. 'I could make a fair guess.'

Penny's chin came up.

'Cowardice,' he said, although she had not asked. 'Sheer blue funk.'

'An informed opinion is always interesting,' she said with heavy irony.

He shrugged. 'Apart from that, he said you were gorgeous though you didn't seem to know it. And un-touchable. Well, to be honest the word he used was frosty, but I don't think he can have meant that. Anyway, it's not the right word.'

'Thank you,' said Penny drily.

'No. No. It's only right to be fair.' He slanted a teasing look across the table at her. 'Frosty, you're not. Bad-tempered and combative, yes. Cold, no.'

It was her turn to raise an eyebrow. She was rather proud of the way she managed it.

'You seem to have drawn an awful lot of conclusions about me in such a short time,' she said in a neutral voice. 'I thought academics disapproved of leaping to conclusions.'

His smile—his real smile—she found, crinkled up the corners of his eyes. It was fascinating. She looked quickly away.

'Oh, they do. They do. A lot of real academics don't approve of me either.'

'Either?' she echoed, puzzled.

'Any more than you do,' he pointed out softly. 'It's very sad.'

Penny snorted. 'Much you care about that.'

'Not a lot, in general, I agree. I don't have any terribly British ideas about wanting my opponents to respect me. Though sometimes it can be a nuisance,' he added reflectively.

Penny was bewildered. 'A nuisance? Why? How?'

'When the opponent is a long-legged, green-eyed blonde,' he said deadpan.

It took her a couple of crucial seconds to assimilate. When she did she blushed scarlet. Zoltan watched the colour flood up under the delicate skin with every appearance of appreciation.

'I—you—do you——? How dare you?' she choked.

'Bad-tempered,' he murmured. 'Combative. Not a hint of frost.'

And he leaned forward and touched the back of his hand to her warm cheek.

Penny shot away from him as if his touch were an electric shock. Which in a way it was.

'Don't touch me,' she almost shouted.

He was looking at his hand, shaking his fingers ruefully.

'Wow. Does that often happen?'

'It——' She bit off the insult she was about to hurl at his head. It was uncontrolled, adolescent and it showed how badly rattled she was. She did not want to show Zoltan Guard any such thing. She counted to ten and said dangerously, 'I don't often get mauled by guests in my parents' house, no.'

His eyes twinkled. 'Now, Mike never said you were a fantasist.'

'I——'

'Come on, honey, admit it. Just a hint of exaggeration there?'

She said, 'I do not recall inviting you to touch me.'

He grinned. 'That's the problem, huh? In England men wait for an invitation? Preferably in writing, no doubt.'

Penny was shaking with anger. She reminded herself that he was a guest and that just because he had no manners it was no excuse for letting her own standards drop to the level of the classroom. The primary call room, if she consulted her instincts. She would have liked to throw things.

Instead she said as coolly as she could manage, 'Do you make a career of being rude to complete strangers? Or is it just a hobby?'

He laughed. 'Poor Cinderella,' he said. 'Don't glare daggers at me. I won't tell anyone.'

'Tell them what?' she demanded, in a voice that could have come out of the refrigerator behind him.

'That you're knotted up with frustration.'

Their eyes met again. This time Penny was beyond even trying to disguise the blaze of anger in her own. Her earlier unwelcome suspicion was returning all too vividly.

She was remembering, all too clearly, Sue Flynn's laughing warning. The whole family had taken great pains to make certain that Penny and Penny alone met this man tonight. And stayed alone with him.

'How dare you?' she said, not much above a whisper.

'Don't like the truth?'

Her voice was deadly. 'I don't like people I have never met making assumptions about my sexual feelings and then throwing them in my face on the strength of a couple of hours' acquaintance.'

There was an icy little silence.

Then Zoltan said softly, 'Who said I was talking about sexual frustration?'

It was like a blow in the stomach. Penny gagged.

'Aren't you?' she challenged, recovering, but not quickly enough.

'I wasn't,' he said thoughtfully. 'But since that is clearly what you think—and you should know—I ask myself...' He left it unfinished.

Penny wanted to be anywhere but in the kitchen. She wanted to be with anyone but this man with his worldly, uncaring amusement. She wished it were a hundred years in the future. Or thirty seconds in the past and she could keep her stupid, stupid mouth shut.

None of that was possible, of course. Ignoring the embarrassment was not easy. Nor was the horrid sense that she had dug an elephant trap for herself and jumped right in it. But she was an independent lady who had put her life back together after disasters much worse than an impetuous remark in argument with a stranger. And he would be gone in twenty-four hours.

She swallowed and ignored the slight ringing in her ears. It might, she told herself, even be a good thing in the end. At least it got her determination to avoid involvement out in the open. If her family had concocted some sort of conspiracy to pair her up with Zoltan Guard it was no bad thing to let him know the score, even though she would not have chosen that way of doing it.

She realised suddenly that she had not even considered the possibility that he, too, might be an unwilling victim. Oh, no, she thought. If there was some sort of family conspiracy then this man would be part of it, she was sure. He was not the sort of person that anyone would plot against or involve against his will. Not if they valued their life.

Though it was difficult to see why he would agree. At least it was difficult at first. As soon as she thought about it she could see exactly why he would take it on. He probably looked on it as a challenge. He would find that entertaining, she thought. Keeping boredom away for another couple of days! At my expense, thought Penny, raging with suspicion.

It only needed one confirming detail and she would be sure.

'Are you married?' she demanded harshly into the silence.

The decided eyebrows flew up in comical astonishment. He slanted a wicked look at her. The look said that the amusement was to be shared. Penny refused to share it. She stared at him implacably.

The smile died. It was replaced by a slow, interested consideration which made her shift uncomfortably. But she was shaking, tense with the need to know. She stuck to her guns.

'Are you?'

He shrugged, his face closing suddenly. 'No.'

Any unmarried man, Sue Flynn had said. Penny was so angry she could barely speak. She felt she would choke with the humiliation. And underneath there was the cold little sense of betrayal.

How could they? Her mother and Celia—how could they? They had not even met the man, now she came to think about it. Just because they wanted a neat pairing off to tidy up the seating arrangements at the wedding, she thought bitterly.

She said, 'I think there may be one item on which you have been misled.'

'More of Mike's faulty briefing?'

She did not smile. 'Probably. I am not in the market for an affair.'

To her satisfaction, and for the first time since they had met, Zoltan Guard looked as if she had really startled him.

He began, 'Mike——' Then comprehension dawned. Penny saw him realise where she was going. Unforgivably he looked amused again.

'Mike never told me you were in need of a little masculine appreciation, if that's what you're worried about,' he told her kindly. 'I worked that one out for myself.'

Yet again he had seized the initiative, throwing her into confusion. Penny blinked.

'*What*?'

'You don't have to tell me you don't want an affair,' he went on calmly. 'It's written all over you.' He helped himself to more wine and looked her up and down. 'Bad clothes. Bad temper. Left at home to tend the pots because you don't like parties. All the evidence says you're seriously antisocial. Which must be voluntary with looks like yours.' He shrugged. 'Bad self-image, obviously.'

The embarrassment burned up in a heady slow rage.

'So you think what I need is some flattery to give me a better idea of myself?' Penny said with dangerous charm. 'Sorry. Correction: *masculine* flattery.'

Zoltan Guard laughed, the blue eyes gleaming. 'Appreciation was what I said, I think.'

Penny dismissed that with a flick of the fingers.

'What's the difference? I——'

She broke off, startled, as he got up from his chair and came round to her side of the table. He perched on the corner, one long leg swinging, while he looked down at her thoughtfully. He did not touch her. He looked as if he was laughing silently.

'If I said you were a sweet little creature who made my heart beat faster, that would be flattery,' he explained helpfully. 'If I say that you've got skin a man wants to touch and green eyes he could drown in, that's appreciation.'

The green eyes in question sparkled militantly. 'It's also nonsense,' Penny told him roundly.

He shook his head in rebuke. 'It must be a long time since you let anyone get within stroking distance.'

Her heart jumped. 'Mike *did* say something,' she accused.

'No. All my own observation, I assure you.' He looked down at her thoughtfully. 'But everything you say confirms it. No men in your life, mmm? And, I suppose, Mike and Celia disapprove?'

'My whole family thinks they can run my life better than I can,' Penny said drily. She looked him up and down in a very fair imitation of the way he had inspected her. 'And they've got another recruit by the looks of it.'

He laughed, flinging up his hand in a dueller's gesture of surrender.

'Not me. I don't want to run your life, honey. I don't want to run anyone's life.'

Her eyes gleamed. Quickly she veiled them.

'So you *don't* want to drown in my eyes, after all, Professor Guard?' she taunted softly.

She had underestimated her opponent. He gave a chuckle. 'Temporarily, yes. Permanently, no. I'm not into permanence.'

'Surprise me,' Penny said acidly.

His eyes flickered. 'And as you said to me earlier, what is it to do with you? As I'm only passing through, I mean?'

Penny stood up and looked down at him. All her anger, her disappointment and the hurt at her family's betrayal suddenly boiled up.

'I don't like you, Professor Guard. I don't like you. I don't trust you. I advise you not to rely on whatever my future brother-in-law said about me. He knows as little about me as you do. I will, however, tell you two things about me which you may find worth remembering. One is that I don't play games. The other is that if you try and "shake me up", as you call it, I shall make you sorry you ever laid eyes on me.'

CHAPTER THREE

THERE was a long, crackling silence. Zoltan's eyes never left her face. At last he pursed his lips in a soundless whistle.

'You don't beat about the bush, do you?' he said.

Penny pushed her hair back. She met his eyes unflinchingly.

'All right,' he said. 'You don't play games, you don't like me and you don't want an affair. What,' he added mildly, 'makes you think there is any danger of it?'

'I don't,' she said at once.

He shook his head. 'I don't buy that. Since you feel the need to warn me so comprehensively you must have at least some feeling that an affair is on the cards. Rather a brief one, as I leave tomorrow,' he added, that hateful laugh in his voice again. He put his head on one side and thought about it. 'Because I kissed you?' he hazarded.

She flushed. Her eyes fell. 'It didn't help,' she said stiffly.

'So, kissing you is a contributory but not a sufficient cause to put you on the defensive,' he mused.

She looked up. She was dismayed to see that his eyes were amused—and more than amused. There was also a distinctly speculative light in them. Her spine stiffened.

'If you tell me I'm interesting again, I shall throw the stew pot at your head,' Penny said dangerously.

At that he laughed out loud. He flung up his hands, both of them this time, high above his head like a cornered cowboy.

'You're boring. You're boring,' he said swiftly. 'I've never met a more boring woman in my life. Honestly.'

Penny surveyed him. 'Tell that to my mother,' she said drily.

Zoltan blinked. The heavy brows flew up. As he failed to answer she stood up and went back to the Aga. She picked up the heavy pot.

'I will,' he said hastily. 'Any time. "Mrs Brinkman," I will say, "you have a boring daughter."'

Penny put the pot down again, not without some relief. Even with its contents considerably diminished it was too heavy to hold for long.

'Lovely,' Zoltan added mischievously, 'but boring.'

Penny flung him an exasperated look.

'It's true, you know,' he told her conversationally.

He lowered his arms and crossed them over his chest. He was still perched on the corner of the kitchen table. He swung one booted foot negligently as he subjected her to a leisurely scrutiny.

'What is?' Penny demanded, suspicious of that silent inspection.

'You're quite lovely. Even,' he allowed with a grin, 'when you're spitting mad.'

'Thank you.'

He shook his head, his mouth tilted in a wry expression. 'And you don't believe a word of it.'

'I believe you,' said Penny coolly—and untruthfully.

She just could not bear the odious patient tone in his voice. As if he knew everything in the world there was to know and she were just a child. That would stop him dead in his superior tracks, she thought.

He looked taken aback. *Good*, she thought. She realised, of course, that there could have been no better proof of the childishness of her reactions. She did not care. She set her teeth and made it worse.

'I'm an artist,' she said hardily. 'I've got a mirror. Of course I know I'm lovely.'

Somewhere inside, her wiser self was looking on in blank amazement. Penny had not behaved like this since she was a carefree art student, still experimenting, still hopeful. It was exhilarating.

Zoltan flicked up one eyebrow. His eyes were bright with laughter.

'Oh, an *artist*. Of course. Mike never told me that. He said you were a hospital administrator. You look,' he added candidly, 'like a hospital administrator.'

'Good,' said Penny.

He shook his head. 'You're the most perverse woman I've ever met.'

'I'm flattered,' Penny said sweetly.

'Yes, I can see that you would be.' He looked at her unflatteringly. 'Would you like me to pass that on to your mother as well?'

She did not react to the mockery. 'If you think it would be helpful,' Penny said with composure.

He looked bewildered. 'Helpful for what?'

So he was not going to admit the conspiracy. Well, she was not really surprised. She set her teeth.

'To stop her getting the wrong idea,' she snapped.

His brows twitched together. 'What sort of wrong idea?'

Penny hesitated. Then, 'That one wedding leads to another,' she said, goaded.

Zoltan stood rock-still.

'One——?'

'The wedding effect,' Penny said, remembering Sue Flynn. She clasped her arms in front of her, feeling suddenly cold.

'Ah. That effect.' He strolled over to the window and looked out into the dark copse that kept the kitchen shaded and cool.

'You've heard of it?'

He cast her an amused look over his shoulder.

'Hungary is no different from the rest of the world. At any wedding the old women are going round to the unmarried girls, saying, "Please God, your turn next." It's human nature.'

'Then human nature could do with some attention,' Penny muttered.

'Indubitably. However, you're in no danger from me. I'm not into marriage.' He sent her a wry look. 'And I like my affairs to be a little less of an assault course.'

She stared.

'I mean,' he said, his eyes glinting, 'that it takes more than twenty-four hours to seduce a porcupine. Even for one of my famous charm.' He smiled kindly. 'And, no matter what your family might have told you, I haven't got more than twenty-four hours. I've got a board meeting in Brussels on Monday and a lecture to prepare first. I only fitted in the wedding with a shoe-horn. So you can relax,' he added acidly. 'You're quite safe—at least from me.'

'Oh,' said Penny, fiercely embarrassed.

Zoltan did not notice. He was staring intently out of the window. He said with sudden urgency, 'Turn the light off.'

'*What*?'

'Lights. Out.'

She began to object. But there was something in his voice that demanded obedience. It went against all her instincts. Half resentful, she clicked the lights off. In the abrupt ensuing darkness she stood very still, suddenly a little afraid.

His voice was soft. 'You say everyone is out toasting the bride?'

'Everyone but you and me.' Her voice didn't sound like her own.

'So those characters crossing the lawn are not here by invitation?'

A hand motioned her imperatively. She saw the movement in the shadows. Her every instinct was to stand firmly where she was. But she had to know what he was looking at. Fuming inwardly, she went to his side. Her temper was not improved when, without hesitation, he took her hand and pointed it silently.

About to protest, Penny froze. He was perfectly right. There were three of them, moving quickly over the grass where the croquet hoops would be set up tomorrow. As far as she could make out they were wearing dark clothes. They were carrying sinister-looking bags, not unlike Zoltan's own.

He bent and said against her ear, 'Does anyone know you're here?'

He was too close, too comfortable with being too close—unlike herself. But now was hardly the time to say so. Swallowing, Penny shook her head. 'I don't know. Perhaps not. Mother probably said everyone was going out with Celia. I mean, she wouldn't think of saying I wasn't going because I never do.'

'So anyone who wanted to burgle the house would think it was empty tonight?'

Penny nodded. 'Except for the wedding presents.'

'What?'

'They're all laid out in the library. I told Mother it was silly and vulgar. But she said people liked to see their presents.'

'Valuable?'

She tried to think. 'I don't know. Some of them might be. Michael's very successful and his boss is rich. And Celia is a model. She's successful too. There could be some jewellery, I suppose. I don't take much notice...' She swallowed. 'The police. I'll call the police.'

He had not taken his eyes off the hurrying figures.

'You can try.'

He let go her hand and she flew across the kitchen, hardly noticing when she banged her hip painfully on the corner of the hall table. She lifted the phone off its cradle. There was no sound from it at all.

'Dead?' he asked softly.

Penny began to shake. 'Yes.'

'Any alternatives? Cellular phone? Car phone?'

She shook her head. 'My mother has one. But she'll have taken it with her. She always does.'

He did not waste time exclaiming.

'Where are those guys going, do you think? Straight to the room where the presents are?'

She went back to him, skirting the table more carefully this time. There was only one of the men visible now. She shuddered.

As if by instinct, a long arm came round her. Penny removed it.

'The famous charm working on autopilot?' she said acidly.

'Porcupine,' he said softly. Though there was a slight edge to it, she thought with satisfaction. 'Where?'

She tried to put herself in the burglars' place. 'N-not the study. It's on the first floor. Maybe the drawing-room. There are big French windows there. They wouldn't have to do any climbing.'

'Burglar alarm?'

'Not on,' Penny said. 'We're here, aren't we?'

'Yes, but they don't know that. So first they'll want to disable the burglar alarm,' he pointed out. 'Where is it?'

'The works, you mean? I'm not sure. They laid a cable through the flowerbed, I think...'

He moved, looked down at her in the darkness. 'Can you lock the drawing-room door into the hall?'

'Yes, but...'

'Let's get to it,' Zoltan said. 'While they're still cutting the wires of the burglar alarm.'

'But...'

'No, it won't stop them, or even hold them for long,' he murmured, as if he was agreeing with something she said. 'But it will buy some time while we think of what to do next.'

'*We*! Huh. So far all you've done is give me orders.'

'Don't be tiresome, there's a good girl,' he murmured.

'Tiresome——' Her voice began to rise.

He turned and kissed her rapidly on her open mouth. It was the briefest touch of the lips but its effect was electrifying. Penny gulped, gagged, and would have hit him—but he had already let her go.

'I know you're in shock. But save it for later.'

Zoltan was already moving to the kitchen door. He moved like a cat, silent-footed and neat. He motioned her past him and let her lead the way to the drawing-room. The door stood open on grey empty shadows. Silently he flowed past her and pulled the door shut, locking it with the heavy brass key. He took the key out and pocketed it, looking round.

Her father had bought a heavy refectory table which stood just inside the front door. Zoltan went to it, sized it up and then, to Penny's horror, flexed his shoulder muscles and picked it up.

He set it down across the door.

'A bit more time,' he said. She could hear the grin in his voice. He wasn't even breathing hard.

'Any more doors to the drawing-room?'

Penny hadn't thought of that. 'There's a sort of archway through to the dining-room. It's got a bookcase in it. You have to know that the bookcase is a door...'

'Sweetheart,' Zoltan said, 'whoever is out there, cutting the burglar alarm right now, has done their homework. Take me to the dining-room.'

Odious, superior man. And what made it worse was that he was right. Fuming, she went with him and they locked that door too. They piled the table and dining chairs up against it in a veritable obstacle course and she followed him back silently to the kitchen.

Once there, Zoltan locked that door too. He stood with his back to the door, listening.

Something nasty had just occurred to Penny. She said in a strangled voice, 'What if they've got guns?'

'Armed robbery?' Zoltan shook his head. 'Streets of New York, sure. Not a professional job in the English countryside.'

In spite of herself she moved closer. 'But——'

'You carry a gun if you think you're going to need it. You won't need it in an empty house. And if you did get caught, by some bad luck, then it would treble the sentence. Think about it, sweetheart,' he advised.

Penny was so offended by this casual lecture that she stopped trembling and stepped away from him. Zoltan, unaware, was concentrating on the problem in hand.

'Now, where did they come from?' he said in a musing tone.

Penny shuddered. 'You mean—are they local?' she said, bewildered.

'No, honey. I mean where have they left their wheels. They didn't walk here from the station,' he added drily. 'And they didn't drive up to the front door either.'

'Oh,' she said, enlightened. 'No, they wouldn't. There's a bell you set off if you come up the drive. The Warreners in Keepers' Cottage would hear it.' She thought about it, frowning. 'I suppose they could have come through the wood. There's a bridle-path of sorts.'

'Big enough for a van?' he asked swiftly.

Penny tried to remember. 'A small one. At least, I think so.'

'And they would have dumped the car in the wood, climbed through your hedge and come across the lawn,' Zoltan deduced.

Penny was beginning to see where this was leading.

'No, you can't,' she said in quick alarm. She was not talking about his theory. 'They could have left someone in the van on watch. They could come back. They could——'

'Hush.'

His fingers lay briefly against her cheek. Penny jumped. But this time she did not feel like protesting. Her heart was beating uncomfortably fast. Although they were speaking in whispers, she could still hear the amusement in his voice.

He said reasonably, 'Why should they have left anyone on guard? They don't know there's anyone in the house.'

Penny was beginning to shake again. 'They soon will,' she hissed. 'The moment they find that obstacle course we've just been building.'

'Which is why I must get to that van quickly,' Zoltan agreed coolly.

In the distance there was a crash, followed by the sound of tinkling glass.

'Well, they're in,' Zoltan said.

To Penny's amazement he sounded calm. No, more than calm—pleased. As if he was relishing the battle of wits. She strained to look up at him in the darkness. She could not make out his expression. But she could see the set of his jaw.

'*Please* don't go out there,' she said.

But he was withdrawing his arms, putting her away from him, moving catlike and silent to the kitchen door.

She flung herself after him. This time she managed to avoid the furniture. She hung on to his arm.

'You're not going out there without me,' she said in a ferocious whisper.

He looked down at her. 'You'll be perfectly safe...'

'I will. You won't.' She wanted to yell at him. It put a strain on her throat talking with this intensity at nil volume, she thought. 'It's just as much of an obstacle course out there, you know. Without me you'll fall into a ditch or something. Probably bring them on top of you. You need me. I'm coming. You can't stop me.'

He didn't want her to come. Penny could feel the resistance in the hard muscles bunching under her fingers. But he had not taught logic for nothing.

'OK,' he said reluctantly. 'But you do what I say. All right?'

'But——'

The arm under her hand was as unyielding as iron.

'All right?' he repeated softly.

Penny swallowed her protests. 'All right.'

'Come on, then.'

He possessed himself of her hand. She stiffened. He laughed under his breath.

'Can't afford to lose each other,' he murmured, taunting her. 'Still want to come?'

'I'm coming,' she said between gritted teeth.

His fingers tightened briefly on her own. Then he was letting them softly out of the back door. He was moving fast but he still took the time to put the deadbolt down behind them. No one was going to follow them that way. Penny realised with reluctant respect that she was in the hands of a man who didn't leave things to chance.

The back door opened on to a gravelled area. The crunching of their steps sounded appallingly loud to Penny, like gunshots in the dark. He stopped and pulled her close against him.

'We need to get on to grass, preferably under the trees, before we work our way round. Is that possible?'

She nodded. He put her gently in front of him.

'Show me.'

She led the way, her heart thumping. They tiptoed the three or four steps to the protection of the cherry tree.

'This is what we used to do as children,' Penny said. Her teeth were chattering. She felt cold and scared, disorientated and slightly disbelieving at the same time. She gave a strained laugh. 'Playing highwaymen——' Her voice started to rise.

Zoltan squeezed her hand. She subsided abruptly. She stood beside him, quivering like a hunted animal. He put an arm round her and held her against him strongly. He did not speak. Penny took several long breaths. She felt the frightening beginnings of hysteria dissolve.

'I'm sorry,' she muttered at last.

In the dark she felt him shrug—smile. How could you feel a man smile in the dark? Penny thought. This was crazy. But she could. It was like standing under a sun-lamp.

'Nothing to be sorry about,' he murmured into her ear. 'Ready to go on?'

She nodded, hoping he could not feel her expression in his turn. Her lips were compressed into a tight line and her jaw felt rigid with the effort of controlling her alarm. She was not proud of herself. Who would believe she was a cool, competent professional woman these days if they could see her shivering like this?

He did not take her hand again. He let her lead the way, skirting the lawn carefully in the deeper shadow provided by the bushes and shrubs at the back of the flowerbeds.

'Mr Lambton is going to go mad when he sees our footprints all over his flowerbeds,' Penny muttered. 'He moaned enough about the men who came to put up the marquee. He's been getting the garden ready for the wedding for weeks.'

Zoltan chuckled quietly. 'We all have our crosses to bear.'

A crash came from the house. Penny looked over her shoulder in alarm. The intruders had closed the curtains in the drawing-room but it was clear that they had turned the light on. From the sounds emerging into the still night it was clear that they had discovered the barriers barring their way out of the room. She shuddered a little.

Zoltan sent her a quick look, then overtook her and increased the pace. He had obviously identified the break in the hedge that she had been making for.

It was not easy scrambling under the tangled bushes in the dark. She got several scratches and more than a little debris in her hair and down her shirt. Zoltan set a punishing pace. She was soon breathing hard.

At the gap in the hedge he paused and reached back a hand to her. Penny took it thankfully. He vaulted lightly over the confining fence, half hidden by the greenery, and pulled her through after him.

Once in the wood he stood very still, looking round him. The shadows of the trees were enormous, engulfing them. Penny began to feel safer.

'Through there,' she said. 'That's the bridle-path.'

Zoltan had been right. As soon as they found the path they found the van. There had been no attempt to hide it in the undergrowth.

'They're confident,' Zoltan remarked.

He strolled round the van, trying its doors. The back one gave under very little pressure. It swung open with a grinding sound.

'Hinges want oiling,' Zoltan said critically.

He put one hand on the floor of the van and leaped up into it.

Penny thought about telling him to be careful and decided against it. She thought she had never in her life seen a man who looked more capable of taking care of himself. Or one less likely to be careful, she thought wryly.

He was making a thorough investigation of the van.

'Not very professional,' he said disapprovingly from its depths. 'Young and opportunist by the look of it. Certainly they have been drinking. No dedicated burglar would do that.'

He emerged clutching a couple of empty lager cans. Penny looked at them and winced.

'They're going to make a mess of the house, aren't they?' she said. 'If they're not professionals, I mean. They could get vindictive, couldn't they?'

'It's possible.'

'Oh, hell,' she said. 'That's all my mother needs, just before Celia's wedding. I wonder if there's a chance of leaving home before tomorrow.'

Zoltan laughed but he looked at her curiously.

'Your mother is not as philosophical as you, obviously.'

'She's spent a year getting ready for this wedding,' Penny said with feeling.

'Then we'd better stop them before they turn the place into a garbage tip,' he said lightly.

Penny stared, torn between hope and alarm. 'What do you mean? I thought we were going to make a break for it.'

He leaned up against the side of the van. He looked very tall in the moonlight-dappled shadows. There was a distinct breeze among the trees but he didn't seem aware of it. Penny shivered.

He seemed like one of the heroes out of legend, standing there. While she felt small and scared and very mortal.

'We have a choice,' Zoltan was saying. He did not sound in the least concerned. 'We can put the van out of action, get to your nearest neighbours and call the police.'

Penny swallowed. 'Or?'

'Or go back and stop any further mayhem,' he said tranquilly.

'Oh,' she said in a hollow voice.

She thought he was looking at her with a good deal of amused comprehension.

She was certain of it when he said, 'Or both.'

'How——?'

'You go for the phone,' he said gently. 'And I'll stop the riot.'

Penny was shaking her head even before he had finished speaking.

'That's ridiculous. You can't possibly go back in there on your own. There are at least three of them.'

In the dark she saw the wide shoulders lift in a shrug. She also made a discovery.

'You're enjoying yourself,' she said accusingly.

He did not try to deny it. 'Hell, I haven't had so much fun in years.'

Penny's tension found an entirely understandable release.

'You're completely irresponsible,' she raged, forgetting to keep her voice down in her exasperation. 'You're treating this whole thing as if you were a schoolboy. We should have run for help as soon as we saw them on the lawn.'

'I thought we were doing rather well,' Zoltan said mildly.

Penny glared at him. In the dark he could not see it, of course, but it relieved her feelings.

'This is not a *game*.'

'No, it's much more entertaining.'

She made a noise like a steam kettle coming to the boil. It surprised her. She had not made a noise like that since she was a child.

'Be serious.'

'OK,' he said, quite unoffended. 'Seriously, you head off to the friendly neighbours. And I'll have a chat with the boys about the error of their ways.'

'You are not going back to the house on your own,' Penny said positively.

'I'm quite able——'

'*No*,' she interrupted him.

'But by the time the police get here they could have spray-painted the drawing-room,' Zoltan pointed out.

'What do you think they'll do instead if you go down there on your own?' Penny flung at him. 'You don't *know* they're not armed.'

He shrugged again, laughing. 'Maybe with the odd beer can. I can handle that.'

She shuddered again. He would have seen that, she realised. Knowing he would have seen it—and had every right to think her the most appalling coward because of it—Penny could have screamed.

Instead she said tartly, 'Oh, can't you treat this seriously for a minute? We should both get out now.'

'And let your mother have hysterics all over your sister's wedding?' he challenged softly.

Penny was horribly torn. It was a choice between facing Laura Brinkman in despair or three drunken burglars, possibly armed. Neither prospect was attractive. But Laura's regrets, Penny thought, were likely to go on longer than any bruises would last. She made her decision.

'I'll come with you.'

He was startled. And not at all pleased, she thought. 'But——'

'I'm not arguing,' Penny said. 'Whatever we do, we do it together.'

There was a moment's silence while their wills met and clashed. The moon caught his hair, turning it to silver. In the shadows his eyes glinted like a sword-blade. She had the fancy that, just for that second, they were on another planet—heroic, alone and opposed, strangers who knew each other better than lovers. Penny's breath caught in her throat.

Then he gave a husky laugh.

'I'll remind you of that.'

'What?' So strong was the picture in her head that she barely registered what he said.

'Skip it. Not immediately relevant.'

She had the feeling that he was laughing at some private joke. She was about to demand enlightenment when across the distant lawn the lights of the drawing-room seemed to blaze briefly. She stared. He followed her eyes.

'Ah,' he said with satisfaction. 'Developments.'

Penny swallowed. There was a figure on the lawn. It was not particularly furtive but it was moving fast. It was coming directly for the place where they stood in the shadow of the van.

'Now, that,' said Zoltan in his lazy, laughing voice, 'is very helpful.'

'Helpful?' Penny gasped.

'Divide and rule,' he reminded her. 'Back into the bushes with you.'

She did not protest. She might not understand what Zoltan was doing but it was only too clear that he knew exactly. At his silent gesture, she retreated into the wood. She found a friendly witch hazel and huddled under the slender branches, breathing in the fragrance of its blossom without appreciation. She looked back at the van.

Zoltan was nowhere to be seen. But the door at the back was swinging slightly. They must have forgotten to close it, Penny thought in sudden anguish. She measured the distance. Was there time for her to close it before the intruder came through the hedge?

But no. He was there already, climbing over the drunken fence. He did not even pause when he saw the open door. He climbed straight into the vehicle and began to rummage noisily.

Penny saw a shadow move below the van. Or did she? Surely—yes—or——?

Her heart was thundering. She put a hand to her side to ease the pain of a stitch. Her eyes stared till they ached. Then she saw it again.

Zoltan's long-legged figure stepped silently out of the shadows. The man was getting clumsily out of the van, carrying an armful of tools that looked heavy. Zoltan's arm flicked sideways. Penny's hands flew to her mouth. The man fell without making a sound. There was a muted grunt from Zoltan as he fielded the tools.

Carefully he put the tools on the ground. Then he was down on one knee by the intruder, efficiently removing his belt and using it to tie the man's hands behind his back.

Penny came out from under the witch hazel at a running crouch.

'What have you done?' she hissed.

He turned towards her and put a finger to his lips. His eyes glittered in the moonlight.

'You've hurt him,' she accused in a furious whisper.

'He'll live,' he whispered back.

He didn't sound either regretful or worried, Penny noticed.

'There was no need for violence.'

He sent her an ironical look. But all he said was, 'Open the van doors,' in the same indifferent tone.

He hefted the man to his feet and then tipped the dangling body over his shoulder. He looked down at Penny.

'He'll be more comfortable lying down,' he said mockingly.

Her lips tightened. She turned on her heel and flung open the van doors with an exaggerated bow.

'Thank you.'

He stepped up into the van without any apparent effort at all. He must be immensely strong, Penny thought. For some reason it was not as comforting a reflection as she might have expected.

He laid down his burden and just turned the man's head, checking his breathing. Satisfied, he stepped lithely down on to the moss-covered path.

'One down,' he said lightly, 'two to go. Back to your foxhole and see what we get next.'

Penny went. She thought his flippancy deplorable and his attitude downright dangerous but now was not the time to say so. Or indeed, anything. So she went.

For an age, it seemed, nothing else happened. Penny became aware of the breeze turning to a cold wind as clouds covered the moon. She wished she were nearer to Zoltan; or even that she knew where he was.

Nothing stirred in the wood except branches and small nocturnal animals, cheeping and squeaking as they scuttled about their business. She might have been alone. For a moment she even wondered if he had left her in the wood while he went back to the house in pursuit of the other intruders. But even as she started to straighten and peer about her, she realised that he would not abandon her.

It was odd that she should be so certain of it, Penny thought with a slight shock. But she was. Truly as if they were strangers who knew the depths of each other's hearts.

That is crazy, she said to herself.

She had no time to ponder further, however, because there was activity coming from the house again. This time there were two of them. And they were not just trotting across the lawn to fetch a crowbar. They were moving with a silent purposefulness that made Penny press her knuckles hard against her teeth to suppress a whimper of dismay.

They came over the fence cautiously, one looking round, guarding the other. Zoltan would not be able to step up behind these two and knock them senseless. They backed round the van, their eyes darting, their backs tight against the vehicle's sides. They looked fit and ready to take on anyone.

But that was not the worst of it. They had things in their hands. At first Penny thought they were tools of some sort—maybe a spanner or a wrench. Then, turning cold to the marrow of her bones, she realised what they were. She had never, she thought with a sort of detached despair, seen a gun in real life before.

Please let Zoltan keep down and let them go, she prayed silently. I wish we'd never started this. I wish I'd insisted on going for the police. I wish——

And then one of the shadows moved. Penny's teeth drew blood. She wanted to close her eyes, to shut out the carnage she was sure would follow. But she could not.

With a start she realised that there was now three figures stepping warily round the van, their backs pressed against it. As she watched disbelievingly one of them seemed to touch the other on the shoulder and, as he turned, fell him with one of those silent, horizontal blows she had seen before. Penny winced—but this time she did not protest.

Suddenly the stalking silence was broken. The van began to bang and rock as if of its own accord. With a start she realised that Zoltan's prisoner must have recovered consciousness. The two circling figures were both plainly startled by the commotion. One turned and was face to face with the other. Penny saw him raise the thing that was not a spanner.

Without thinking, she was hurtling out from under the witch hazel, screaming.

The gun froze, shifted, turned in her direction, shifted again uncertainly. It happened in a split-second but it was long enough. The other shadow flung itself upon him and they were grappling, rolling to and fro among the moss and leaf-mould.

There was another gun, Penny thought frantically. When the other man went down he had been carrying a gun. Desperate, she looked round.

Some accident of the moonlight caught a dull gleam. She made a dive. It was a cold, ugly thing but she scrabbled it up and held it to her breast as tight as a favourite bear.

Someone was coming off very much the worst in the tangle of arms and legs on the ground. Penny thought longingly of Keeper's Cottage, the Warreners and their telephone. But she could not leave Zoltan. He might need her. Or at least her weapon—if she could make a convincing display of knowing how to fire it.

There was an ugly series of grunts. Then a thump. One man fell back. The arms and legs resolved themselves into two figures, one unmoving. A tall shadow unfolded himself and stood up. He looked down at the prone body.

Penny groped for a decent hold on the gun. The man did not turn his head. He seemed unaware of her.

She swallowed and turned the gun.

'Don't shoot,' said Zoltan Guard, a grin in his voice. 'There's quite enough cleaning up to be done before the wedding already.'

She jumped. She let the gun fall with equal relief and fury.

'You——'

'Give me your belt, sweetheart. I need to tie these monkeys up.'

She fumbled the required article out of its confining loops one-handed. The gun bumped against her thigh.

He took the belt, trussed up the two men on the ground, and came back to her.

'Is there any other item of my clothing you would like?' Penny asked icily. She was shivering uncontrollably but she was damned if she was going to let him see it.

He grinned. She saw the gleam of his teeth in the moonlight.

'Not just at the moment.' He put a hand out and tipped her chin to look up at him.

I am an adult, independent woman, Penny thought incredulously. How dare he pinch my chin as if I'm a schoolgirl? How can I be so stupid as to stand here and let him?

She removed his hand and stepped back. Unfortunately, she had forgotten the gun. It banged against her leg, causing her to stumble. Zoltan reached down his other hand and hefted it easily out of her grasp.

'Mrs Brinkman,' he murmured, 'if this is your boring daughter I don't think I can cope with the others.'

And, to Penny's silent outrage, for the third time that night, he brushed laughing lips against her own.

CHAPTER FOUR

PENNY stood very still. There was the same electric tingle, unwelcome but unmistakable. From the gleam in the blue eyes Zoltan Guard was well aware of her reaction. She winced at the thought as at the flick of a whip.

'I must call the police,' she said briskly, stepping away from him.

Even with the distance of several feet between them, she could still feel the warmth of his lips. She was dismayed. In the moonlit wood he looked impossibly attractive. Something inside her reached out to him. I don't want this, Penny thought. Just the possibility, the imagination of attraction made her wince as if at the touch of fire. She saw him take note of it.

But all he said was, 'Good thinking, Batwoman.'

He glanced at the bodies on the ground. One of them was stirring with a groan.

'I'll lock these beauties in the van. Then I'll join you.'

He did. But not before Penny had spoken to a bored duty officer who suddenly became a lot less bored at her news.

'Sounds as if you got a regular little gang there, Mrs Dane,' he said approvingly. 'Hang on.' There were some clicks on the line and he came back to her. 'The first car should be with you in ten minutes.'

It was six. The police arrived just after Zoltan had strolled back into the kitchen. It seemed natural that he went out to meet them. Even more natural that he took them over to the van. But it did nothing for Penny's temper. Here he was taking matters out of her hands again, she thought, irritated.

She set to work dismantling their makeshift barriers, pulling the furniture back into place with an energy born of a rising fury.

By the time Zoltan and the senior policeman came back to the house the rooms were restored to their previous order and Penny was hot, dusty and spitting mad.

Zoltan identified her mood at once; she saw from the way his mouth tilted. It did not placate her.

'Mrs Dane can tell you more about what happened than I can, Sergeant,' he said smoothly. 'I'm only a visitor. She was the one who realised the gang must be after the wedding presents. And she worked out where their transport had to be parked. I just—er—provided a helping hand.'

The sergeant was not deceived by this modesty. Nor was Penny. Zoltan's intention to keep her sweet was blatant, she thought. She ground her teeth.

But, in the face of this graceful acknowledgement, she could do nothing except be gracious in her turn. Or not if she wanted to keep any semblance of dignity. Oh, he was an expert manipulator, she thought, seething.

'Trapping the burglars was entirely Professor Guard's work,' she said curtly.

The sergeant smiled. He had clearly never thought anything else. He sent the odious man a look of admiration.

'I'll need a statement from you, sir. And you as well, of course, Mrs Dane.'

Zoltan looked down at her. There was a gleam in his eye that the innocent sergeant must have thought was solicitude. Penny, seeing the gleam under the downswept lashes, knew different.

'Of course. But not tonight, mmm? It's been fairly stressful. And Mrs Dane has had a shock.'

He put an arm round her waist. It was more of a challenge than a support. But the policeman did not know that. He gave a sentimental sigh and nodded.

Penny whisked herself out of the provocative embrace.

'I have had no bigger a shock than you have,' she told Zoltan coldly. 'I'm perfectly capable of giving the police a statement about what happened.'

The sergeant said soothingly, 'No need to worry about that tonight, Mrs Dane. We've got enough to hold those three varmints. Your boyfriend's identified them.'

Penny stiffened. Zoltan's face was an elaborate mask of innocence. The sergeant did not notice. He was chuckling reminiscently.

'Bit of a formality, that, seeing as they were tied up with your belts. Still, that's all we need to charge them tonight. Someone will be down to take a detailed statement later. Probably next week some time.' He looked at his watch. 'But no need to keep you good people from your bed any longer. You'll be glad of your rest tonight,' he added. 'Shock's a funny thing. Takes people different ways. You want to treat it with respect. Well, I'll say goodnight.'

Penny said nothing. Zoltan, after a quick look at her, said goodnight for both of them and showed the helpful sergeant out.

He came back to the drawing-room, eyeing her warily.

'My *boyfriend*?' Penny's harsh question was an accusation in itself.

Zoltan's lips twitched. 'An understandable mistake,' he murmured.

'Not unless that's what you told him. Did you?'

'Now, why would I do that?' He sounded hurt.

'I don't think there's anything you wouldn't do if you thought it was funny,' Penny said grimly. '*Did* you?'

He shrugged. 'He may have assumed something. It hardly seemed necessary to take him into the exact nature of our relationship.'

'We do not have a relationship,' Penny said in a strangled voice.

'Well, quite.' One eyebrow flicked up. His smile was bland. 'But it would only have confused him if I'd said that, wouldn't it?'

She glared at him, unable to deny his reasoning, but deeply suspicious of it at the same time.

His voice grew coaxing. 'Look, the man was here to collect some criminals. If he finds a man and a woman alone in the house and jumps to the obvious conclusion, what does it matter? He will have forgotten it as soon as he gets back and starts writing out the charge sheets.'

Penny said between her teeth, 'It was not the obvious conclusion. I——'

The smile was back in his eyes. 'Oh, yes, it was,' he said gently.

The indignant words died on her lips. 'What?' she said blankly.

'He's a good detective, your policeman. He picked it up at once.'

Penny did not believe it. He could not be saying what he seemed to be saying. The shock-induced anger leaked away. It was replaced by something much more complicated. Though it probably did nothing for her shock levels, she thought wryly.

'I don't understand,' she said, hoping she was telling the truth. If her suspicions were right she was heading into a situation she had not foreseen, much less invited,

and she did not have the faintest idea how she was going
to handle it.

'No, I know you don't.' Zoltan's expression was
thoughtful. 'I find that—intriguing.'

Somewhere deep in her breast Penny's heart closed up
tight like a threatened sea anemone. The tension under
her ribcage was so fierce it almost hurt. Involuntarily,
she put a hand to her side, to ease the vestigial pain.

She was hardly aware she was doing it. Zoltan was
aware, though. She saw one eyebrow flick up in a curious
expression of disbelief, almost of regret. Following his
glance, she dropped her hand to her side again swiftly.

'What do you mean?' she said, not really wanting an
answer.

In the same gentle tone he said, 'It's not just the skin
and the dangerous green eyes, you know.'

She shook her head. 'I don't know what you're talking
about.'

'I'm afraid you do. You may not understand it. But
you know what I'm talking about, all right.' He was not
laughing any more. If anything, he sounded almost grim.

Penny turned a shoulder and began to push a brocade
sofa back into place.

'You're wrong,' she said over her shoulder. 'I haven't
the slightest idea.'

She lined the sofa up in its former position, plumped
up the cushions and straightened, ignoring him. The
picture above it had been knocked crooked, she saw.
She began to straighten that too.

A long arm came over her shoulder. She went very
still. Zoltan eased the dipping corner of the picture until
the bottom edge was precisely horizontal. She could feel
the warmth of his unhurried breathing on the back of
her neck. It was disturbing.

'Look at me.'

'I——'

'Don't dare?' he taunted softly.

Penny's chin lifted at that. She whipped round, prepared to tell him that she was very happy to dare anything he could challenge her with. It was a tactical error. Powerful arms closed round her before her confused brain had even managed to register how much too close he was.

Too close and too gorgeous. And he knew it. The unquestioning confidence was there in the easy way he held her, the laughing mouth, the arrogant tilt of the head. Registering all that amused assurance with a sinking heart, Penny suddenly saw something else as well: a tiny flame in the blue eyes.

As she stared up at him in bemusement it flickered into hot life. His arms tightened, jerking her against his muscular length. She gasped.

Which meant her lips were already parted when his mouth closed over hers. And this time it was not a kiss without passion—on either side, Penny realised with a slight shock.

They were so close that she could feel his heart thudding, his blood drumming in his veins. She could feel, too, that for all that magnificent assurance he was trembling very slightly. And, for all her anger, she was trembling even harder and clinging to him as she had never clung to anyone in the whole of her life.

Without lifting his mouth from hers he turned their locked bodies until they collapsed on to the sofa. Penny thought he gave a breathless laugh at the success of the manoeuvre. It sounded triumphant. That should have ignited her anger again—or at least put her on her guard. But it did not.

Lying among the cushions, she snaked her arms round his neck and kissed him with a demand as great as his own. It set him on fire. The grip of his arms relaxed. Then his hands became imperious. Penny gave a soundless gasp. She arched to a searching sensuality she had never imagined in her wildest dreams. She was beyond remembering, beyond thinking at all—except of how exquisitely gentle his touch was.

She began to shiver like her childhood pony before a horse show—half excited, half terrified. It made her cling to him all the harder, her eyes tight shut.

He was saying something in a language she did not recognise, crooning it against her skin as his kisses travelled. His bent head pushed aside the tangled shirt. Without her realising what was happening he had already dealt with the buttons. Now he was pulling aside her fragile underwear. She felt his mouth on her breast. It was a sensation like drowning. She arched into it, wanting to lose herself in that lovely oblivion.

But something was wrong. Something was happening. The darkness behind her tight-shut eyelids was shot across with lightning. In the distance there was the noise of a car engine... a voice...

Penny surfaced reluctantly. Zoltan muttered a protest against her skin, not stirring. Penny looked down at the gleaming head against her pale naked flesh and blushed wildly. She began to struggle.

His hands tightened. 'No...'

'Someone's arrived,' she hissed.

For a moment she thought he was not going to let her up. She had a brief, startling vision of her mother and sister walking into the drawing-room to find her half-undressed wrapped around a stranger. It brought her back to reality as nothing else could have done.

'Let me up,' she said frantically, beginning to push at him.

For just another second he resisted. Then a door banged, unmistakably.

Zoltan raised his head and inspected her flushed face.

Desperately embarrassed, Penny struggled with underwear. She pulled at the cotton shirt to very little effect. It must have wound itself round her while she writhed in his arms, she thought, wincing.

'Please.'

He lifted himself off her then, sat her up and buttoned the shirt swiftly round her. As if she were about six, Penny thought. She was irrationally annoyed at the alacrity with which he obeyed her.

'If this is another burglar, the police should start giving you a discount for bulk purchase,' he murmured, getting to his feet.

Penny followed suit. She tugged at the waistband of her trousers, which had unaccountably come undone.

'It will be my father. I recognise his voice.' Her voice sounded stiff and unnatural in her ears.

She did not look at him. She could not. She was still trembling to the core from that sensual onslaught.

Zoltan, however, seemed unmoved. 'The great actor?'

She nodded. He smiled. Even without looking at him she knew he was smiling, amused.

'I don't think much of his timing,' he said drily.

Penny blushed fierily. Zoltan's eyes narrowed.

'Do you want me to head him off?'

She stared, uncomprehending.

'While you—er—tidy yourself up,' he explained.

She winced again. No doubt he was seeing what anyone would see—a tremulous mouth and a dazed, dazzled look. She knew that look. She had seen it in the mirror every night when she was first in love with Alan. There was even a mirror above the fireplace now. Out of the shadows her haunted face looked back at her.

What is happening to me? He doesn't want an affair any more than I do. He just uses that damned charm of his without noticing.

Except that he had noticed the effect it had on her, Penny thought. And had pursued his advantage ruthlessly. She looked at him now. In the semi-dark he was laughing, relaxed, unconcerned. But he had not been unconcerned when she was in his arms just now. So why had he kissed her? *Why?*

He reached out a hand to her but she brushed it away, straightening her clothes with fingers that still shook.

'I'm fine,' she said, shaking her head. 'Fine.'

'Penny——'

She could not bear any more of that meaningless, too-powerful charm. She brushed past him. Head high, she went back to the kitchen. Just in time, as it turned out.

The kitchen door banged back on its hinges. A strong breeze sent a flurry of fallen wistaria blossom across the floor. Behind them appeared a wavering shadow.

'I'm home,' sang out the intruder.

Two matching suitcases were dumped inside the door and a tall figure followed them in, weaving slightly. He made two or three passes at the outer door before managing to close it.

'Hello-oo.'

Zoltan was at her shoulder. He held her strongly. She could feel his heart beating in steady hammer-blows under her shoulderblade. A long sweet shiver went up her spine. She fought it.

'Let me go. My father will see.'

He said in her ear, 'You're joking. He'd be lucky to see an oak tree in that state.'

'What?'

'The father of the bride,' he said, with an edge to the even tone, 'has obviously been celebrating. Unlike her sister.' He let her go.

Penny bit her lip. She went to her father's side and slipped an unobtrusively supporting hand under his elbow.

'Hello, Charles. I thought you were staying in London tonight.'

'Too noisy.'

He allowed himself to be guided to the kitchen table. He surveyed its forgotten contents and his face brightened.

'Wine.' He reached for the bottle.

Zoltan, laughing again, found a glass and poured it for him.

'Thankee,' said Charles Brinkman in his best stage pirate.

Penny made sure that he was propped against the table before she removed her hand. Coffee, she could see, was required. Lots of it and fast. He needed to be sobered up before her mother and sister got back.

Charles took a long swig of wine. Then, registering that the friendly face was not familiar, he lowered his glass. A look of confusion crossed the famously handsome features.

'Which one are you?'

Zoltan smiled. 'Which what?'

'Son-in-law,' explained Charles Brinkman.

To Penny's acute eye, Zoltan shuddered. But he said politely enough, 'I'm afraid I don't have that honour.'

Charles nodded sagely. 'Too many son-in-laws,' he remarked in self-pitying tones which made it all too clear, if that had been necessary, that the wine was not his first beverage of the evening.

Zoltan chuckled. 'Comes with the territory. So many gorgeous daughters,' he explained as Charles looked puzzled.

Charles looked vaguely round the kitchen. His look of puzzlement deepened when his gaze fell on Penny. She flinched. All it needed to close a perfect evening was for her father to explain why this particular daughter had provided the worst possible candidate in the way of sons-in-law, she thought savagely.

'Hadn't you better go to bed and sleep it off, Charles?' she snapped before he could speak.

Zoltan's eyes narrowed. But Charles beamed.

'That's my girl. You always look after me. Always look after all of us...' He was becomingly muzzily sentimental.

Penny said crisply, 'If you don't go to bed now you'll be caught by Mother and the bridesmaids.'

It worked. He heaved himself to his feet, reaching absent-mindedly for the bottle. Penny removed it from his grasp. She replaced it with a bottle of mineral water from the fridge.

She could feel Zoltan watching her, watching Charles. She urged her father to the door.

'Don't forget to drink the water,' she instructed. 'If you have a hangover tomorrow Mother will never forgive you. Especially if you mess up your speech.'

He looked at her reproachfully. 'Never fluffed a speech in my life.'

But he stuffed the plastic bottle under his arm and went out. Penny listened as he tacked noisily up the stairs. She heaved a sigh of relief.

Zoltan said, 'You got rid of him very summarily.'

She was startled. 'I'm sorry?'

'Didn't even tell him about our adventurous evening. Just packed the poor old guy off to bed.' He leaned against the kitchen wall and folded his arms over his chest, inspecting her. 'Don't you like your family?'

For no reason that she could think of, Penny found herself flushing. 'Don't be ridiculous,' she said.

His eyes were searching. And not laughing any more.

'They want a lot of sustaining,' she burst out under that dispassionate gaze. 'A lot of attention. It's sometimes more than I can bear.'

'You don't know how lucky you are to have anything to bear at all,' Zoltan said softly. 'I can't remember the last time I saw my father. And as for my mother——' He shrugged. 'She never bothered where I was or with whom. Even when I was half a world away. And here you are, all set to go to war because you think your family want to fix you up with an escort so you can have a nice time at your sister's wedding.'

Put like that it sounded petty in the extreme. Penny was torn between indignation and a weird desire to vindicate herself, to wipe that look of lurking contempt out of his eyes. Indignation won, but only just.

'What is it to do with you?' she said heatedly.

'Well, you seem quite clear that I've been elected the escort under reference,' he drawled. 'So you might say I have a vested interest.'

She said between her teeth, 'You have no interest in me. Nor I in you.'

'You keep saying that.'

'Because it's true.' He looked sceptical. Her temper rose a notch. 'It's self-evident.'

He shook his head. 'If it were self-evident you wouldn't have to say it.'

'I keep saying it,' said Penny, with desperate calm, 'because you seem to need reminding of it.' She added waspishly, 'Which, given your views on affairs, I find hard to account for.'

His mouth slanted. 'I have nothing against affairs. I just don't like to rush them.'

Penny met his eyes and found them quizzical. The contempt had not exactly gone but it had been pushed to one side, she thought, temporarily put on one side while Zoltan amused himself baiting her. She wished he did not have such instant success in doing so.

She said, 'Well, that rules me out, doesn't it?'

'Not,' he said, 'necessarily.' He strolled forward.

Penny became horribly aware of her heart racing. The blood pounded so loudly in her ears that she was afraid he would hear it. She remembered, all too vividly, how she had writhed in his arms.

She retreated behind a chair with more prudence than dignity and spoke rapidly.

'I know I went a bit crazy before my father arrived but you have to believe that was completely out of character. You said yourself, I was in shock.'

'Yes,' he agreed in a thoughtful tone, 'I think you were.'

Penny looked at him uneasily. There was something in his tone that she was sure would be unwelcome if she could only fathom it.

'What do you mean?' she said suspiciously.

His smile had a hard edge. 'That for an experienced woman, which I take you to be, you are extraordinarily reluctant to recognise your own feelings.'

Her hands clenched hard by her sides. Realising, she straightened them quickly.

'You're imagining it,' she said curtly.

'I don't think so.'

'I was in shock because of an armed burglary,' Penny declared, her voice rising. 'I had every reason——'

'You were in shock because you were responding to me,' he said quietly. 'Until your father arrived you'd forgotten where we were and you didn't know what was going to happen next. What's more, you didn't care.'

Penny stood very still. 'No,' she said in a voice of horror.

He just looked at her, faintly frowning.

'No.'

'You need to take a good long look at your feelings, I think.'

She swallowed. All the same she managed to send him a hard, defiant look.

'And what feelings are those?'

'Attraction, excitement...'

She shrank. It was all horribly familiar. That was what Alan had offered, demanded, imposed... She shut her eyes. Oh, God!

But Zoltan Guard did not know any of that and she was not about to tell him.

She pulled herself together and said with rather shaky sarcasm, 'You flatter yourself.'

'...set against fear and cowardice.'

That was safer ground. Penny glared at him. 'Are you calling me a coward?'

'Yup.'

She thought of the horrors of her marriage, of the irascible consultants that only she could deal with, of the life she had built out of devastation.

'You're crazy,' she said calmly. 'No one's ever called me a coward.'

He was watching her with an odd little smile. 'OK. Prove it.'

'I don't have to——' She stopped.

His smile grew. He did not say, Point proven. He did not have to. Those weary blue eyes said it for him.

It was like conceding him the victory without even attempting to fight. Penny's self-respect could not endure it. She took a deep breath.

'How?'

The steep lids fell. 'Come to bed with me,' Zoltan Guard said gently.

CHAPTER FIVE

THERE was a moment when Penny thought she had not heard properly. She shook her head, trying to rid it of the distortion through which her own subconscious mind must have filtered his words. An embarrassing distortion—and worrying evidence of exactly what was preoccupying her subconscious mind, she thought, disturbed.

Then, slowly, she realised that Zoltan had said exactly what she thought he had said. And the sheer outrageousness of it silenced her. She stared at him, her brain whirling.

One dark eyebrow flicked up. 'There's no need to look so dismayed. It was an offer, not a command.'

An *offer*. Penny stared at him for a disbelieving moment. Just for a moment she had a vivid picture of herself entwined with those strong limbs, all that electric concentration bent on her and her alone. Her breath shivered in her throat.

And then common sense reasserted itself. Along with it, for the first time that night, came her sense of humour. It was a huge relief. Penny pushed a hand through her hair and looked at him wryly.

'I can't believe you said that.' The germ of a laugh quivered in her voice.

Zoltan's eyes narrowed. 'Believe it.'

'I'd rather not,' Penny said firmly. 'You've embarrassed me quite enough for one evening.'

'How have I embarrassed you?'

She looked at him speechlessly. Then irrepressible laughter began to bubble up. If there was a faint note of controlled hysteria in it, he failed to point it out. And Penny herself was beyond noticing.

Zoltan watched her without comment, his eyes hooded. At last she choked to a halt. She rummaged for a handkerchief, failed to find one, and mopped her eyes on the back of her hand, looking round for the roll of kitchen paper. Finding it, she tore off a sheet and blew her nose vigorously.

'I'm sorry. I shouldn't——' The convulsive laughter threatened again and she drew a steadying breath. 'It's just that this is all slightly outside my experience. And when you asked how you'd embarrassed me——' She broke off, strangled, and blew her nose again.

'Outside my experience too,' Zoltan said with a hint of crispness. 'I've never had a lady laugh in my face before.'

'Oh. I'm sorry.' Penny was genuinely taken aback. She was even briefly contrite. 'I didn't mean to be rude.'

He was indifferent. 'My ego will stand it.'

It sounded as if it would too. Her contrition dwindled somewhat.

He was looking at her with that curiously detached interest again.

'But I'm still interested in the answer. Does sexual attraction embarrass you, then?'

What was left of her contrition contracted to a microdot and disappeared.

'It must be perfectly obvious what embarrassed me,' she countered swiftly. 'The same as would embarrass any other halfway sensible person. Or do you normally ask women to bed the first time you meet them?'

His eyebrows flew up. There was an odd expression on his face; it almost looked as if she had startled him. But then that lazy self-possession took over again.

'Depends on the woman. And the time,' he drawled.

Penny looked at him levelly. 'Another old Hungarian custom?'

He laughed aloud at that. 'Honey, I've been out of Hungary a long time. I learned my courting rituals on the Californian beaches.'

So that accounted for the accent, Penny thought. And the tan. And other things.

'I see where you get your high embarrassment threshold,' she told him affably.

He shrugged. 'Embarrassment is a waste of time. You want something, you go for it. Maybe you get hurt.' Under the lazy eyelids, the glance he bent on her was keen. 'Getting hurt is a pain. But it's better than letting embarrassment bounce you out of trying.'

Penny shook her head. 'Good try,' she said. 'The answer is still no.'

'Yes, I can see it is,' he agreed without apparent concern. 'I'm still interested in why.'

She hesitated. It must be her tiredness—or some odd integrity that she sensed in him that demanded honesty— but suddenly she wanted to tell him the truth. Suddenly serious, a little shy, she said, 'Have you ever been in love, Zoltan?'

His body seemed to tense.

'Yes.'

'Often?'

'Enough.'

'Well, I've only been in love once. I was nineteen and I wanted to give him the moon. I did my best to.

Everybody said I was crazy and he—didn't want the moon anyway. The trouble was we found it out too late.'

Zoltan was very still. 'That's why you're embarrassed?' He sounded disbelieving.

Penny shook her head. 'That's why I'm out of the game.' She hesitated. 'I've played all my chips, you see. There's nothing left. There hasn't been ever since. I suppose I'm a one-man girl who chose the wrong man. My family all think I should try again. But I know—I'm not like that.' She looked him bravely in the face. 'Can you understand that?'

He said in a strange voice, 'Nobody ever since? One throw and that was it?'

Penny nodded.

'You're right,' he said with feeling. 'Your family don't understand you. That was one hell of a gamble.'

'I know now. I didn't at nineteen.'

'So now you don't take any risks at all.' He paused, watching her face. Then he diagnosed slowly. 'I'd say a green-eyed blonde who looks like you and doesn't take risks gets embarrassed a hell of a lot.'

She smiled a little. 'No, I can usually deflect anything that looks potentially embarrassing. You've given me more sticky moments this evening than I've had in the last five years put together.'

'So I've shaken you up after all?' He did not sound particularly pleased with his victory.

There was no point in lying. He was too shrewd. Anyway she was too emotionally drained. Her chin lifted. 'Yes.'

He said nothing. There was a brooding expression in the blue eyes. Her chin came down.

'Not a great evening one way and another,' she said ruefully. 'And one hell of a day coming. I don't know

about you, but I need my sleep. Do you want anything
else before I go to bed?'

Even as she said it, she thought, That could have been
better phrased. But he did not take it up, make a joke.
In fact he ignored it.

'So I've shaken you up.' The self-mockery was almost
bitter. 'Well, at least you can comfort yourself that it's
mutual,' he said harshly.

That shook her out of her weary calm. Her eyes flew
to his, shocked.

'Oh, yes,' he said, with more than a touch of grimness.
'I'll go off to bed like a gentleman and I won't come
creeping round your door—even if I knew which it was.
But don't think either of us is going to sleep tonight.
Because we won't.'

He was right, of course.

Penny tucked herself into the single bed she had had
from childhood and, for the first time in her life, could
not get comfortable in it. She tossed and turned, lost
her bedcovers, knocked over her alarm clock, heard the
bridesmaids' party returning...

In the end Penny gave up and turned the light on. It
was three o'clock. She shivered. Although it was nearly
summer, the dead hour of the night was as cold as
December.

She remembered Zoltan's strictures on the English
climate. Was he, too, awake and cold in his room under
the eaves?

She hugged her arms round herself. What on earth
had possessed her to tell him so much? It was more than
she had ever told her concerned family, more than she
had said to any of the occasional boyfriends who took
her out to dinner from time to time and ended up

wondering vainly why they never got any closer. More even than she had told Sue Flynn, the friend and confidante who knew more about her than anyone else.

Yet here she was spilling it all out to Zoltan Guard like an adolescent on a radio phone-in, she thought, disgusted with herself. I was nineteen. I was in love. There's nothing left. God, it was pathetic. How he must be laughing at her if he was awake.

She pulled the blanket up round her shoulders against the cold. Would she have been warmer in Zoltan's arms? It was an involuntary thought and it shocked her. But once it was there she could not quite banish it at once. Would she have felt happier? Safer? Or once more terrifyingly at risk? Once she had dreamed of sleeping in Alan's arms, cherished and secure. And look what had happened to that.

Penny shook her head, banishing the traitorous thoughts. More of the wedding effect, she told herself grimly. She had not imagined herself in a man's arms since long before Alan left. Now was not a good time to start. At least if she wanted to retain her peace of mind. There were safer ways of getting warm.

She got out of bed, found bedsocks and an old velvet dressing-gown and climbed back into bed. Even so, it was not until the light began to show grey round the wistaria leaves outside her window that she finally slept.

Inevitably perhaps, she was late for breakfast. She had dark circles under her eyes and a tense look about the jaw that, she knew, was all too likely to give rise to comment. She paused in the doorway, bracing herself. Everyone else was already there.

Laura looked up, her eyes preoccupied. 'Morning, darling. Overslept?'

Penny nodded, relieved. Normally her mother would have demanded an immediate explanation of her washed-out appearance and uncharacteristically late arrival at the breakfast table.

Zoltan looked up quickly. She saw him take in the signs of sleeplessness at once. His mouth tightened.

He was looking good. No signs of a bad night there, Penny thought ruefully, in spite of what he had said last night. She did not know whether to be glad or sorry.

There was an empty seat opposite him. She slipped into it, not quite meeting his eyes. They were alert. They swept over her in a comprehensive survey that brought a faint colour to her cheeks.

Fortunately her mother did not notice that either. She was pouring coffee. She handed it across to Penny.

'The flowers haven't arrived,' she said in a distracted way. 'I've phoned the florist but they don't answer.'

Charles snorted. 'There were half a dozen women taking whole trees into the marquee when I came down,' he said.

Laura shook her head. 'That's the Women's Institute. They are doing the marquee and the church. I *told* you, Charles. The florist from London is supposed to be doing the flowers in the drawing-room and all the bouquets. It's *Jennings'* present to Celia.'

'Then they won't have forgotten, will they?' Charles said reasonably. 'A London florist isn't going to forget a top fashion magazine's order for flowers for a top model's wedding, are they? Too much free publicity,' he added with professional sympathy.

Laura ignored that. She did not like the more commercial aspects of her beautiful daughter's wedding. On the whole she had been fairly successful in pretending they did not exist so far, Penny thought with amused affection. But if Charles, less sentimental about these matters, started rubbing it in, he would find himself with a full-scale row on his hands. Laura was already pretty wrought-up, she thought.

She said in her quiet voice, 'When did you call them, Mother?'

Charles gave another of his massive snorts.

'She's been doing it every hour on the hour since the dawn chorus started. I'm not surprised they haven't phoned her back.'

Laura looked as if she might cry. 'Well, florists have to get up early to go to market to buy the flowers.'

'If they're still buying the flowers the blasted things aren't going to be sitting here in the drawing-room with bows in their hair, are they?' said Charles irritably. 'Stands to reason.'

Hangover, deduced Penny.

The bride reached for a fourth piece of toast and covered it lavishly with butter and marmalade.

'Don't fuss, Mummy. If the worst comes to the worst Penny can make me up a bouquet from the garden.'

'Thank you for your vote of confidence,' Penny said drily.

Celia gave her a most unmodel-like grin. 'Do you remember those presentation bouquets we used to make for Daddy?'

Penny gave a startled chuckle. 'Nettles and bindweed, you mean? You want to walk down the aisle carrying stuff salvaged from the compost heap?'

'Well, bindweed is pretty,' Celia said in a judicial tone.

At her mother's look of horror, she collapsed in giggles.

'She doesn't mean it,' Penny said soothingly as Laura began to get to her feet in protest.

Charles grinned. 'You're naughty girls, winding your mother up like that.' He said to Zoltan in explanation, 'When they were small, I was up for one of the European awards where they gave you flowers—men and women alike. The girls overheard me talking about it to Laura and decided to help out.' His voice was warm with reminiscence. 'They staged presentation ceremonies every night after school. They weren't allowed to pick flowers from the garden, of course, so they had to use weeds. They took it in turns to receive the award but as far as I can remember it was always Penny who made up the bouquets.'

'An artist even then?' asked Zoltan teasingly.

There was a warmth in his eyes which made Penny glad that there was someone to answer for her.

Celia nodded. 'She was the only one who was any good at it. Leslie's and mine fell apart and Angel put stinging-nettles in hers which brought everyone out in a rash.'

'No stinging-nettles,' Penny murmured, as one making a note.

'I think I'll just go and ring the florist again,' Laura said, rising.

She hurried out. Charles picked up his paper. Celia laughed. She was so happy she shone, Penny thought.

'Poor Mummy. It will come out all right. It has to on a wonderful day like this,' she said buoyantly. 'Is there any more coffee, Pen?'

'Good lord,' said Charles, reading, '"Wife of twenty years gets injunction against husband." You'd think it wouldn't take her twenty years to notice the man beat her up.' He looked round the edge of the paper. 'Yes, thank you, darling, I'll have some too.'

Penny stiffened slightly. Zoltan saw it. She realised it too late, as his eyes narrowed across the table at her. Another betrayal of her private feelings. Why did he have to notice? Nobody else had. Damn, damn, damn.

She got up. 'The pot is cold. I'll make some more.'

She went to the cupboard. She could feel his eyes on her—thoughtful, assessing. *Damn.*

Celia said dreamily, 'Today is the start of the rest of my life.'

'Yes, poppet,' said Charles. 'Not that it's exactly a revolution. You've been living with the man for long enough.'

Celia was unabashed. 'We wanted to be sure before we made a commitment.'

Charles shook his head, clearly only half convinced. 'Well, at least you know he won't beat you, I suppose,' He shook the paper. 'Did you read this? I don't know why your mother thinks Hollywood is such a den of iniquity. It seems to me it all happens in the Home Counties. This woman claims her husband beat her up twice a week for twenty years. If it took her twenty years to leave him then she must have liked it.'

Penny felt her skin go cold, as it had in the long-ago past. She kept her back turned to them and switched on the coffee grinder. It was too loud to make an answer possible.

'Ouch,' said Charles, when the noise died away. 'That's not a thing to do to a man with a hangover, darling.'

'If you had an ounce of decent feeling you wouldn't have a hangover,' Penny said lightly, not turning round.

She found filter papers and tipped the coffee competently into one. She measured water into the glass tank, reconstructed the machine and switched it on.

Charles assumed his noblest voice. 'A man's entitled to get drunk when he gives away his last little girl,' he said.

Celia crowed with laughter. Penny gasped and turned round in spite of herself. She caught Zoltan's eye at once. There was a question there, but it was also brimful of laughter. Suddenly her own lips twitched. She sat down on one of the kitchen chairs, shaking her head.

'Charles, you are outrageous,' she said frankly. 'None of us has been your little girl for fifteen years.'

But Charles was enjoying playing the regretful father.

'Do you remember your wedding, Pen? I was so nervous I lost your bouquet. And your mother cried through the whole thing.' He sighed reminiscently.

Penny winced. All desire to laugh left her abruptly. What could she say? *You weren't nervous, you were furious. You didn't want me to marry him. That's why Mother cried too. And you were both right.*

No, that wasn't a possibility. For one thing, you didn't talk about your own marital disasters at someone else's wedding. For another, her family didn't know exactly what a disaster it had been. It had become a matter of pride to keep it from them in the end.

'I remember,' she said without expression.

Celia shuddered. 'Don't talk about losing bouquets. I'm not superstitious but there's no need to go looking for bad luck.'

Zoltan leaned forward to Penny. 'You were married from this house too?'

Penny did not answer. But Charles was only too willing to do so for her.

'It wasn't like this,' he assured him with a grimace. 'Pen was still a student. She never liked frills anyway. It was just a family party.'

'A student?' Zoltan was frowning slightly, as if the news surprised him. 'So young?' His eyes narrowed suddenly, as if he'd remembered a crucial clue in a game of wits. 'Nineteen?' he asked softly.

Double damn. She should never have told him that. Penny nodded briefly, not allowing him to meet her eyes.

'Pen always knows her own mind,' Charles said. There was a faintly defensive note in his voice.

And rushes headlong to disaster following it, Penny thought wryly. She did not say it, though. Her father knew that her marriage had been as big a mistake as he had predicted. Fortunately he did not know exactly how big a mistake. There was no need for Zoltan Guard to know anything at all.

The coffee was ready. The kitchen was full of the comforting aroma. She got up and brought the jug to the table.

Her father held out his cup. Celia pushed his newspaper out of the way. Her eye fell on the article.

'You know, it is odd,' she said, with the confidence of one possessing a sunny nature and a devoted lover. 'I mean, why didn't she leave him if he beat her up?'

Penny's hand shook a little. She steadied the coffee pot and poured carefully into her father's cup.

'Maybe she didn't have anywhere else to go,' she said levelly.

'But there are refuges,' Celia said, puzzled.

'Maybe she was afraid.' Penny pushed the cup towards her father, gave some to Celia and at last, reluctantly, looked at Zoltan. 'More coffee?'

The eyes were frighteningly acute as he passed his cup across to her.

She took it, looking quickly at Celia and her father. But no, knowing her well, they still detected nothing.

Oh, if only she had not been so indiscreet last night. If only she had *thought*, instead of allowing herself to be swept away by the strangeness of it all. If only she had not given Zoltan so many clues.

'It is easy to be afraid when you are in a violent relationship,' Zoltan said, his eyes on her face.

Penny studied the stream of coffee as she poured. She could feel his gaze on her face like a heat-lamp, she thought in confusion.

'I suppose so,' she said colourlessly.

Charles snorted again. 'Violent relationships! Psychobabble. If a man hits a woman then any woman worth her salt walks out on him the first time he does it. If she doesn't, she's just asking for more,' he announced.

Penny felt as if he had tipped ice water over her. She felt her spine freeze, her whole flesh and nerves turn to ice in one juddering moment of shock. Her hand shook. Hastily she put the coffee-pot down, heedless for once of whether it marked the wooden table. She could feel the blood leaving her face.

Zoltan leaned forward and took the cup away from her.

'You'd think so, certainly,' he said easily.

He stood up and went to the window so that her father had to shift slightly to carry on talking to him. He leaned against the worktop, cradling the coffee in front of him. He looked, she thought suddenly, as if he were conducting a seminar. For the first time she could see him as an academic.

'But it is extraordinary what the human animal can get used to. Convince itself is normal, even.' His voice was dispassionate. 'There is a basic tendency to inertia, of course. Psychologically speaking, the individual fears that any change in one's circumstances will be for the worse.' He chuckled suddenly. 'Michael told me that the English call it Murphy's Law—anything that can go wrong will. And then unprecedented action is particularly difficult for an individual. Groups reinforce each other—whether they are football fans or rocket scientists—but the isolated individual takes on the whole world. And there are few people as isolated as the woman in a violent marriage. One can understand how it happens.'

The words flowed over her—measured, unemotional. Penny drew steadying breaths, pressing her hands together out of sight of her father. Slowly she could feel the blood begin to flow again. She poured herself coffee and gulped it down.

Her father shrugged. He looked unconvinced. 'You may be right. I've never known anyone like that.'

Oh, haven't you? thought Penny with wincing irony. Did I do such a wonderful job of disguising it? Or did you just not want to see?

Celia said compassionately, 'Poor things. It must be awful not to have a family to back you up.' She reached out across the tablecloth and squeezed Penny's hand affectionately. 'If it were me, I'd run to my big sister.'

Penny smiled but it was an effort. Oh, no, you wouldn't, she thought sadly. You're too like me. You'd keep it quiet and hope it would change and not tell a soul.

She said impulsively, 'Be happy, Cilly.'

Celia smiled. 'I will. I am.' She added mischievously, 'Even if we have to raid the compost heap for my bouquet.'

Charles said, 'Well, your mother won't be. Go and find out if she's spoken to the wretched florist yet, will you, love?'

Celia went obligingly. As soon as she'd gone, he leaned forward.

'Can you really make up some sort of bouquet for her, Pen? If there's been a hitch, I mean?'

Penny said doubtfully, 'Not out of the garden. There's not enough in flower. Well, maybe something for Celia but not the bridesmaids as well. And that big urn in the drawing-room will take some filling.'

Zoltan moved. He said lazily, 'Is there anything stopping you going out to buy more flowers locally?'

Penny jumped. 'I suppose not,' she said slowly.

'Brilliant,' said Charles enthusiastically. 'Take someone with you. There'll be a lot to carry.' He looked meaningly at their guest.

Zoltan looked amused. 'I was just about to offer.'

'There's no need,' Penny said stiffly.

'Yes, there is. You said it yourself. That damn great urn takes half a tree to fill it up. In fact you'd better take the estate car and load the stuff in the back.'

Penny hesitated. She did not like driving the estate car which was a great deal longer and heavier than her own runabout.

Charles, who was well aware of her prejudice, beamed.

'Zoltan can drive,' he said with apparent inspiration.

Zoltan's amusement deepened. 'Delighted,' he said.

There was nothing she could do, Penny realised. It was perfectly obvious that they were being manoeuvred. It was also obvious that Zoltan thought it was funny—and she was not going to be able to avoid it without being rude or so elaborately evasive as to invite questions. Neither of which would do anything to add to the happiness of Celia's day.

'Thank you,' she said with restraint.

He tilted his head, laughing down at her. 'Any time.'

She looked at her watch. 'If I'm going to do it, we'd better get going.'

Charles nodded. 'Do that. Not a word to Laura.'

Penny looked surprised.

'I'm going to hold the line that professional florists don't let their customers down,' he said. 'Then she won't start to panic until you've got some more flowers back here.' He pulled out his wallet and rummaged through it. 'You don't want dollars. What—oh, yes, here it is. I cashed a cheque yesterday. Take that. It probably won't be enough so——'

'I can put any excess on my credit card,' Penny assured him.

'Thank God for plastic.' Charles grinned. 'I never thought I'd live to hear myself say that.'

On the kitchen wall, the telephone began to ring. He went to answer it, fishing a set of car keys off the hook in the memory board beside it.

'Hello. Oh, hello, Jonas. Lost your map?' He tossed the keys to Zoltan, who caught them one-handed. 'Yes, of course I can tell you how to get to the church. Got to get there myself, haven't I?' He waved them out of the kitchen, saying into the telephone, 'Got a pencil...?'

'Coming?' Zoltan was at the kitchen door.

Penny went, hoping her reluctance didn't show.

'Don't look so worried,' he said, knocking that one on the head as soon as they were out of the door. 'I promise not to jump on you in the back of the car.'

'Don't be ridiculous,' she said, leading the way to the garage. 'It never occurred to me that you would.'

'Then you don't know anything about Californian courting habits,' he said blandly. 'When I was growing up it was standard behaviour.'

'One would have hoped you had grown up by now, however,' she pointed out acidly.

He laughed. 'Some things you never forget.'

She unlocked the garage door. 'Well, try,' she advised him. 'We haven't got time for silly games.'

'Especially as you don't play games,' he agreed.

Penny looked at him sharply but his face stayed bland. He followed her into the garage and identified the car without difficulty. It was wedged tightly between Celia's open-topped cabriolet and her mother's car. Neither was well parked.

'I'll get the keys and move one of those,' Penny said.

'No need.'

Zoltan vaulted lightly over Celia's car and opened the door of the estate. It was the narrowest possible gap but he eased himself through it, holding his ribcage in and laughing. He drove the car out into the sun without adding a mark to any of the closely packed cars. For some reason the lazy expertise annoyed Penny.

'Very proficient,' she said, getting into the passenger seat and closing the door unnecessarily hard.

'The word,' Zoltan told her drily, 'is professional. While I was in college I parked cars for a living.'

He let in the clutch and they were away.

'You parked cars in Hungary?' said Penny, boggling at this unlikely scenario. 'Where?'

He laughed. 'No. No. California. My father would not have allowed me to soil my hands with automobiles when I was at home. I was supposed to be a boy genius.'

'Oh, I see. Did you do an exchange with an American university?'

'No.' He was cool. 'I emigrated. When I was fourteen.'

She was surprised. 'So long ago? That shows how little one knows about the rest of the world. I always assumed it wasn't permitted.'

He smiled. 'It wasn't.'

'What?'

'I was a political refugee,' he explained. 'I went over the border at dead of night, expecting to be caught at any moment.'

She said, 'But you can't have been a political refugee at fourteen. It's—you were a *child*, for heaven's sake.'

Zoltan looked down at her. 'I was never a child.'

'*What*?'

He shrugged. 'I was the only son of a man who had once been a genius. He didn't hold with childhood. And unfortunately the system supported him.' They turned on to the main road. 'Where now?'

'Right at the crossroads.' She was struggling to digest the information. None of it made sense. 'What do you mean? How can he have been a genius once? Geniuses don't go off,' she protested.

He sent her a quick look. 'They do if they're mathematicians. I've always been grateful I wasn't only a mathematician. There's probably some chemical reason for it. Most mathematicians have done their best work by the time they're thirty. Earlier, even. At twenty-five my father had worldwide acclaim. He was reading papers all over the world. At forty he was forgotten.'

Penny's eyes narrowed. 'Are you saying you were his second chance?'

His eyebrows rose. 'Clever,' he approved. 'Something like that, certainly.'

She shook her head. 'What happened?'

'Nothing very terrible. I was gifted. Extraordinarily gifted. So I was taken away from my parents and sent to school with my peers. All over the Soviet Union at one time or another. I only went back to Hungary when I was thirteen.'

Penny thought of her own disorderly childhood. The schools had changed but there had always been one or the other of her parents and her sisters.

She said, 'That's terrible.'

'That's what I thought,' Zoltan agreed. 'I blamed the Communist regime, of course. I swore I would get out and lead my own life as soon as I could. It was a terrible shock when I got to the West to find that gifted children aren't treated so different here. Although I was older then. Getting to see that human nature isn't so different, no matter what the political organisation. But it was still a shock. In fact,' he added thoughtfully, 'that was probably my last illusion.'

Penny had a crazy urge to apologise to him for the loss of that illusion. She even opened her lips to speak. Then she looked at him, tall and powerfully compact, with laughing eyes and that devil-may-care tilt to his head, and thought better of it. This was not a man who needed sympathy from anyone.

As if he were reading her mind, he said, 'I've done just fine without illusions. Although I suppose there was one that was not so great to lose.' He did not take his eyes off the windscreen this time. 'That love-affair you were asking about last night.'

Penny blushed. 'I wasn't. I——'

'Yes, you were. Quite rightly.'

'I had no right——' she began uncomfortably.

'You had every right if you wanted to know.' Zoltan drove carefully round a blind corner. 'Do you?'

Penny stared at the road with concentration. She had met him less than twenty-four hours ago. He had laughed at her and ordered her around and nearly taken her into some very dangerous territory indeed last night. He also seemed to know exactly whenever something was important to her, no matter how carefully she monitored her reactions or how obliquely she spoke. And she knew nothing at all about him. She made up her mind.

'Yes,' she said.

'It was a long time ago,' he said evenly. 'I was young. Though not as young as nineteen. She was everything a young man dreams about, I suppose—beautiful, beautifully brought up, clever, well-connected.' He checked their speed over a hump-backed bridge. 'On reflection I think I was probably as much in love with her family as I was with her. They were all clever and they lived in this wonderful house in New Hampshire.' He looked sideways at her. 'Not unlike yours in some ways.'

Did that account for the reserve she sensed in him? The slight air of mystery which he had shown no desire to dispel?

'Do we remind you?' she asked tentatively.

'In some ways. Not all. They were a very competitive family. You—well, you have your differences but you look after each other. I can see that now. They just wanted to beat each other. Katherine most of all.'

'I see,' said Penny. 'Did she want to beat you too?'

He smiled. It was a mirthless twist of the lips.

'Yes and no. Yes, she wanted to win; she was ferocious if she didn't. No, she didn't want to live with a man who was beaten by anyone—even herself.'

'It sounds like hell,' Penny said involuntarily.

'It had its moments,' he admitted.

'Were you married?'

'That was the only stupidity I didn't commit. She wanted to. But I—wasn't sure. It went on too long, though, while we battled it out. In the end she said it was my fault it hadn't worked. And in part she had to be right. But she was hyper-competitive before she met me and it's gone on since. I'm told she's on her third husband now.'

Something in his tone made her look at him.

'Still carrying a torch, Zoltan?'

He shrugged. 'No. The burn-marks, maybe. It taught me hard but it taught me well. No permanent relationships.'

'I see,' said Penny again.

And she did. Rather too clearly for her own peace of mind. After all, what was it to her if Zoltan Guard was not going to consider permanent commitment? She barely knew the man. And yet it hurt, somewhere secret and deeply private; it hurt rather a lot.

'She's a main board director of the family bank now. That was what she wanted me to do, of course. Said there was no future in the academic life. She'd have hated it if I'd got to the board before she did, too. Anyway, that wasn't for me.' His voice grew amused suddenly. 'In fact I did a consultancy project for them last year. It was a bit small for me really, but I thought I owed her old man. He was good to me in his way. Even lent me money once.'

She said, 'Do academics do consultancies for banks?' although she was not in the least bit interested. She was only interested in keeping his eyes off her until this fierce little pain died down.

'All the time. I'm much in demand.' He laughed. 'So much that I name my own price these days.'

She gave a sudden choke of laughter. 'And my mother thought you were a starving academic who could do with a square meal.'

'Last night I was.' He sent her another of those quick looks. 'In all sorts of ways.'

'Yes, well. Turn left at the next roundabout,' Penny said uncomfortably. 'It's not much more than a village but they might have some flowers here. Through the traffic lights, and it's the second parade of shops.'

He followed her instructions. She leapt out, expecting him to wait for her in the car. But he got out and strolled into the shop after her.

'You get flowers here?' he said, looking round at the racks of local organic vegetables.

'Well, I'm not sending my sister down the aisle clutching a cauliflower,' snapped Penny, unaccountably disturbed by his warm presence at her shoulder.

He laughed. 'From what I saw this morning, I wouldn't think she'd care.'

'My mother would,' Penny said unanswerably.

The shopkeeper came out to greet them. Penny explained the problem. The shopkeeper shook her head.

'I get my flowers from Meadowbanks fresh every day,' she explained. 'I'm on my own this morning so I didn't go over.'

Penny's heart dropped to her toes. She looked at her watch.

'Maybe there's time to get to Shrewsbury if you put your foot down,' she said.

Zoltan did not move from the spot. He smiled at the shopkeeper lazily.

'How about if we went to Meadowbanks?' he asked.

The woman looked doubtful. 'Well, they really only sell wholesale.'

'That's no problem. The lady's father says we need the equivalent of half a tree,' he said with a grin.

She smiled back. The famous charm working again, Penny thought sourly. She danced with impatience.

'No—I mean just to trade,' amended the shopkeeper.

'Come *on*,' said Penny. 'We're wasting time.'

'But if we were collecting flowers for you we would be buying for the trade, wouldn't we?' he suggested.

The shopkeeper nodded slowly. 'I suppose I could give you my card. They know me, of course, but...'

'You call them and say you're on your own and can't get out there but neighbours are picking up your order,' said Zoltan fluently. His grin widened. 'It's even true.'

The shopkeeper nodded. 'I could do that.'

'Fine. Then all we need is a list of whatever you want. Do you pay Meadowbanks cash or put it on account?'

Penny watched in deep dudgeon as he and the woman organised the mechanics of paying for the flowers. From the slightly bemused expression on the woman's face she guessed that he was either offering her particularly generous terms for the flowers or was overwhelming her with that charm.

'I suppose you think you're very clever,' she said when they were back in the car.

One eyebrow flicked up. 'Angry with me?' he sounded amused and not very surprised.

'I don't like the way you order everyone around for your own convenience.'

'On this occasion for your convenience,' he pointed out. 'And I don't order. I just smooth the path to help people to do what I want. Just show them it's what they want to do too, really.'

Out of nowhere came his voice from last night. 'It was an offer, not a command.' Penny flushed brilliant scarlet. I wish I would stop doing that, she thought furiously.

'Oh, is that what it is? Well, you're suspiciously good at it.'

'I ought to be,' he said calmly. 'It's my job. Well, the well-paid bit of my job anyway.'

'*What?*'

He looked down at her, his eyes dancing. 'You, my dear girl, have just had the benefit of several thousand dollars' worth of management advice. Implementation thrown in, too. I shouldn't be too rude about it if I were you. My clients wouldn't like to hear I'm giving it away for free.'

They collected the flowers, along with the shop-keeper's order. Penny was allowed to go out into the gardens to choose her own flowers. She did so, her eyes daring Zoltan to go with her. He laughed, shrugged, and stayed in the run-down office.

Back on the road to the manor, the back of the car piled with flowers and greenery, Zoltan said idly, 'Why didn't you have this sort of wedding as well? When you were nineteen and so in love?'

Penny lifted her head, surprised.

'Your father mentioned it at breakfast,' he reminded her.

'Oh. Yes.' She smiled. Choosing the flowers had exercised a calming effect on her temper. 'Partly it's not my style. Partly—— Well, you may as well know. My family weren't ecstatic about my marriage anyway.'

He nodded as if it was what he had expected. 'I bet you were stunning at nineteen,' he said softly. 'Stunning, head over heels in love, disapproving parents. I bet you weren't even pregnant.'

Between astonishment and outrage, Penny gave a choke of shocked laughter. 'How do you know that?'

'Because you gambled all your emotional resources on one man,' he said slowly. 'If there had been a child you wouldn't have been able to. You would have had to keep something back for the baby.'

Penny was silenced. 'You're too clever,' she said at last with a little shiver.

'I'm interested,' he said, not denying it. 'Tell me about your husband. What happened to him?'

She looked out of the window. The sun had come out and made the surface of the road gleam as if it were melting. She could face it as long as told him just the bare facts.

'He died,' she said. 'Two years ago. He was killed in an accident.'

It was the truth but not the whole truth. She wondered if he would notice the evasion. He did.

'And that's all you're going to tell me.' He did not sound annoyed about it. 'Well, leave it for the moment. Tell me instead how you met. Was he as young as you?'

Fact again. She could handle facts. Penny shrugged.

'No. He was a painter. He borrowed a studio down here for the summer. I was at art college. He gave me lessons. We fell in love. We married. End of story.'

'I usually think of marriage as the beginning of the story rather than the end,' Zoltan said.

'That,' muttered Penny to the passing road, 'depends on the story.'

She did not say it loudly. She did not expect him to hear. But of course he did. He reached out a hand and covered her own.

'One day you will tell me,' he said. It sounded like a vow. 'One day you will tell me the whole story.'

CHAPTER SIX

Fortunately he was not able to demand any more revelations because at that moment the manor's entrance came into view. Penny drew a sigh of relief.

None of the family was anywhere to be seen but the ladies from the Women's Institute reported that Mrs Brinkman was very agitated—and the flowers had still not arrived. Penny went into the kitchen and set about finding the wherewithal to make bouquets. Before she had even begun to look the Women's Institute produced stiffened wire, secateurs, and other refinements she had never even imagined when producing her earlier creations.

Zoltan, to the expressed admiration of the entire Women's Institute party, carried in boxes of flowers without complaint. Penny suspected darkly that it was his charm at work again which won her three volunteers to help with bridesmaids' bouquets.

Whether it was or not, she was grateful. The whole business took much longer than she had expected. Finally she dressed the big urn in the drawing-room in fifteen minutes flat.

Leaving one of her kind helpers to trail leaves artistically, she took the stairs at a run. Zoltan, holding the urn, flashed her a wicked, intimate smile. As one, the Women's Institute sighed. Breathing hard, Penny flung into her room and dragged her new outfit from the wardrobe. In the act of doing so, she caught sight of herself in the long mirror on the back of the old-fashioned door to the wardrobe. She stopped, arrested.

For the first time in months she surveyed herself. It was a pleasant enough image that met her eyes, she allowed dispassionately. Undistinguished, but there was nothing absolutely ugly about it. Tall—above the average. Probably too thin but that was fashionable and she did not worry about it. In the years with Alan she had gone from worrying about youthful plumpness to concern that her skeletal condition would cause comment. Now she was just grateful to be back within the average range and seldom thought about her figure. In comparison with the voluptuous Celia, though, there was no doubt that she looked like a beanpole, she thought now.

Penny felt the first stirrings of dissatisfaction with her appearance that she had felt for years. She put her hands on her hips and squared up to it. Her chin lifted a little.

The smart new haircut had left a cluster of curls clinging to the soft curve of her neck, accentuating the graceful length. It also made her look absurdly young and vulnerable, Penny saw now, with a little shock of displeasure.

'I am not vulnerable,' she told her image grimly.

The mirror image looked back at her, disproving her claim. Her eyes looked enormous under the level brows. They had gone the colour of her jade pendant. They always did that when she was on edge, she thought disgustedly. It was one of the ways Alan had been able to tell when she was most vulnerable...

She caught herself. She was not going to think about Alan. She was not going to do any more remembering today. Marriage was in the past; she had dealt with it and, as she had told Sue Flynn, she knew its price. She was not in the market for another relationship, especially not some fleeting, volatile exchange with a man she did not understand—who seemed to understand her all too well.

She thought of his fingers at the back of her neck last night and shivered again. All too well in all sorts of ways.

She turned away from the mirror. What was happening to her? You would almost think she was in love with the man, the way she kept referring back to incidents much better forgotten. Keep a hold of yourself, she thought. After this weekend is over you aren't going to see him again.

She shivered for the third time. It was the safest thing, she told herself. She should be grateful that she could say an uncomplicated goodbye to him before she got too involved. But she could not quite banish the oddly forlorn feeling it gave her.

'Stupid,' Penny told herself aloud, fiercely.

She stripped off her jeans and loose sweater without once looking back in the mirror and went to run her bath. After a soak in the scented water she felt steadier. She slipped on her old towelling robe and padded out into her bedroom to fetch fresh underwear.

There was a knock at the door. Bent over her weekend case, Penny froze momentarily. He wouldn't, she thought. He *wouldn't*. Not in a house full of people, any one of whom might see him and draw the right conclusions. Not when they would all be gathering in the local church in an hour and he would have to look her family in the eye.

Oh, but he would, another part of her mind thought. He was the only man she had ever met who was really, deeply indifferent to what people thought of him. Even Alan at his wildest had still cared about other people's good opinion. But not Zoltan. He would probably not even notice, Penny thought.

Her lips twitched and she straightened. She would have to send him away, of course. But she liked that indifference to public opinion. It was one of the things she found most attractive about him, she thought unguardedly.

'Careful,' she muttered, catching herself.

She tightened the towelling belt and opened the door.

'This is not very sensible——' she began. And stopped.

It was not Zoltan. It was Celia. Her sister was wearing a silky kimono pulled untidily over a froth of white underwear and a long hooped petticoat. Her hair was piled high and she had a veil and a pretty coronet of fresh flowers in the blonde silkiness. She had lost her earlier luminous glow. Her expression was closer to panic.

'Come in,' Penny said, concerned.

Celia nodded. She was trembling slightly. Penny saw the way the much-photographed lips shook. She slid an arm round Celia's shoulders.

'Sit down,' she said practically. 'What's wrong?'

'Mummy.' Celia's normal guileless blue eyes were shadowed with distress.

'Ah,' said Penny.

'She's been in my room going on and on and on...'

So that was why there had been no members of the family around when they got back. She poured her sister a glass of mineral water from the bottle on her bedside table and put it into her hand.

'Calm down, love. I take it the flowers didn't arrive?'

'No. The van broke down on the motorway. How did you——?'

Penny told her about Charles' rescue plan. 'When we got back and the Women's Institute said the flowers hadn't arrived, I just sat down and did you a bouquet,' she said. 'I should have come and told you—but to be honest, Cilly, I just went at it hammer and tongs because of the time.'

She cast a surreptitious look at her watch. Celia didn't notice. She was too busy bursting into grateful tears.

'I told her you'd do something. I *told* her. But she kept saying there weren't enough flowers in the garden and I'd have to carry a hymn book or something and it was all Daddy's fault.' Celia sniffed. 'Why didn't Daddy say?'

Penny thought privately that Charles had probably got too annoyed at her mother's reproaches. He had a notoriously short fuse and he was not very happy about having his home turned upside-down, even for a beloved daughter's wedding.

But she said diplomatically, 'He probably thought he'd better not until he found out whether we'd managed to find any flowers in time.'

Celia raised eyes like drowned cornflowers.

'We?'

'Charles sent Zoltan Guard with me as chauffeur-cum-native bearer,' said Penny briefly.

'Oh.'

A small complacent smile flickered briefly across her sister's lovely face. It disappeared so quickly that Penny could not even be certain she had seen it. I am getting paranoid, she told herself.

'He's nice, isn't he?' Celia said airily.

'He's an opinionated, devious man with a nasty habit of amusing himself at other people's expense,' Penny said roundly.

Celia blinked. 'I thought he was rather glamorous,' she said in a small voice.

'Oh, he's that as well,' Penny said bitterly. 'No doubt he's given you a burst of the world-famous charm?'

'*What*?'

'His description, not mine.'

Celia giggled. 'Mike says every woman thinks he's a knock-out,' she said in congratulatory tones.

Penny's eyes narrowed.

'In that case,' she said with dangerous quiet, 'why did you send me to the station looking for Albert Einstein last night?'

Celia took a hasty sip of water which turned into a prolonged coughing fit. When Penny had thumped her none too gently on the back she got her breath and denied ever doing any such thing.

'Anyway, I didn't know what he would be like. I've never met him until today. I don't trust Mike's opinion, after all. Men are never reliable about other men, are they?' Celia said, desperately trying to retrieve the situation.

She was not successful. Penny looked at her broodingly.

'You set me up.'

Celia gave her a dazzling but tentative smile. 'Only a little. Honestly, Pen, I just wanted you to have a nice time. It seemed so miserable all the rest of us being happy and having our men to hold our hands and you not having anyone. I sort of couldn't bear it. Not on my wedding-day.'

Penny shook her head. 'The trouble with you is you're a hopeless romantic. Didn't it occur to you I might not *want* anyone?'

Celia dismissed that as frivolous. 'Pride gets you no-where,' she said sagely. 'You wanted someone once.'

Penny winced. Celia looked intrigued. She was staring at her sister unblinkingly. The tears seemed to have subsided.

'What did go wrong for you, Pen?' she asked.

Penny bit her lip.

'Lots of things. It was wrong from the start. We just didn't know enough about each other.'

'And you couldn't find out after you were married?' Celia sounded disappointed, just like the little sister who had cried herself to sleep complaining that Fanny Price had married the wrong man. 'He was so gorgeous. I remember when you got married—I envied you so much. I thought, I'll never find a man as lovely as that. And you seemed so in love.' Her eyes grew misty again.

'Infatuated is the word,' Penny said sharply.

Celia looked at her wonderingly. 'Would you have got back together again? If he hadn't died like that, I mean.'

'No.' It was uncompromising.

Celia was disappointed again. 'But he adored you. I remember the way he used to look at you. Sort of smouldering.' She gave a little wriggle. 'It used to make my insides melt just to see it.'

Penny remembered that look too. Even across the years it still had the power to make her throat close and the palms of her hands sweat. Because, unlike Celia, she knew what came after.

'We were divorced,' she said levelly. 'I didn't do that lightly. I considered very carefully whether I could go back to him before ever I petitioned for divorce. I couldn't. The marriage was over.'

It should never have begun, of course. But you didn't say that to your sister on her wedding-day. In spite of her restraint her sister looked a little alarmed.

'Oh, God, what if something like that happened to Mike and me? I couldn't bear it without Mike. I really couldn't. He can hurt me so easily. I know I ought not to let him. That it's weak and silly and I ought to be ashamed of myself. But I can't help it.'

Tears seemed to threaten again. This wedding, Penny thought with resignation, was going to deplete her emotional reserves for the next fifty years one way and another. Oh, for the peace of the office and the bellowing of offended consultants! She applied herself to soothing her sister's nerves.

She said gently. 'You and Michael are different people from Alan and me. It isn't as if you don't know each other. You've lived together for over a year. You talk. You trust each other. That's why you're getting married. It's silly to say you mustn't let him hurt you. If you love each other, of course you can hurt each other. It's part of the deal. You can't say, I'll marry you but only a bit, and then I'll be safe from being hurt. It doesn't work like that.'

Celia stared at her.

'Alan hurt you,' she said slowly, on a note of discovery.

Penny did not blink. 'Divorce is a nasty business. I've no doubt I hurt him too. Look, this is a crazy conversation for your wedding-day.' She hugged her sister. 'You're in love with Mike. The sun is shining. And you don't even have to walk up the aisle carrying a cauliflower,' she added irrepressibly.

Celia looked startled. 'A cauliflower?'

'We got the flowers from the greengrocer's in the village.'

Celia grinned. 'That would have made a nice feature in the family album.'

'Well, you can forget it. You've got a bouquet of camellias and maidenhair fern with a few grape hyacinths thrown in for something blue,' Penny said. She turned her hands over for inspection. 'I've scratched myself all over with that blasted chicken-wire doing it, too. So if you don't carry it I shall personally strangle you.'

'You'd be in the queue after Mummy,' Celia said, undisturbed by the threat. She stood up and kissed Penny's cheek. 'You're the best sister in the world, Pen.' She sighed. 'I just wish there was someone nice for you.'

'Wish all you like but don't do anything about it,' Penny said firmly. 'Please.'

'What?'

'I'm told it's a syndrome called the wedding effect. My friends have been warning me about it. The urge for one successful wedding to spawn another,' Penny explained. 'Matchmaking between unmarried parties present. Largely undertaken by the bride and her mother, I understand,' she added darkly.

Celia giggled again.

'I wouldn't dare. And after today Mummy will probably pay you not to marry again,' she said cheerfully. 'She was going to lie down on her bed with cologne-soaked pads on her eyelids when last seen.' She grinned. 'So you're quite safe.'

Penny thought of the man who had been dominating her thoughts for the last twenty-four hours. *Safe*? She was shaken by a little laugh. Celia watched her from under exquisite eyelashes.

'Unless the gorgeous prof makes a play for you off his own bat, of course.'

Penny blushed faintly. 'Don't be ridiculous.'

'Why is it ridiculous? He was asking all sorts of things about you this morning. I'd say he was distinctly interested.'

'Oh, *interested*.' Penny laughed dismissively. 'Yes, I'll give you that. He kept saying last night how interesting I was.'

'Well, you are,' Celia said stoutly. 'Especially as you seem to have been frightfully brave about the burglars. I gather we aren't telling Mummy in case she has the heebie-jeebies. But Zoltan was telling Daddy you were an absolute heroine through it all.'

Penny blushed deeper. 'Exaggeration,' she said gruffly.

'Zoltan didn't seem to think so.' Celia examined her nails. 'Honestly, Pen, I think he's really smitten.'

'You're letting the romance of the wedding go to your head,' Penny said drily. 'That man has never been seriously smitten in the whole of his life.' And as her sister looked disbelieving she added in a goaded voice, 'He *told* me he didn't believe in permanence.'

'Permanent what?' asked Celia innocently.

Penny shot her a cool look. 'As I recall, he was discussing drowning in my eyes at the time. Quite temporarily, as he pointed out.'

Celia gave a crow of laughter. 'How wonderful. In that case I think you might just as well start writing out your formal surrender now.'

'Surrender? You're talking nonsense. Why on earth should I?'

'Because I don't see any red-blooded woman resisting Zoltan Guard,' Celia said simply. 'Not for long, anyway.'

'He won't be here for long,' Penny said.

But she was disconcerted. And just a little uneasy.

If she was aware of it then Celia was shrewd enough not to say any more. She swallowed the last of the mineral water.

'I suppose you haven't got a real drink?' she said wistfully. 'I could really do with a glass of champagne.'

'Wait for it,' Penny advised. 'The place will be awash with the stuff in a couple of hours.'

There was another knock on the door.

'This is like Paddington station,' she muttered, going to open it.

Celia helped herself to a tissue and blew her nose loudly.

'No, it isn't. You can get a drink on Paddington station,' she said with a grin. Her equilibrium seemed fully restored. 'Who...? Oh,' she ended on a long note of surprise. She sent her sister a mischievous look.

Penny was speechless. All she could think was, He did dare. I should have known. Silently she stood aside to admit her visitor. Her hands went quickly to check the tie of her old robe. She tightened it anyway.

Zoltan Guard gave them both an impartial flash of that dazzling smile and strolled into her room. Suddenly it seemed smaller.

'Funny you should mention that,' he said. 'I was thinking along the same lines myself.' He produced a silver-topped bottle and began to strip away the foil in a businesslike fashion.

Celia gave a long sigh. 'Champagne,' she said dreamily.

'Inspired,' Penny said, with something of a snap. 'Celia was just demanding it.'

His quick glance said he noted her flicker of annoyance. From the way his mouth just tilted, very slightly, Penny concluded that it amused him. She tugged her towelling sash even tighter and glared at him.

He withstood it with equanimity. 'Very understandable,' he said soothingly. 'Glasses?'

Celia detached the glass from the carafe of water on the washstand and gave it to him.

'Penny doesn't go in for secret drinking. Or even public drinking,' she informed him chattily. 'This could be a challenge. Oh, what about the tooth-mug?'

She went into the bathroom. Penny found Zoltan was very close. He was laughing down at her, his amusement silent and undisguisable. She opened her mouth to remonstrate when, to her total astonishment, she was caught up in a whirlwind kiss. This time it did not feel as if he was experimenting to see if he liked it. Or demonstrating any other philosophical point. It was almost fierce.

'Where's your tooth-glass, Pen?' Celia called.

Penny put out a stunned hand to ease her hurried breathing. She had no breath to answer.

'Did Mrs Davies move it?' Celia called.

Penny closed her eyes, shutting out the unwelcome vision of Zoltan Guard's amusement and the imminent prospect of her sister walking in on them and drawing the all too obvious conclusion.

How dare he? she thought. But that was silly. She had only to open her eyes and view the matter of fact way with which he had returned to the champagne bottle to know exactly how he dared. Because he did not give a damn about what anyone thought.

'Oh, it's all right. I've found it,' Celia called.

Penny took three sharp steps backwards, leaving as much space between them as the furniture permitted. Her sister emerged triumphantly, bearing aloft the rose-covered tooth-mug Penny had owned since she was a child. She was shaking her head.

'Only one, though. Someone will have to drink out of the bottle.'

'I don't want any,' Penny said hastily.

Celia looked impatient. 'This is my wedding-day, for heaven's sake. You're going to have to indulge a bit today. It wouldn't be sisterly not to.' She held out the mug to Zoltan. 'Penny is virtually teetotal,' she explained, grimacing. 'Not so much as a glass of wine at Christmas. It's very boring.'

One of those heavy eyebrows flicked up. Penny knew he was storing it away, just as he had stored away every other damned thing she had told him since she met him off the train last night.

But he did not say anything. Instead he cast an experienced eye over her dressing-table and swooped. Unceremoniously tipping a tumble of trinkets on to the cloth-covered top, he presented her with an open lotus dish that Charles had brought back from China.

'There you are,' he said. 'You'll lose some of the bubbles but it will look wonderfully decadent.'

Celia giggled again.

He poured the wine for the three of them and then silently toasted Celia. They all drank, Penny barely sipping at hers.

'Wonderful,' said Celia after a long swallow. 'Oh, this is better than sitting and listening to Mummy complaining about how conventional Handel is.' She gave Penny a quick, conspiratorial look. 'Or anything else either.'

Zoltan's eyes narrowed.

Celia finished her drink and put down the tooth-mug. She peered in the mirror. The coronet of flowers was now distinctly lopsided.

'Well, if Mummy sees me now she really will have something to complain about,' Celia said cheerfully. She gave Penny a quick hug. 'Thanks for everything, Pen. You keep us all sane, you know. Oh, God, is that the time? I must *fly*.'

She whipped out of the door and let it crash behind her with a thump that sent dispossessed costume jewellery all over the floor. Penny groaned.

'She is very fond of you, isn't she?' Zoltan said in a thoughtful tone.

Penny was scooping up daisy earrings and a malachite ring.

'We're sisters.'

'Doesn't follow. I know sisters who are at each other's throats,' he said tranquilly.

'Well, we aren't. We've always got on very well.'

He was mildly surprised. 'Always? Even in your competitive teens?'

Penny laughed. 'I never competed with any of my sisters. We are too different. Leslie is brainy, Angel is dedicated to her dancing and Celia—well, you've seen her. She was always going to be the beauty of the family. Not much point in competing with her.'

She looked up, smiling. She was crouching on the carpet with the little trinkets in her hand. Just for a moment she surprised the oddest expression on his face. Almost as if he was angry. Her smile died.

But the expression was only there for a second. He sat down in her pretty painted cane chair. He should have looked ridiculous with his long booted legs propped against the feminine frills of the dressing-table. But he

did not. In fact, Penny thought, startled, he looked as
if he belonged there.

He smiled crookedly down at her.

'So when Celia was planning to be the beauty, what
did you want to be when you grew up? A hospital administrator?' he asked with gentle irony.

Penny stood up, brushing carpet fluff off her robe.

'Of course not.'

'Well, then?'

There was something about the way he said it that
convinced her he was not going to give up until he got
his answer.

'I wanted to paint,' she said reluctantly.

'A painter,' he said thoughtfully. 'Did you go to
college? Did you study it?'

She put the trinkets down carefully on the dressing-
table.

'For a while.'

'What does that mean?'

She flung away from him. 'I didn't finish my course.'

It was odd, she thought, with the part of her mind
that was not wincing away from the admission, how
much that failure still hurt all these years later. She
looked out of the window blindly, biting her lip. Below,
the tradesmen's vans were beginning to leave, she saw.

'We ought to be getting ready.'

Zoltan ignored that.

'Was it your choice?'

Penny was watching the caterer's van as if her life
depended on it.

'What?'

'That you didn't finish your art course,' he elucidated
gently. 'Who took the decision? You or the college?'

What would he say if she told him the truth? Penny thought wryly. That neither she nor the college had decided. That Alan had come to the end-of-term exhibition, seen her work and the sales she had achieved, and had gone off on a bender of imperial proportions. That she had spent her twentieth birthday sitting by his bedside persuading him that he did not want to kill himself. That she had never gone back to college after that one, too-successful end-of-year show.

She shrugged, not answering.

But he was not to be deflected.

'Did you lose interest? Get bored?'

'There were other things I—wanted to do,' she said carefully.

Wanted! Well, she supposed she had wanted to then. She had been full of love and trust and optimism then. She had thought her love could cure Alan of his demon of alcoholism and his even deeper demon of jealousy.

Well, she had been wrong. She was no judge of men and no judge of her own emotional strength either. It was important to remember that, Penny thought.

'What other things?' said the soft, implacable voice behind her.

She shrugged again, not answering.

'How old were you?'

There seemed to be no harm in telling him. 'Twenty.'

'One year into that gambler's marriage of yours? Or less?'

Penny froze. She turned to face him. He was still sitting there, his boots on her dressing-table, looking at her over the top of his glass. He wore an expression of blandly social interest but she was not deceived.

'Why do you keep asking me things like that?' she said in sudden despair. 'Why do you keep digging and digging and digging? Why can't you leave me alone?'

'Why does it upset you so much?' he countered softly. 'All you need to do is tell me to mind my own business.'

'I have,' Penny said. She flopped down on the stool with a sigh. 'It didn't seem to work, as I recall.' She passed a hand over her hair in a distracted way.

'Do you still paint?'

'When I have time.'

'Ah.' He nodded thoughtfully. 'Another area of frustration. Your best energies going on stuff you don't believe in and only the time when you're tired left to paint. I can relate to that.'

Penny straightened. 'What do you mean, *another*...?'

He gave her an enigmatic smile.

She said hurriedly. 'Oh, good heavens, look at the time. We ought to be changing.' She remembered that sports bag and looked at him with misgiving. 'Will you—er—be changing?'

He laughed. 'There's plenty of time and you know it. Yes, I will be changing. I'm waiting for the iron.'

It was so unexpected that Penny was blank.

'What?'

'Iron,' he repeated calmly. 'The material is supposed to be crease-resistant but I'm sure your mother could tell. So I asked another of your sisters—Leslie, is it?—if I could borrow an iron to smarten it up a bit. I'm in a queue, I gather. We're stacked up until your father has dressed.'

Penny was surprised into a laugh.

'I bet you are.'

'Yes. I gather your mother was worried by his lack of progress,' Zoltan said.

His expression was neutral yet she knew he was laughing. Now, how do I know? Penny asked herself, bemused.

He stood up. Picking up the lotus dish she had put down on the dressing-table, he strolled across to her.

'You forgot your champagne.'

Penny took it. There didn't seem to be an alternative. 'I don't drink very much.'

'Less than a glass of champagne won't hurt you,' he said comfortably. 'It might even stop you looking as if you're expecting to be ambushed.'

'*What*?'

'It's not very flattering, you know.'

Penny was bewildered. 'I haven't the slightest idea what you're talking about.'

He smiled at her. 'Then let me show you,' he said gently.

He put his hands out and grasped her by the shoulders. Penny tensed. She began to pull away. But he was not going to kiss her, she found. Instead he marched her to the full-length mirror and stood her in front of it.

His hands looked very strong and tanned against the old white robe. It was beginning to gape a little, Penny saw, as the ancient belt relaxed its knot. She stood very still in his hands, hoping it would get no worse.

He shook her very gently. 'Look at yourself, Penny Dane,' he said softly. 'You should be in battledress with a Kalashnikov in your hands. I've never seen a woman so jumpy.'

Penny swallowed. She looked at the image in the mirror; without make-up she looked ivory-pale, the green eyes enormous. And, yes, he was right; her eyes were full of wariness and a flinching knowledge of the possibility of hurt.

Lying, she said again, 'I don't know what you're talking about.'

'Oh, I think you do. And I want to know why.'

In the mirror he seemed immensely tall and muscular compared with her slenderness. She could feel the warmth of him, the steady beat of his heart behind her shoulderblade. She had not been this close to a man in this room since she had left Alan. It would be so easy to shift her weight a little, to lean back against him, letting her head drop against his shoulder, the blonde hair fanning out against the darkness of his shirt.

Her whole body seemed to sigh at the thought. So easy. Dangerously easy.

Suddenly Penny could not bear it. She pulled out of the light hold which was not—not quite—an embrace.

'We've got no time to play silly games. Let me go,' she said in a stifled voice, although physically she had already removed herself to the window.

He flung up his hands, palm outwards, laughing.

'You're free. I still want to know the answer.'

'You're imagining things. If I'm a little tense it's because there are a lot of things that can go wrong at weddings,' she said defensively.

'Yes, I considered that,' he agreed. 'But you like your future brother-in-law. There are no rivalries between you and your sisters. Your mother might be a bit overwrought but you're all used to it and you can handle it. So I ask myself, What is it that gives her that look of—desperation?'

Penny was startled. 'You're imagining it.'

Zoltan smiled. 'No.'

'But——'

'You've looked on the edge of desperation ever since I arrived last night,' Zoltan told her levelly. 'At first I thought it was because of me—you didn't know me, after all. A lot of women might find that a bit daunting, having to meet someone they didn't know and keep him entertained for a whole evening. But not you. That wasn't what worried you. You could handle it and a great deal more with one hand tied behind your back. Just as you handle me.' He was rueful.

'I don't,' protested Penny.

'Oh, but you do. You're very civilised about it, of course. Very hospitable, very polite. But every time we approach something you don't want to talk about, the notices go up. Protected area! It makes it very difficult to know what's going on in your head.'

Penny found she still had the lotus dish of champagne in her hand. In spite of her prejudices, she drank. It was cool and pleasant and the bubbles seemed to have a calming effect, she found gratefully.

'Why should you want to know what's going on in my head?' she said.

'It seems a reasonable first step.'

Her eyes widened. 'First step to what?'

'To wherever we're going.'

Penny did not pretend to misunderstand him. She did not think there would be much point. Zoltan Guard did not seem to care too much about the social niceties. He would certainly not let her get away with it.

She shook her head with decision. 'We're not going anywhere,' she said firmly.

'Oh, but we are,' he said with equal firmness. He seemed amused again.

Penny took another revivifying mouthful of champagne.

'You're mad,' she told him. 'We've known each other less than twenty-four hours. You asked me to go to bed with you and I said no. End of story.'

He chuckled. 'On the contrary. Start of story.'

'You mean that because I turned you down you have to keep after me till I agree?' Penny was incredulous. 'Oh, get real, please.'

'I told you, when I start a project I see it through to the end,' he told her tranquilly.

Penny glared. 'I am *not* a project.'

'Yes, you are. And likely to prove one of the most difficult I've ever set my hand to.' He sounded thoughtful.

'You will not set your hand to me,' she began hotly.

But there was another knock on the door. She jumped and fell silent, bewildered and indignant.

Zoltan took in her confusion, smiled at her with odious reassurance, and strolled over to the door.

It was Leslie. She was carrying coat-hangers.

'Pen, have you seen Mike's professor? I've ironed——'

She stopped short, taking in Zoltan's easy smile and her sister backed up against the window with flushed face and eyes darting green fire. If Penny looked hot and bothered, Zoltan looked completely at home. Leslie was flustered.

'Oh, I'm sorry,' she said. 'I didn't mean to interrupt.'

Penny did not say anything. Anything she could think of would only make it worse. Now there were two of her sisters who thought she was having a dance round the maypole with Zoltan Guard, she thought grimly. He, she could see, was well aware of the undercurrents—and hugely amused by them.

'How very kind,' said Zoltan smoothly. He took the coat-hangers from Leslie. 'I came to ask your sister if she would like me to drive to the church, since we will be going in the same car. I'm told that driving is ruin to smart high heels.'

'Er—how thoughtful,' said Leslie. She looked at Penny with faint anxiety. 'Are you all right, Pen?'

'I'm fine,' Penny said through clenched teeth. 'As you say, Professor Guard is all consideration.'

'Yes,' agreed Leslie, happily unaware of sarcasm. 'Steven wouldn't think of a thing like that.' She gave Zoltan an approving smile. 'Will you be long? Mummy's getting in a tizz and Daddy wants to give everyone a drink before we go off to church.'

'I've already had a drink,' said Penny. 'I don't want any more.'

Leslie's eyes widened slightly as she took in the champagne bottle. Her eyebrows rose but she contained her surprise. She prepared to go.

'Well, get a move on, anyway. Mummy wants to pin corsages on everyone. The bridesmaids have thrown her out and I think she's feeling a bit spare.'

'I'll be down as soon as I'm dressed,' Penny promised.

Leslie's eyebrows went a fraction higher. Zoltan met her startled gaze blandly.

'I also,' he assured Leslie, closing the door on her courteously but firmly.

His shoulders, Penny saw, were shaking with suppressed laughter.

'What's funny?' she said with uncharacteristic belligerence. 'Are you laughing at my family?'

He strolled over and took the lotus dish away from her.

'You really aren't used to alcohol, are you?' he said musingly. 'You can't have had more than a thimbleful and you're ready to do battle with the world already. I can see you're going to be a cheap date,' he added in self-congratulatory tones.

Penny choked. 'I am not going to be any sort of date...'

He just smiled.

'I'm not.' She was almost shouting. She had thought of a number of crushing things to say to the hateful man. So it was sad that the one that came out was the weakest. 'What would my family say?'

He threw back his head and laughed aloud at that.

'Why are you laughing? Don't laugh at me. I won't have you laughing at me,' she cried, taking a hasty step forward.

Her foot somehow got entangled with the hem of her robe. She stumbled. Zoltan caught her in a competent, unimpassioned embrace. He gently pushed the hair that had flopped forward out of her eyes.

'You don't have to fight me too, you know,' he told her, laughing quietly. 'If you're taking on the world, I'm on your side.'

'I am not——'

He held on to her. Quite suddenly she stopped resisting.

'What were you laughing at?' she muttered.

'At the idea that you cared what your family thought about you and me,' he told her, the sculpted lips twitching at the memory.

Penny was puzzled. 'Why?'

'Well, my darling, you've done your best to give them the impression that we have already reached an—er— accommodation.'

She stared up at him. He laughed softly.

'Did you think that your reputation for immunity would stand up to anything? Come on, Penny, be realistic. What would you think if you went into one of your sister's rooms and there she was swigging champagne with a man and wearing nothing but a robe that was on the point of falling off? What would your conclusion be in those circumstances, hmm?'

Penny took herself smartly out of his arms.

'How do you know I haven't got anything on underneath?' she demanded, her cheeks burning.

'Experience,' he said with deplorable sang-froid.

She tugged the robe so hard she almost wrapped it round her twice. All of a sudden she felt rather cold.

'I'm surprised you're not ashamed to admit it,' she said grimly.

'Are you?' He was interested.

She gave an exasperated sign. 'No. Not really. You're not ashamed of anything, are you?'

'If I'm not ashamed to do it, I'm not ashamed to admit it,' Zoltan said tranquilly. 'It's a very simple principle but it works. You should try it some time.'

'I don't do things I'm ashamed to admit,' Penny flashed.

'That wasn't quite what I meant,' he said drily. 'I mean, that policy doesn't leave a lot of room for you to do much, does it? You seem to be ashamed to admit such peculiar things.'

'I'm not. I'm an independent person and I do what I want——'

He was very close, she realised, breaking off.

Under her breath, not quite knowing why, she said, 'No.'

But it was too late.

CHAPTER SEVEN

ZOLTAN'S breath stirred the curling tendrils that lay against her throat. His body was not only muscular, it was alarmingly exciting—and it was between her and the door.

'Now, look,' said Penny, arching her throat to avoid his kiss, 'be sensible...'

'Sensible is no fun,' he murmured, turning his face into the fall of hair at the back of her neck. 'Your hair smells like the garden did last night. Mmm. I love English gardens.'

Penny gave a sweet, involuntary shiver. She repressed it.

'Thank you. That's because I've washed it,' she said, determinedly prosaic.

He gave a low laugh. She felt the small turbulence along the surface of her skin. In spite of herself she shivered again.

'You're amazing,' he said.

Every woman thought he was a knock-out, Mike had said. He knew what he was talking about, Penny thought in rising concern.

'I may be amazing. I am also unavailable,' she said firmly.

'Unavailable?' he murmured against the soft vulnerable skin below her ear. 'I don't think so, you know.' He kissed her throat lingeringly. 'I—really—don't—think—so.'

Her head fell back. In spite of herself, it seemed, her body was responding to him. And he knew it. Her pulse quickened.

Heaven help me, thought Penny.

She strove for a normal tone. 'Look, we really don't have time for this...'

Zoltan laughed huskily. 'How much time do you want, honey?'

Briefly Penny shut her eyes. 'My sister is getting married in less than an hour,' she said on a rising note. 'I'd like to be there.'

He raised his head. His eyes were as blue as the cobalt tube in her paintbox. They weren't laughing any more, Penny saw. She began to feel seriously alarmed.

As soon as he saw her expression, he smiled.

'Let me go,' she said breathlessly.

His smile widened. 'Persuade me.'

Penny felt horribly foolish. She turned her head away. 'I shouldn't need to,' she said in low voice.

He ignored that. 'Kiss me, Penny. Let's see where it takes us.'

Her breath fluttered in her throat at the thought. She winced.

'You're not exactly chivalrous, are you?' she said bitterly.

'No,' he agreed without noticeable regret. He pushed the robe away so that he could kiss her shoulder. 'I suspect too many men have been treating you with chivalry for too long. It gives you too big an advantage,' he murmured.

The feel of his lips on her skin made her shiver deep inside. Suddenly she felt silken, scented, precious...

'Oh, God,' said Penny under her breath. Even when she had been at her youngest and silliest and utterly dazzled by Alan, he had never made her feel like this.

'Kiss me,' Zoltan said again.

He raised his head. Their eyes met. She searched his face. There was no softness there. Just curiosity and a strange implacability which somehow she had almost expected.

'*Why?*' Penny said, almost to herself.

He shrugged. 'There is reason and there is need. This is not reason.' His eyes were intent. She had the feeling that he was looking into her deepest heart.

Penny could not look away. Time seemed suspended.

'Oh, lord,' she said at last on a long sigh.

At once his arms tightened. But there was no need. She was reaching for him eagerly. They kissed almost desperately.

He slid his arms under the robe. His fingers touched her spine, ran softly up and down it. Penny shivered in animal delight. She pressed closer, her hands nearly frantic in the crisp hair.

He was plucking the robe away. Helplessly, she dropped her arms from his neck. The unglamorous towelling slid silently to the floor. Penny swayed.

At once he gathered up. Before she knew what was happening he carried her to the bed and was beside her. He held her face between his hands and kissed her from chin to hairline and back, lingering at the corner of her mouth tantalisingly. Penny squirmed round, seeking his mouth. But he held her off, touching butterfly kisses all around her lips until she moaned deeply.

Then, as if she had pulled a trigger, Zoltan turned on his back and pulled her on top of him. His hand swept down her naked body in explicit demand. His hand was not entirely steady.

He's laying claim to me, Penny thought, shocked. She caught her breath. But she was too deep in the sensual delight to remember the principles that had got her through the last arid years. Too deep to remember basic common sense.

'Kiss me,' Zoltan said again. She thought that he too had forgotten everything except the fierce demands of the body.

And then, impossibly, unbelievably, there came another knock on the door.

Penny shot up on the bed as if someone had flung cold water over her.

'Pen? Pen? Are you in there?'

It was her mother. She looked round frantically for her robe. Any of her sisters would go away if she didn't answer, but Laura thought she was still licensed to walk into any of her daughters' rooms without permission.

'Just a minute,' she called. Her voice was so thick she hardly recognised it.

The robe was on the floor. She hauled it up. One of the sleeves had got itself inside-out. She was tousled and fiery-cheeked by the time she had her arms through both sleeves.

Zoltan was unmoved, she noted. He leaned back on one elbow, watching her with undisguised appreciation. In the circumstances, it was hardly tactful. It did nothing at all for Penny's self-possession as she wrenched the door open.

Fortunately the bed was masked from the door. She ran her hands through her disarranged hair.

'Darling!' Laura looked at her in dismay.

Penny looked down at herself in sudden horror. But the robe was in place and any tell-tale marks from those hectic moments in his arms were decently hidden under it. Her mother's expression was reaction to her state of unreadiness, she realised.

'I know. I know. I—forgot the time.'

On the bed, safely hidden from Laura, Zoltan grinned. Penny avoided his eyes at once. But she felt the colour rise in her cheeks.

'But, darling, we'll start leaving for the church any *moment*,' Laura said with pardonable exaggeration.

'Yes. I know. I'm sorry. I'll be downstairs in ten minutes,' Penny said desperately.

Laura looked dissatisfied. 'You'd better hurry. Shall I help you to dress?'

'*No!*' It was almost a scream.

Laura's eyes looked as if they were about to brim over. Clearly she had had the same treatment from Celia and the bridesmaids, Penny thought. Normally she would have relented and let her mother in. But in the circumstances it was out of the question.

Laura said, 'Darling you've done the flowers beautifully. But it's made you dreadfully late. You'll need someone to do your hair. It's a mess.'

She made as if to come in. Penny took a firm grip on the door. Zoltan flung himself back on the pillows and raised his hands in a gesture of surrender straight out of a hundred westerns.

He could afford to think it was funny, Penny thought sourly. He was not having to bar the door.

'No, Mother.'

'But——'

'Mother,' said Penny with the resolution of cold panic, 'you are holding me up. If you want me downstairs in ten minutes, go *away*.'

Laura blinked. Penny did not blame her. She had never spoken like that to her sweetly old-fashioned mother in her life. She closed the door firmly.

She turned back to Zoltan. His shirt was unbuttoned and hanging out of his jeans, she registered. She folded her lips together. She was not going to succumb to embarrassment now. For one thing there was no time. For another, she didn't see why she should feel embarrassment when Zoltan clearly regarded the whole thing as a huge joke.

She picked up the hangers with his suit on them from the chair where he had tossed them.

'There,' she said in an angry undertone. 'Take them and get out.'

In spite of the interruptions Penny was ready with time to spare. It was just as well. She found her mother tearful and her father impatient.

She also found that Zoltan was before her. He had changed into the pale suit. With it he wore a crisp midnight shirt that made his eyes look bluer than ever. The bridesmaids were impressed. Penny was less so. Especially when those eyes swept over her.

'Mmm. Very glamorous,' he murmured.

'Thank you,' she said coolly.

The silk dress was new, a swirl of arctic greens and apricot that echoed the gold lights in her hair. It also, Penny was registering now, flattered her slimness and her long elegant legs in ways she had not realised. When she had seen it at a design school exhibition she had fallen in love with it. She had thought that that was entirely because of the way it suited her colouring. Now, under Zoltan's amused appreciation, she became conscious of the way the soft stuff clung as she moved.

'Very demure,' he said. It sounded as if he was laughing privately. His eyes lingered at her breast, outlined too clearly for Penny's peace of mind by the exquisite cut of the dress. 'You're a very subtle lady, aren't you?'

The look in his eyes made her feel hot. There was more than laughter there. All of a sudden she remembered what it had felt like to be in his arms.

The trouble was it had felt so right. Not just warm and exciting but *right*. As if she was meant to be there. As if they shared all the tenderness in the world. As if she loved him.

Oh, no, thought Penny. Oh, no, I can't handle that. I can't have fallen in love with him. I can't. Not in this space of time. Not when I've put all that behind me. Not when all he wants is a brief fling. And only that at the instigation of my loving family.

Heaven help me get through this wedding, she thought, conscious of her eyes filling.

Zoltan looked at her consideringly. 'Why is that every time I pay you a compliment you look as if I've strapped you on the rack?' he asked.

Penny shifted her shoulders. 'You're imagining it.'

'No, I'm not.' He touched her lashes, retrieving an unshed tear with one long finger. Penny stared at him, startled. Their eyes met. He looked serious, the lurking laughter briefly banished. As she watched the handsome mouth twisted. He seemed to hesitate.

For a moment she thought he was going to kiss her, there in the crowded room with all her family and friends around them. She went very still. Half of her wanted him to, desperately. Half of her was sad. Not without love, she thought forlornly.

They were interrupted.

'Pen, you're a *genius*.' It was Celia, clasping her trailing woodland flowers. 'I've never seen anything so beautiful. Nothing the florists could have done would have been half so gorgeous.'

'Yes, it's lovely. So unusual,' said Laura, more dubiously.

Celia was her ebullient self again.

'I'll do the same for you next time,' she told Penny naughtily, before dancing away.

Laura shook her head. 'Oh, dear. She never thinks. Don't worry, darling.' She laid a soft hand on Penny's arm. 'You're very happy as you are. It's perfectly all right to be a professional woman on her own these days.' Her tone was, if anything, even more dubious. 'Oh, no, Minky darling, don't...'

She darted off to stop a junior bridesmaid eating her posy.

Beside her, Penny was aware of Zoltan laughing silently.

'There you are. You're licensed to get rid of your escort,' he said in her ear. 'I wish that didn't make me feel redundant.'

'Oh, God. Mothers,' she moaned. 'The embarrassment!'

'Think yourself lucky. My mother walked out when I was three and didn't walk back until my annual salary hit six figures. In dollars.'

She looked up at him sharply. He sounded indifferent enough but a thing like that would hurt, she thought. Add it to exile at fourteen and the banker's daughter who had not loved him enough and you had a man who meant it when he said he was not into permanence.

Penny said gently, 'You haven't had a lot of luck with families, have you? Not like me.'

He said, 'I thought you thought your family was a pain.'

Penny said, 'I think you've taught me different.'

His eyes gleamed. 'You mean I'm reinstated as escort?'

She drew away. 'Don't push your luck,' she said lightly. 'I must see about the cars.'

There was the usual confusion as both her mother and her father had issued instructions. Penny sorted it out, had a brief word with Leslie and Angel, and was soon marshalling people into transport for the church.

Laura went with Angel and her husband. That left only Penny herself, and the two formal limousines for the bridesmaids and Celia and her father. She gave a long sigh. No disasters so far, she thought, as she went to her car.

'End of Act One,' an amused voice said in her ear.

She raised her head, startled.

'You haven't forgotten me?' Zoltan said reproachfully. He was leaning negligently against the open passenger door. He had obviously been waiting for her. 'You weren't really thinking of dispensing with my escort?'

There was a warmth around her heart. Penny found herself smiling at him unreservedly. As if they were already lovers, she thought, with a superstitious quiver in the throat. He held out an imperative hand.

'Come on, Cinderella, hand over the keys. I'm your coachman for the day.'

She surrendered them without a struggle. 'Heaven.'

He ushered her into the car as ceremonially as if he were a professional chauffeur.

'Tired?' he asked, swinging in beside her.

'A bit. I didn't sleep well,' she said without thinking.

She encountered a wry look.

'Tell me about it.'

She fought down a blush. 'And all that rushing around this morning was a bit nerve-racking. Of course, if I'd realised I was in the hands of a professional management consultant, I wouldn't have worried.'

'Interesting. I would have said you'd be more likely to run me out of town,' Zoltan said drily. 'I didn't get the impression that you were exactly appreciative of my efforts this morning.'

'No, I wasn't very gracious. I'm sorry,' Penny said simply. 'I don't know what got into me.'

'Don't you?' he murmured. 'We must talk about that later.'

He put the car in gear. He drove with easy competence, Penny saw, as if he had been driving her ancient car all his life. He followed her directions to the church without fuss and slotted the car into the minimal space that had been left for it in a single powerful manoeuvre.

Watching the strong brown hands on the wheel, Penny felt that little shiver of awareness again, like the touch of a moth's wing. It was gone almost before she realised. But just for an instant she had remembered those hands on her body, had wondered what it would be like if he touched her again. It left her dry-mouthed and unsettled.

What is happening to me? she thought. I don't feel like this about men. Any men. I don't wonder about them touching me. I don't want to be touched. I don't like being touched.

But she had let Zoltan Guard touch her, she remembered. She had forgotten that she had disliked it, that it had left her feeling unsafe and vulnerable. She had wanted it. And it wasn't she who had stopped it.

If her mother had not knocked at the door then who knew what she would have wanted—or where it would have ended?

She did not meet his eyes as he helped her out of the car. She had the impression that he was laughing again, though.

He did not touch her. It was as if he knew he did not need to. As if he had picked up her thoughts and knew that she already carried his touch like a brand.

They walked into the church side by side. Penny was very conscious of the warmth of his body across the decorous distance that separated them.

All through the service she stayed conscious of him, though he was across the aisle.

She sat and stood and sang the familiar hymns mechanically. The ceremony she had not admitted she had been dreading flowed past her. Even the old words of the marriage vows, which always made her wince, did not hurt today. And when they came out into the sunshine she was dry-eyed.

'A beautiful service,' everyone said. 'A radiant bride.'

'Such a handsome man,' sighed old Mrs Carpenter sentimentally.

Penny looked at Zoltan where he stood talking to one of Mike's old university friends. The silver hair was dramatic against that even tan. The proud carriage of the head made him look like an emperor.

'Yes,' she agreed, swallowing. She tried to wrestle her reaction into something conventionally excusable. 'Of course, it's an unusual combination—white hair with such a young face. And those amazing blue eyes. Really blue eyes are always startling, aren't they?'

Mrs Carpenter looked at her oddly. 'I was talking about the bridegroom, dear,' she said.

'Oh,' said Penny, nonplussed. She flushed a little. 'Oh, yes, of course.'

'They make a handsome couple, don't they?'

They did. Penny agreed with just a hint of constraint. Mrs Carpenter went to kiss Celia while the photographer was chivvying the bridesmaids into a neat composition. Zoltan came back to her.

'You look flustered.'

Her eyes slid away from him. 'The church was hot,' she said defiantly.

The heavy brows rose. 'I thought it was distinctly cold in there.'

He was right. Penny shrugged. She was not going to explain the real reason for the discomfiture he detected.

'What are you wearing under that dress?' he asked, amused. 'Long woollen underwear?' He turned slightly, masking her from the crowd, and added in a mischievous undertone, 'That wasn't what it looked like to me.'

Penny felt her cheeks warm. She looked anywhere but at him, praying that the betraying colour would subside.

'That's not very funny,' she said, with an iciness worthy of her mother. 'Or in very good taste.'

Zoltan was unabashed. 'That depends on your point of view.'

Penny dared a single look at him. It was like flame.

'From my point of view,' she elucidated, 'I would prefer it if you did not refer to that unfortunate incident.'

She sounded like a Victorian governess, she thought in despair. She was not surprised when he chuckled.

'I just bet you would,' Zoltan agreed.

'Then don't.' She was crisp.

'Can't do that.'

'Why on earth not?'

'From *my* point of view,' Zoltan said gently, 'it wasn't unfortunate. Or an incident either, if by that you mean something that happens only once. I'm going to do my best to see it happens again. Preferably as soon as possible. Only next time I intend to make sure we aren't interrupted.'

Penny gasped. He laughed again. He took her cold gloved hand and slipped it into the crook of his elbow.

'Smile,' he advised. 'We're under observation.'

He was right. The official photographer was not the only man wielding a camera. Celia's godfather, for one, was crouching among the gravestones, directing an expensive lens in their direction. Hurriedly Penny adjusted her expression.

'Let go my hand,' she said under her breath, her smile fixed on the middle distance.

His only answer was to tighten his fingers perceptibly over her own.

'Let *go*.'

'Certainly not. No sensible man ever surrenders an advantage.'

So they were locked together when her mother came up. Laura had recovered but the aunt who accompanied her was still distinctly damp around the eyes.

'Such a lovely service,' she said. 'So touching.'

'They always are,' Laura said, with a touch of sharpness.

Penny swallowed suddenly. She had not cried in church. But the memory of the soft look on Celia's face as she spoke the old vows caught her suddenly by the throat. Her mother looked at her narrowly.

'It's certainly powerful stuff,' Zoltan agreed easily. 'In any language.'

The elderly aunt looked at him with approval.

'I understand you aren't married, Professor?' she said, avoiding Penny's indignant eye.

Zoltan grinned. 'Never have been. Too big a risk.'

That would not shock Aunt Mary as much as he probably expected, Penny thought with a certain satisfaction. She had married off three adventurous and reluctant sons herself.

Sure enough, Aunt Mary was saying serenely, 'That just means you haven't met the right woman yet.'

Penny had underestimated him, she found. The handsome face stayed calm, politely interested. True, a faint tremor ran through the arm under her fingers. But whether it was a superstitious shudder or pure amusement she could not tell. She suspected the latter.

She was certain of it when he said gravely, 'You could be right.'

Penny ground her teeth and hauled as unobtrusively as she could manage at her hand. To no avail. Aunt Mary's eyes sharpened.

Laura said, 'Darling, we must go and line up for the family picture.'

Zoltan let her go then. But not before he had raised her hand to his lips and sent a sizzling look down the length of her arm. It made Penny long to hit him. It also sent Aunt Mary's eyebrows up to the brim of her hat and brought a worried frown to Laura's brow.

'Darling,' she said again.

The photographs took a long time. The May winds tossed hats and veiling about unpredictably. The photographer's professional amiability grew strained. By the end Penny was shivering in her silk dress.

She retreated to the shelter of a holly bush while the final shots were taken.

'Let's go,' said a familiar voice in her ear.

She jumped. He took her arm masterfully.

'Come on.'

'I can't,' she said. She looked wistfully at the church door where her father had one arm wrapped round Celia and the other placed on the shoulder of his new son-in-law while her mother and sisters looked on. 'My family... I ought to wait for them.'

'You're cold,' he said crisply. 'Wait for them at the house.'

'But——'

'They want any more snapshots of you, they can take them in front of the radiator,' he said. 'I'm taking you back.'

It was too tempting. Penny went with him without a struggle.

In the car he said, 'Poor old Cinderella. You just don't have any self-defence at all, do you?'

'What do you mean?'

'There you are jumping again whenever your family clap their hands.' He sounded annoyed.

Penny sighed. 'You don't understand. It's a convention to wait for the bride and groom to leave the church first.'

He slanted a look down at her. 'Even when you're incubating pneumonia?'

'I'm not——' She broke off as she was overtaken by a deep shiver she could not attempt to disguise. 'Damn,' she said.

He laughed. Reluctantly Penny smiled.

'Do you never get tired of being right?' she asked.

The blue eyes gleamed. 'So you agree I'm always right?'

She remembered their earlier encounter. And his conviction that she was not unavailable, in spite of her claim. She felt the faint colour rise in her cheeks and was grateful that his eyes were on the road.

'You clearly think so,' she said repressively. 'Personally I doubt it.'

'That's because you haven't known me long enough,' he said soothingly.

Penny allowed herself a mocking laugh. 'That's a matter of opinion,' she muttered.

He shook his head. 'You'll see.'

She eyed him unflatteringly. 'There's nothing wrong with your ego, is there?'

'There's nothing wrong with any of me,' he said superbly. 'It was your lucky day when you found me, Cinderella.'

'Somehow I doubt that,' Penny said, thinking of the maternal reproaches she would face for leaving the church early.

'You'll see,' he said again.

Penny didn't answer. She was learning that you did not get the better of Zoltan Guard by argument. The only possibility was avoiding action.

Accordingly she retired to her room as soon as they got back to the house. She sat in front of the mirror and retouched her make-up carefully. No need to add blusher, she saw ruefully. She did not emerge until there was enough noise to proclaim that the party was in full swing.

When she came downstairs her parents and Mike and Celia were still in the receiving line, greeting the last arrivals. But everyone else was circulating in the flower-decked rooms. The scullery already showed several cases of empty champagne bottles and the hired waiters were spinning in and out of the kitchen as if battery-powered.

Penny helped herself to a champagne flute and a bottle of fizzing mineral water. She entered the drawing-room unobtrusively and lodged the bottle of mineral water behind an urn of trailing roses. Other family weddings had taught her that if you wanted to drink and didn't want to drink alcohol then it was a good idea to set up your own private cache.

She looked round for her sisters. They were deeply engaged with old friends or new acquaintants. She did not admit that she was looking for Zoltan Guard as well but she located him anyway. He was talking to a couple of men she did not recognise. Friends of Mike's, obviously. Maybe fellow former pupils of Zoltan's. Penny turned away, telling herself she was relieved that her escort duties seemed to have come to an end.

Now it was time for other duties. She straightened her shoulders and began to circulate conscientiously.

It was a big wedding. The party seemed to go on for ever, Penny thought. She talked and drank her mineral water and stood on elegant heels until her head rang with the noise, her throat tasted like a vitamin pill and her feet ached. If only she could leave now. But there was the meal and the speeches to come. Briefly alone, she thought longingly of Zoltan's cavalier way with wedding conventions.

'Let me take you away from all this,' said a voice in her ear. She was coming to know that note of amusement all too well.

Penny choked. For some reason her heart gave a convulsive jump at the unexpected words. She had not even known he was anywhere in the vicinity. Or had she? It was uncanny the way she had been thinking about him just the moment before he spoke, she thought.

Penny coughed hard, cleared her throat, and mopped watering eyes. She brought her breathing back under control. She took a fortifying swig of mineral water and turned to face him.

'I seem to have heard that before,' she said.

'You'll be hearing it again,' Zoltan said, amused.

The blue shirt really was startling, the way it was reflected in his eyes. And brilliant blue eyes smiling straight down into your own were a disconcerting experience, Penny found.

'You have a one-track mind?' she asked faintly.

He considered the point.

'I've never thought so. You seem to have a peculiar effect on me,' he told her with candour.

Penny recovered herself. She raised her brows. 'Should I be flattered?'

'That rather depends on whether you like having that effect on me.'

She snorted. '*Like* it? You think I mean to encourage you to make fun of me?'

'I'm not making fun of you, Cinderella.'

She sighed. 'What else would you call it?'

Just for a moment he seemed to hesitate. She tipped her head on one side to look at him, her whole attitude a challenge. He looked back at her, his mouth slanted in a wry expression.

'I think we need more time for this discussion. And some privacy,' he said, a rueful note in his voice.

For a moment Penny did not understand him. When she did, she took an involuntary step backwards, her amusement dissolving in a quick response to a danger signal. The blue eyes narrowed, taking in that instinctive retreat.

'Complete privacy.' His voice was suddenly steely.

Penny was saved from having to answer by the announcement of the meal, set out in the marquee in the garden. She was seated at the same table as Zoltan but at a distance. She did not know whether that was a relief or an annoyance. She only knew that her first feeling was of sharp disappointment.

Careful! she said to herself. He'll be gone by tonight or tomorrow at the latest. And, no matter what he says about attraction, the first thing he told you was that it was purely temporary. Remember that!

She concentrated hard on her neighbour, a distant cousin of her new brother-in-law's.

Once or twice she looked up and found Zoltan looking at her. There was a faint frown between the black brows. She shivered a little, although it was anything but cold in the big tent. She did not think anyone had ever looked at her with such serious intentness before. It was as if he wanted to have all her secrets laid bare for him.

She looked away. Well, he was not going to. Nobody knew all her secrets. She had worked hard to banish them to outer darkness. No casual philanderer was going to bring them roaring back into the light.

There were speeches. Penny listened with half an ear to her father's polished performance. It set in stark contrast Mike's brief, embarrassed speech, to say nothing of the best man's rambling tissue of drunken innuendo. She winced inwardly. Even these days it brought back other drunken ramblings, without the hearty laughter and friendly goodwill. It was an effort to smile, though she applauded conventionally when the best man was at last persuaded to sit down by his amused well-wishers.

Throughout it all, she was conscious of Zoltan. Not that he was looking at her all the time. In fact, thought Penny ruefully, she seemed to be more conscious of him when he was paying attention to his neighbour, a vivacious redhead who borrowed a studio in the summer.

Get a hold on yourself, she told herself. It doesn't matter to you who he talks to. After today you'll never see him again. And just as well.

Tables began to break up. The men on either side of her went to join their girlfriends. Penny pushed the uneaten food away from her and looked at her watch. She was conscious of a faint throbbing at her temples.

'There you are,' said a voice above her head. Not Zoltan's for once, Penny thought in quick amusement. This was slightly slurred, very friendly and not in the least dictatorial. She looked up with a smile.

It was the inebriated best man. He collapsed on to the little gilt chair beside her and helped himself absent-mindedly to her untouched glass of champagne.

'Wonderful wedding,' he said, beaming.

Penny tensed. She could not help herself. It was an instinctive reaction that she supposed she would never now get rid of. But he was a nice enough man when sober and his present intoxication was not taking a threatening form. So she calmed her pulses and kept her smile in place.

'I'm glad you're enjoying it.'

'Got a bit worried about m'speech,' he confessed. 'Glad it's over.'

Penny could appreciate that. He looked at her expectantly. Clearly words of appreciation were called for.

'It was a very friendly speech,' she said diplomatically.

He was pleased. 'Mike and I—friends since school. Even went to university together.'

'Oh?' She sought for a neutral topic. One presented itself. 'Do you know his old tutor, then? Professor Guard?' she asked casually.

'Old Zoltan?' The beaming smile became a beacon. 'Course I know Zoltan. Used to recycle his girlfriends when he'd finished with them.'

'*What*?' Penny did not believe she could have heard aright.

But her cheerful companion nodded. 'Devil of a fellow, old Zoltan. All the girls used to fall for him. Never had a girl student who didn't.'

Penny found she was not surprised. Zoltan's whole manner had indicated as much. It must have taken years of sexual negotiation to perfect that elegant technique. So why did she feel somehow betrayed by this information? It was no more than she would have expected if she had thought about it.

She said in a chilly voice, 'And you took the surplus off his hands?'

The best man detected something wrong. He blinked at her.

'Made an awful nuisance of themselves, some of them,' he offered as a palliative. 'Used to lie in wait for him when he came home. Smuggle themselves into his room. The works.' He contemplated their shared past with evident regret. 'Never seen anything like it. One girl wrapped herself round him like a boa constrictor. Took two of us to get her off.'

Penny stiffened. She had responded to Zoltan in a way she could not remember responding to anyone in her whole life, ever. Would this uncomplicated young man have described her as a boa constrictor? She had an uneasy feeling that he would. She gritted her teeth. It was unnerving to find that she was one of an army.

'He must have been grateful for your help,' she said acidly.

He looked doubtful. 'Soft-hearted chap. I said to him once, "Zoltan," I said, "you can't let these silly little creatures take over your life." But he could never bring himself to say a rude word to them, even when they were mega-inconvenient. Used to feel sorry for them, I suppose.'

Penny winced. Not that Zoltan Guard had any reason to be sorry for her, she reminded herself. He might call her Cinderella; he might even detect that she carried secret scars but at least for the moment he had no idea what they were. And it was going to stay exactly like that, she promised herself.

The best man had finished her champagne. He reached out for the bottle in the middle of the table and emptied it into the glass he had appropriated. At the same time he shifted the fragile chair closer to hers.

'Always make me feel sentimental, weddings,' he confided.

His smartly trousered leg pressed uncomfortably against hers. Penny changed her position unobtrusively.

'Do you go to a lot of them?'

'Weddings? All the time. M'friends are falling like flies these days,' he told her.

He downed his wine. He was watching her somewhat muzzily over the top of the glass.

'You married?'

Penny hesitated.

'I'm not,' he said encouragingly.

He had clearly misinterpreted the reason for her hesitation. She needed to deflect his attention from herself. Choosing her words carefully, Penny said lightly, 'Never found the right woman?'

He looked briefly morose. 'Oh, I've found her. She——' he hiccuped suddenly '—she wants another chap.' He shook his head, banishing depression. He replenished his drink and returned to the subject that interested him. 'What about you? Found the love of your life?'

'Found and lost and it's all a long time ago,' Penny said firmly.

'Loved and lost,' he said, enlightened.

The pressure of his thigh against hers was abruptly renewed. He was almost pushing her off her chair. Penny leaned away from the fumes of champagne.

'You—broken heart. Me—broken heart,' he pronounced.

He put his face close to hers. There was a faint sheen of sweat on his forehead. This had the makings of a full-blown scene, she thought, her heart sinking.

'My heart is not broken,' she said in a voice like ice-water.

But he wasn't listening any more. He was touching. Penny pushed his hand away. He hardly seemed to notice. He was trying to focus on her eyes, she saw. The insistent hand returned to fumble at her smart silk.

Penny felt cold. She looked round. But everyone was occupied—talking and laughing, toasting each other. Nobody was looking at them. Nobody was going to come over and distract him. She was going to have to deal with the man unaided.

Oh, well, she had had plenty of practice, she thought grimly.

She pushed the slender chair back with a sudden jerk. It startled him. For a moment his hand fell away.

'You need some air,' she told him.

A strange expression crossed his face—half cunning, half sulky. He leaned forward and took hold of her chair, his arms on either side of her, pinning her in place. Penny could smell the wilting carnation in his buttonhole. His breath reeked of the wine. She turned her face away, her mouth twisting in reflex disgust.

Too much practice, she thought. She knew from bitter experience what was all too likely to happen next. And her fellow guests would not be able to ignore it, either.

'Please leave me alone,' she said.

She strove to appear calm, although her nails were digging into her palms and her neck ached with the strain of avoiding that greedy touch. It was important to stay calm, not to let her fear and disgust show. Not to give him cause to hurt her.

'Don't mean that,' he said.

It was just what Alan had always said.

In spite of her sensible resolutions, Penny laughed.

An ugly light flashed in his eyes. In a split-second she realised she had made a mistake. Suffused with drink and affront, the heavy face swooped on hers. She tried to break free. But her momentary hesitation had lost her the chance. Unsteady hands took hold of her in a convulsive grip and his breath filled her mouth. Penny felt the horror close down over her. She made a small, high sound of distress like a wild creature about to be mauled.

And then, unbelievably, she was free.

She had closed her eyes instinctively. Now she opened them. Her tormentor was being helped to his feet by Zoltan Guard. He was looking bewildered. Somehow, his chair had toppled over sideways. The helpful Professor Guard was restoring the furniture to an upright position as well. He was smiling.

'Hi, Ian. Great to see you. How's life?'

The best man shook his head. In order to face Zoltan he had to turn his back to Penny. Slowly she let out the breath she had hardly been aware she was holding. Her fists uncurled. Cautiously she stood up. She was shaking badly.

Zoltan flicked her a glance over the best man's shoulder. Penny revised her opinion abruptly. He was not smiling. His mouth was curved pleasantly enough but the blue eyes were blazing. He was furious.

CHAPTER EIGHT

THE best man was despatched smoothly. You could see the professional who was used to dealing with difficult students, Penny thought.

'What you need,' Zoltan was saying sympathetically, 'is a coffee. Black coffee. They're hiding the coffee urn over there, behind the potted palm.'

The other looked at him blearily. 'You're a good sort, Zoltan,' he said. He clearly had no idea he was being got rid of.

'Coffee,' said Zoltan, turning him in the right direction and giving a gentle push to his shoulders.

Penny watched him go. Her breathing slowly returned to normal. She put a hand to her throat.

'Thank you,' she said in a subdued voice.

Zoltan turned back to her. She looked up at him candidly. With a little shock, Penny realised that the calm, easy voice had been a complete deception. The blue eyes were molten with anger.

'What the *hell*,' he said, fury ripping through the quiet voice, 'do you think you were doing with that drunken fool?'

Penny blinked. 'I'm sorry?'

'So you should be.' He was curt. 'How could you let that happen? You're not a child.'

She stared, taken aback. She felt half insulted, half uneasy. How had Zoltan managed to notice what was going on when nobody else in the room had been aware of it? And, more important, why had he noticed? Be careful! her heart warned.

She tried a half-lie. 'What do you mean? Nothing happened.'

His hand shot out and took her by the elbow.

'Then why are you trembling?'

Penny jumped. His touch was electric. She looked round, disconcerted. He made her feel very vulnerable.

'Stop it,' she hissed, reaching for the conventions to armour her. 'People are staring.'

'No one is taking a blind bit of notice,' Zoltan corrected calmly. He shook her elbow a little and repeated, 'Why are you trembling?'

There was no point in saying that she wasn't. The evidence was there for him to feel in the faint tremor of her flesh under his hard fingers. Penny sought for a reasonable explanation.

'You—startled me.'

He looked down at her for a moment. One eyebrow flicked up.

'You're saying it's my fault you're shaking like a leaf?'

She looked pointedly down at the hand on her arm.

'Oh, no,' he said softly. 'You're not getting away with that. I remember what you look like when I touch you.' The blue eyes bored into hers. 'Not sick,' he said deliberately. 'Not scared to death either.'

Penny flushed. Her eyes fell under his harsh inspection.

'You want to know what I think?' he went on in a conversational tone. 'I think Ian scared you out of your mind. I think if I hadn't stopped it when I did, you'd have passed out.'

Penny was shocked. Her eyes flew to his, horrified.

'I wouldn't,' she said in a suffocated voice.

'No? You had your eyes screwed tight shut and you looked like a ghost. In fact, I've seen more colour in a snowfield.' He paused. 'I think you were so scared you were frozen to the spot,' he said softly.

It was uncomfortably close to the truth. Penny's eyes skittered away from his.

'If that's what you think then you don't sound very sympathetic about it,' she managed at last, with rather shaky sarcasm.

'Sympathetic? Because you let yourself be terrorised by a drunken boy?' Zoltan sounded incredulous. 'Of course I'm not sympathetic. You should have got yourself out of it as soon as you realised what state he was in.'

It was so much what Penny herself had been feeling— and failing to achieve—that she burned with resentment.

'How could I?' she flashed. 'He's one of the honoured guests. I couldn't haul off and box his ears. It would spoil the party.'

Zoltan looked amused suddenly. 'I would have said it was more likely to make it, from what I recall of Mike and Ian and their cronies.'

'Then they differ from my sister Celia,' Penny retorted. 'To say nothing of my mother.'

He looked impatient. 'It's academic anyway. You wouldn't have had to lay him out cold. You're a sophisticated woman. You know how to deflect a man without resorting to violence. You did it to me easily enough,' he reminded her, an undercurrent of laughter stirring the smooth voice.

Penny bit her lip. 'That was different.'

'How?'

She glared at him. 'You weren't drunk,' she said, goaded.

'But I was much more serious——' He broke off suddenly. His eyes narrowed.

Her uneasiness increased by the second. Not for the first time, Penny was aware of an acute brain at work behind his neutral expression. He looked her up and down. Not as he had done before. This time it was almost absent, as if he was trying to see where a rather small Penny fitted into some large geometrical pattern that he had in his mind's eye.

'Drunk,' he said slowly.

Out of the crowd someone came up to him. They touched him on the shoulder, said something. He barely moved.

'Hi,' he said, not taking his eyes off her. 'Catch you later.'

The man moved off. Penny began to feel like a laboratory specimen under that implacable analysis.

'I wish you'd stop looking at me like that,' she muttered, protesting.

'Drunk,' he repeated, ignoring it.

'And let me have my arm back.'

He ignored that too. He was looking at her as if he were a chemist who had just found a new element.

'Even last night—when your father came in. You weren't scared when we were running through the garden after unknown intruders. But you were scared then, when he came in. I felt it. You went rigid.'

'No,' said Penny, appalled.

How could he tell? How *could* he?

'I didn't understand it. He's not the sort of tyrannical father a girl would be afraid of, your dad. And you're not the type to be afraid of a tyrant anyway. You're too cool. Too competent.'

'Of course I'm not afraid of him,' she said hotly. But her heart was cold with trepidation.

'No, I guess not. But you were afraid of *something*.'

'I——' She shrugged helplessly.

'He'd been drinking with his agent,' Zoltan said slowly. 'He'd had just a little too much. He was rather charming about it. And he wanted another drink. Only you hustled him off to bed.'

'He needed to be up at a reasonable hour today...'

'And you didn't want him to have any more alcohol.' He watched her. 'That's what you're afraid of, isn't it? Did you think he'd get really drunk? Go out of control?'

Penny thought, he's very nearly there. He's just a couple of steps away from knowing all there is to know about me. She had never felt so naked in her life.

She said numbly, 'No.'

'There's no need to be ashamed of it,' he said, with surprising gentleness. 'He wouldn't be the first over-worked actor to have a drink problem. And if he has it's hardly your fault.'

'He hasn't.'

Zoltan looked at her narrowly. Penny bit her lip. But in the end he obviously decided that in this, at least, she was telling the truth.

'Then——'

Penny took a decision. If she didn't give him some sort of explanation, Zoltan Guard was going to keep worrying away at the problem until he got the right answer, she thought. He liked puzzles too much to let it go. The more difficult they were, the better he liked them. It didn't matter that people might get hurt while he solved them to his intellectual satisfaction.

But she was not a fool. She could tell him something that would satisfy him. Admit the symptom, she thought wryly, and with a bit of luck he won't dig too deep for the cause. And then it can stay my secret.

'Look,' she said, with a great air of frankness, 'I'm a bit worried by people who have had even just a little too much to drink. I'm not proud of it. But I can't help it. I do try to control it. It's a sort of phobia, I suppose.'

'Why?'

Penny jumped. 'What?'

'Phobias have origins,' Zoltan pointed out. 'Where did you pick up yours? And why?'

So much for him not digging for the cause! Penny thought up her answer with lightning speed.

'If you work in a big London hospital you learn to be afraid of drunks,' she told him.

It was even true, she thought, momentarily pleased with herself.

But his eyes stayed watchful.

'You learned to be afraid of drunks in your work?'

She looked away. 'They can be violent. You never know what they're going to do next.' In spite of herself her voice trembled.

Against her will she remembered Alan's face. Too vividly. It sprang to life as she had last seen it, his lips caught back from his teeth in a snarl that was more animal than human. He had not even recognised her by then, she thought. Involuntarily she shivered.

Zoltan said softly, 'I don't believe you.'

Penny jumped and blinked. 'There are studies...'

He dismissed the studies with a shrug. 'I am not quarrelling with you about the typical behaviour of alcoholics. Just about where you learned to fear it.'

At that she was silenced.

The noise of the wedding party swirled and rose all around them. People were enjoying themselves, Penny thought. The hum of conversation was punctuated by laughter. It was all very friendly, very normal.

It might have been a million miles away for all the good it did her.

Penny looked into assessing blue eyes and felt as if she had been abandoned on an ice planet with an alien life-force. A terrifyingly intelligent alien life-force.

He said gently, 'Before I came along just now, you looked as if you were in the middle of a nightmare. And poor old Ian is no werewolf.'

To her horror she felt her throat close with tears.

'I never thought he was,' she said in a choked voice.

It was the gentleness that did it, she thought, scrabbling for a handkerchief. If Zoltan had carried on glaring at her like the Grand Inquisitor then she wouldn't have dissolved in this embarrassing way. She sniffed and tried to pretend that her eyelashes were not wet.

He said something under his breath. She could not make out what it was. It could have been in a foreign language. Or it could just have been exceptionally rude. It sounded fierce.

'We need to get out of here,' he said abruptly.

Penny had found her handkerchief. She blew her nose hard.

'We can't. They'd notice. My mother would never forgive me.'

He gave her an ironic look.

'Oh, all right,' she said crossly, interpreting the look correctly. 'It doesn't matter what my mother thinks.'

'Not just at this precise moment, no,' he agreed.

Zoltan began to move forward purposefully. With a numb Penny held firmly by the wrist, he cleared a path for them through the press of people. Penny noticed the way people seemed just to move aside for him, as if he had only to look in a certain direction and all obstacles removed themselves.

Just like my defences, she thought, worried. What privacy am I going to have left when he has finished dissecting my innermost feelings?

But she still went with him. He was like a stormforce wind. You just bent with it or you broke, she reasoned.

He led her unerringly to the door of her own apartments. It was as if he had lived in the rambling house all his life instead of a matter of hours. But of course he already knew how to find her bedroom. No doubt he had laid out the map of all routes to her door as soon as he arrived, Penny thought bitterly.

He closed the outer door and locked it. Then he took her up to the sun-filled sitting-room.

Penny looked at him warily.

'Brilliant navigation.'

'I can find my way round most places. It's a skill you need if you're a permanent stranger.' He smiled. 'Sit down and relax. I'm not going to jump on you.'

She lifted her chin. 'I never thought you were.'

He considered her for a thoughtful moment. 'No you didn't, did you. You're—an unusual woman, Penny Dane.'

'Why? Because I don't think of you as the big bad wolf?'

She was rather proud of her tone. It not only successfully suppressed the threatening tears, it sounded like the last word in careless sophistication.

She went on, 'I would have thought it was obvious. You can hardly give me a lecture on decent behaviour and then jump on me yourself,' she added, genuine amusement dawning.

Now that they were away from the crowd and her lurching best man antagonist she was feeling better by the moment.

Zoltan's strongly marked eyebrow flicked up. 'Is that what I was doing? Lecturing you on your behaviour?' He sounded faintly annoyed.

'That's what it felt like,' she said firmly.

'I must be losing my touch,' he said in a dry tone.

She sat down on an eighteenth-century couch with a pretty curved back and looked up at him in mockery.

'Would you *rather* I looked on you as the big bad wolf?'

The blue eyes narrowed. Definitely annoyed now, Penny thought. She felt rather pleased with herself. A great deal of her confidence returned abruptly. He might not want her to think of him as an ogre but glamorous Professor Guard didn't want her dismissing him as a pussycat either.

He said with something of a snap, 'I'd rather you saw what was going on under your nose.'

She crossed one leg over the other, clasped her hands round her upraised knee and leaned back. She felt relaxed and almost in control again.

'You think I'm missing something?'

'If you think I give a damn about your good behaviour then you're certainly missing something.' He sounded almost grim.

Penny widened her eyes at him.

'Then why did you rush me out of the party like that?'

He stared at her for a long moment. Then he said slowly, 'Because I thought, God help me, that you needed rescuing. And not just from Ian Springer.'

Penny was silenced. Her mocking confidence faltered. Unwillingly she searched his face, and saw that he was telling the truth. All the mockery drained out of her. She felt cold and vulnerable again. It was not a feeling she welcomed.

She was *not* vulnerable, she reminded herself. She had learned to take care of herself. She had been taking care of herself quite successfully for more than five years now.

She looked away.

'Why should you care?' she demanded at last in an exasperated voice. 'Even if you were right and I did need rescuing—what has it got to do with you? I only met you last night. After the wedding we're most unlikely to meet again. Why did you have to interfere? Why couldn't you leave me alone?' To her consternation, her angry voice broke in the middle of the last word.

'Is that what everyone else does?'

'What?'

Zoltan was looking at her gravely. 'Leaves you alone. You're a pretty solitary lady, aren't you?'

Penny stared. 'What do you mean?'

'The one who doesn't like parties,' he reminded her softly. 'The one who stays behind to meet the unknown guest.'

'Don't start that Cinderella business again,' Penny said dangerously. 'I told you——'

'The one nobody notices any more.'

It stopped her dead. She stared at him in consternation.

He said into the silence, 'The one who takes good care that nobody notices her. I ask myself why.'

She said with an effort, 'You're imagining it.'

Zoltan was unruffled. 'I don't think so.'

Penny met his eyes and read determination in them. She clasped her arms round herself, suddenly cold.

'Let us examine the facts,' he said.

He sounded mildly interested, as if she were some academic subject on the fringe of his discipline, Penny thought in dawning indignation. She did not delude herself, though. However mild his interest, he was not going to leave it now until he got to the bottom of the riddle. She was looking at years of careful defences being breached in less than twenty-four hours, she thought. And all because he found weddings boring and was looking for distraction. This wasn't what Sue Flynn had meant by the wedding effect, but it was going to be just as deadly to her peace of mind.

He cast a comprehensive look round her room. 'You moved in here after you married?'

Penny moistened her suddenly dry lips.

'We couldn't really stay in my old room in the main house. It wasn't big enough.'

His quick look told her that he had noted the evasion.

'But you and your husband lived here? In your parents' house?'

That had been the start of the problem, Penny often thought. Alan had said he wanted to stay there. They didn't have to pay rent to her parents and it was the ideal spot for painting. But it hadn't worked out like that. It hadn't worked out like that at all.

'Some of the time,' she said uncommunicatively.

He let that one go. Instead he looked round the room eloquently.

'He didn't leave much of a mark, did he? What did you do? Clear everything out that reminded you of him? When did you do that? When he died? Or before?'

'How——?' She stopped. Too late. She had been going to ask how he could tell. His expression told her he knew that, in spite of her cutting it off before it was articulated.

His mouth tilted. It was all the answer he was going to give her, she realised. They stared at each other like duellists. The silence hummed with her antagonism.

'When he left,' Penny said at last, curtly.

'It was traumatic?'

She remembered all too clearly. The answer was written on her face.

His voice was unemotional. 'What happened?'

She stood up and moved restlessly to the window. She could feel his eyes on her. The afternoon sun was filling the courtyard with light, turning the old house to honey and the creeper round the door to a flourish of embroidery. It all looked unutterably peaceful. Penny looked at it blindly.

In her mind's eye all she could see was the ill-lit kitchen in the squalid south London flat. The move had been a last-ditch stand to save their marriage. She had been desperate to get away from the claustrophobic atmosphere, with her mother watching every time Alan went out and then telling her exactly how long he had spent away from his canvas. Alan had known the move was necessary as much as she did. But he had still hated it.

Penny closed her eyes, remembering. She could still see the threadbare carpet and the tangle of stained cloths, the smeary canvases that Alan had left in his wake that night. That last terrible night. The night she had promised herself she would never tell anyone about.

She said in a voice as unemotional as Zoltan's own, 'Alan was having trouble with his painting. We—had had difficulties for some time.'

Behind her, she heard him move. Her spine tensed. But he did not approach or speak. That helped. She clasped her hands in front of her and opened her eyes.

'He had been drinking. He drank a lot. Well, I think you've guessed that. He was drinking more and more. I was worried but I didn't realise——'

She broke off. She brushed a strand of blonde hair off her face. Her voice became a shade less steady. 'You don't readily say to yourself, My husband is an alcoholic. Alcoholics are other people. People you read about in newspapers. Not someone you live with every day.'

He said, 'There are usually signs.'

'Oh, there were those all right. Mood swings. Terrible rages. The depression. Sometimes complete withdrawal. There were times when he would go out and not come back for three or four days. I thought——' She bit her lip. 'I thought it was my fault.'

His voice was level. 'Those difficulties you were talking about?'

She flushed. 'Yes.'

'What was wrong between you?' It was still that neutral voice. If it hadn't been, she probably wouldn't have told him.

'He said I had everything. Scholarship to art school. Enough money to live. Friends. Family.' She paused and then added in a low voice, 'He didn't, you see. He ran away from home when he was a schoolboy. After that he was on his own.'

'And you felt you owed him because of it?'

'No!' It was an instinctive, immediate protest, almost a cry of pain. Genuinely shocked, Penny heard it hanging in the air between them.

'I think you did,' he said softly.

This was horrible. She shook her head almost frantically. 'You know nothing about it.'

His mouth tightened. 'I'm willing to bet I know a damn sight more about it than anyone else.' His voice was harsh.

Her head reared up. 'Why?'

'Because, as you said to me earlier today, I've been digging and digging and digging.' Zoltan was drawling again. But his eyes did not look lazy.

Penny took a grip on herself. 'I mean, why do you say that?'

He made an impatient noise. 'I've got eyes and ears. Because everyone else in your family thinks you're a good, cautious, quiet sort of girl who doesn't like crowds and doesn't party a lot.' His voice dropped. 'Whereas I took one look and recognised a gambler. A passionate, reckless girl who punted everything she had and everything she was on love.'

Penny swallowed. 'No. I've changed. I'm not like that any more.' She said slowly, 'They didn't want me to marry Alan because they wanted me to finish my education. They said he wouldn't let me. I didn't believe them. But they were right.'

'What happened?'

She shut her eyes, shaking her head at the weakness of her younger self.

'I got too many prizes. It was a bad time. Alan had a problem with a big canvas. And then someone gave him a commission and he took so long to get started they took it away again. Then I went and sold my stuff in the end-of-term show. It was all too much. He—went on a big drunk.'

'His first?'

'No.' Penny looked down at her hands. 'No, not his first. Just—the first that I knew about. The doctors said that I—shouldn't challenge him.'

'And?'

'And I gave up the art school.'

'And?'

'That's it. That's all.'

His eyes bored into her. It was Penny's which fell.

'No,' he said. 'That's not all. Shall we stop pretending?' His voice was soft. 'It's perfectly clear that your husband hurt you. You married him at nineteen. You finally got out from the marriage—what? Five years ago? Six? And since then you've been melting into the background in case anyone noticed you and hurt you again.'

Penny was perfectly white. She looked at him, her mind a blank.

He said gently, 'I was watching you this morning when your father was reading from the paper.'

Every muscle in her body tensed unbearably.

'He might not believe that women stay with men who hurt them physically,' Zoltan said evenly. 'But I do. If they think it's their fault. If they think they can help.' He paused. 'That's what you did, isn't it?'

There was a terrible silence. She thought, He knows it all. She could not think.

'Tell me,' he said at last, under his breath.

'Nobody has asked me that,' she said at last. '*Nobody*.'

'Then they should have done. And I'm asking now. What happened?'

She closed her eyes. 'Why do you want to know?'

He did not hesitate. 'Because I can't know you properly unless I do.'

She shook her head.

'And I need to know you properly,' Zoltan told her quietly. 'Come on, love, tell me. Then you need never think about it again. Put it behind you for ever.'

'Promises!' she said drearily. 'If I haven't got rid of it in nearly six years, it's not going to go away now.'

He didn't argue. All he did was say again, 'Tell me.'

She shrugged. 'It's fairly ordinary. Alan had a drink problem. He had had one before I met him. That summer he was down here he had been dried out. He was supposed to be starting again.'

Zoltan looked grim. But he didn't say anything. That made it easier somehow.

Penny suddenly found herself saying things she had barely even dared to remember for years.

'He was chronically jealous. Of my background, my financial security, even my place at art school. After that first almighty drunk, I was scared. The doctors wouldn't tell me anything. Except that they seemed to think I was partly responsible somehow. They treated me as if I was his enemy.' She shook her head. All the remembered bewilderment was in her eyes. 'I'd never seen anyone like that before. I was horrified. When he sobered up, he said it was my fault. I made him feel a failure.'

'You didn't go to your parents?'

'I—couldn't. They'd been against the marriage in the first place. Alan already thought they despised him.'

'Was that when he first hit you?' Zoltan asked gently.

Penny flushed. Her eyes fell. 'Yes,' she muttered.

He said something fierce under his breath. 'And no one noticed?'

'I took care that they didn't. It seemed disloyal.'

'So how did you ever get away?' He sounded angry.

'Oh, that was easy.' Penny gave a small bitter smile. 'I'd got a small commission. Alan—took a knife to my canvas. And then he came for me.'

'Hell.'

Zoltan looked bleak with shock.

'I almost expected it by then,' Penny said painfully. 'I'd even sort of half planned my exit route. I ran downstairs to neighbours. The police came and took him away. He was breaking up the flat.'

'And then?'

'Oh, then he was admitted to hospital. The specialist said that it was never going to get better as long as he was living with me. I seemed to drive him to it. He saw me as a rival, apparently, and every time I had any sort of success at all it made him doubt himself. So—I left.'

Zoltan looked at her carefully. 'How did you feel when he died?'

Penny swallowed. But she had told him so much that she was mortally ashamed of, she thought. Why hold back on this one thing?

'Free,' she said honestly.

And then she began to cry.

CHAPTER NINE

ZOLTAN let her cry. He did not attempt to touch her, although he passed across a spotless linen handkerchief at one point. When her tears showed signs of abating he got up and went to her bathroom. He came back with her tooth-mug full of water.

He hunkered down in front of her, presenting it. Penny made a little deprecating grimace, blinked, rubbed the back of her hand across her mouth and accepted the mug.

'Thank you,' she said in a rather watery voice.

He shrugged, his mouth wry. 'Least I can do.'

Penny swallowed some water. 'I don't normally behave like a waterfall.'

'I know you don't. You wouldn't have done now if I hadn't pushed you into it.' He looked at her searchingly. 'All right?' he asked softly.

She nodded, not quite meeting his eyes. He sighed and stood up.

'I wish——' he began. And stopped.

Penny blew her nose hard.

'I must look a mess.' She stole a look at him.

'No.' He looked stern and rather remote.

'Well, I'd better wash my face at least.' She inspected his handkerchief. It was no longer pristine. 'When they say mascara is waterproof they don't seem to count tears,' she said, with a gallant attempt at amusement.

'Yes, do that.' He was curt to the point where he could not have sounded less interested.

Penny flushed slightly. Well, what could she expect? she told herself. He had told her from the start that he was not into permanence. Presumably he was not into floods of tears and self-pity either, no matter how temporary. What was more, she did not blame him.

She went into the bathroom and splashed cold water on her face. She inspected the results narrowly in the mirror. Her eyelids would be puffy for some hours, she thought, but at least the cold water had taken the pinkness out of them.

She blotted her cheeks carefully before reapplying make-up. Normally she did not use much. But she was not an artist for nothing, she told herself firmly. And today was hardly normal. So she went through her whole box of cosmetics, ending with artful and nearly invisible eye-shadow that made her eyes look the colour of malachite and roughly the same shape as Cleopatra's. She dragged a comb through her hair. Fortunately the expensive cut meant that the feathery tendrils fell back into place naturally.

Penny studied the resulting image in the mirror. It might not be what Zoltan Guard was used to in the glamour stakes but it was the best she could do. And Zoltan Guard was going to be on his way in a very few hours, she reminded herself. Her fingers clenched round his handkerchief in a sudden spasm of loss.

This is crazy, she told herself. I don't even like him very much. But at the thought of him going out of my life I feel lonely as I've never felt in my life before. And I've known him twenty-four hours!

Not only crazy but also embarrassing. She must not give any sign of her deplorable feelings to Zoltan, she warned herself. They might not embarrass him, of course. He was the most imperturbable man she had ever met, after all. But they would cripple her with embarrassment whenever she thought about it in the future, she knew. No, her feelings must be buried out of sight. Now.

She went back through the bedroom into her small sitting-room. She averted her eyes as she passed the bed. It was only too easy to remember him lounging there. Was it only this morning? She winced, recalling how she had barred the door to her mother while he lay there laughing.

He was not laughing when she went into the room this time. He was looking out of the window at the sunny courtyard, an expression on his face she had not seen before. It made him look almost grim.

Penny lifted her chin.

'Sorry about that,' she said, in a voice of praise-worthy steadiness. 'I'm better now.'

He turned from the window to face her. His eyes widened slightly.

'So I see.' His look of grimness did not lessen. If anything it intensified. 'Do I gather that you're intending to go back to the party?'

In spite of the grimness he was still breathtakingly attractive. Penny let her eyes slide sideways. She was terrified he would see the hunger in them.

'I can't very well avoid it,' she pointed out reasonably. 'My sister. My home. I have to say goodbye to people.'

'Still other people first?' His voice mocked but he sounded angry. 'You could get out of it very easily. You could go and get that car of yours and we'll make a break for it.'

Her heart flared into hope for a moment. But then common sense reinstated itself. This was a man who looked for temporary satisfactions only. His affairs came with a built-in guarantee of obsolescence. Getting involved with Zoltan Guard would provide her with the second broken heart of her life. And the next one, Penny thought, would be terminal.

'I don't think that's a very good idea,' she said gently after a pause.

Zoltan looked at her moodily. 'No, I suppose not.'

She managed a smile. 'I'm grateful, though.'

The heavy brows twitched together. 'For making you cry like a waterfall?' he asked, with bitter self-mockery.

Her throat ached. But she kept her smile in place somehow.

'You were right. It had to be done some time. I've suppressed it for too long. I'm glad to have told someone. I am truly.'

'Then I'm glad to have been of service.'

But he didn't sound it. He sounded savage, Penny thought.

'I really must go back,' she said. 'Will you come too?'

He shrugged. 'Why not?'

They walked across the courtyard in uncomfortable silence. At least, Penny found it uncomfortable. Zoltan was lost in a brown study and gave every appearance of being unaware of her or anything uncomfortable in their situation.

The party was beginning to break up. As soon as Penny set foot in the front hall, Leslie pounced on her.

'There you are, Pen. You must come and say goodbye to Aunt Catherine.' She smiled briefly at Zoltan. 'Forgive me, Professor. You can have Penny back when she's done her duty.'

The heavy brows twitched together in a black line over the imperial nose. He did not smile.

'But her duty seems neverending,' Zoltan said, before turning on his heel and walking deliberately into another room.

Leslie stared after him, her mouth open.

'Good grief,' she said, awed. 'He wants to take you away from all this. Lucky girl.'

Penny's laugh broke in the middle. 'You don't know how wrong you are.'

Leslie was wearing a small private smile. 'Am I?'

Penny remembered how she had thought there was a conspiracy to matchmake when she had first seen Zoltan. If she had seen Leslie looking like this then, she would have been certain of it. And she would have been as wrong as she could be. Nobody made matches for Zoltan. Not even himself.

She shook her head. 'Completely,' she said firmly. 'The man is heart-whole. And likes his affairs to stay temporary.'

'You seem to know a lot about a man you only met yesterday.'

Penny snorted. 'Considering we spent the evening chasing burglars together——' She broke off, looking conscience-stricken.

'I know,' Leslie said peacefully.

Penny was startled.

'Zoltan mentioned it,' she said. 'He thought you were wrong keeping it from Laura. So do I, frankly. You could have done with a bit of cosseting today. After all, you're probably in shock.'

Penny thought about the way she had twined about Zoltan last night, when she had undoubtedly been in shock. And again today when she almost certainly hadn't. At least until after he touched her.

'Yes, I was probably looking for some cosseting,' she said drily. 'But I'm not going to get it and I don't waste my time chasing dreams. Take me to Aunt Catherine.'

Leslie laughed. 'One day the dreams will come looking for you,' she prophesied. 'Aunt Catherine's over there.'

She nodded in the direction of the study. 'I've got to see a man about transport out of here.'

She whisked off. Penny went in search of her aunt.

Aunt Catherine had installed herself in a high-backed armchair and was holding court.

'There you are,' she greeted Penny. 'Torn yourself away from your young man for a minute?'

Penny flushed slightly. 'No young man, Aunt Catherine,' she said, bending to kiss the wrinkled cheek.

Her aunt looked at her shrewdly. 'So why have you put on eyeshadow for the first time in years? Looks good,' she added fairly.

Penny laughed at her. 'Thank you. But it's for me. Not for any mythical man.'

Aunt Catherine snorted. 'Looked a pretty substantial myth to me. Handsome devil. Difficult to manage, though, I'd have said.'

Penny looked at her in horror. Manage Zoltan? 'I wouldn't even try.'

Her aunt looked amused. 'That's strong feeling. For a myth.'

Penny felt that family affection and the respect due to age had been tried high enough. 'You're a nosy, interfering old woman and it's nothing to do with you,' she told her aunt roundly.

She looked rather pleased. 'You're right, of course. But I'd like to see you happy. And you haven't been.'

Penny was shaken. Her aunt patted her on her arm.

'Go for him,' she advised. 'If he's the one you want then don't let him walk away without telling him.' For a moment the sharp old face looked younger, sadder. 'I did. Never ceased to regret it.'

Her niece was touched—and taken aback. 'I didn't know.'

'Well, now you do. Learn by my mistakes, my girl.'

Penny bit her lip. 'But what if he doesn't want me?'

'From what I've seen,' said Aunt Catherine, looking a great deal less vulnerable, 'he wants you all right. And even if he doesn't, what have you got to lose?'

'My dignity,' protested Penny, wincing at the thought.

'Pride,' said Aunt Catherine dismissively. 'That's all it is. Pride won't keep you warm at night. And I can tell you, it's not much of a consolation either, if you're going to spend your life trying not to think what might have been.'

She hauled herself heavily to her feet and stood up, leaning on her stick. Penny took her arm. Aunt Catherine's face softened.

'You're a good, loving girl. Your marriage was a bad business but it's time you put it behind you.' She touched Penny's hand briefly. 'If you want that handsome devil with the blue eyes, tell him. Chances don't come round twice.'

Penny said, 'I'll remember that.'

'Do it,' her aunt said briskly. 'And now you can see me to my car.'

Penny did. When the driver had tucked the rug round his passenger's knees and driven off at the funeral pace Aunt Catherine demanded, she went slowly back into the house. She had to admit it, a lot of what Aunt Catherine said had echoed her own half-subconscious feelings.

She looked for Zoltan in the house. But he was nowhere to be seen. And she wasn't going to ask, she thought wryly. Leslie's teasing had been quite enough for one day. She wasn't going to give the whole family cause to eye her in the same speculative way.

There was pride and pride, she reasoned. She might— just might—sink it for Zoltan if she was feeling brave enough. But there was no way she was going to expose herself to the cheerful witticisms of her family.

The party had sunk to a desultory state. She saw Leslie, who made a face.

'Everyone is waiting for someone else to move,' she said. 'They know they all need to go off and change before the dance but no one has the energy to start.'

Penny looked at her watch. It was later than she had thought.

'What about Celia and Mike? Can't they start the exodus?'

Leslie cast her eyes to the ceiling. 'Where have you been this last couple of hours? Or perhaps I shouldn't ask.' She had her look of secret amusement again. 'They pushed off ages ago. Celia went up and changed and came down in some amazingly expensive going-away suit and they drove off into the village. Just as if,' she added acidly, 'they really were going away instead of coming back this evening for the dance. No doubt Mummy stage-managed it.'

Penny laughed. 'She wanted everything proper after the disasters the rest of us provided, I suppose.'

Leslie nodded. 'And Celia's too happy to care.' She looked at Penny narrowly. 'What about you, Pen?'

'Me? I'm ecstatic,' said Penny lightly.

'You look it,' agreed her sister drily. 'No, I meant what about the dance. What are you wearing? Do you need a ride?'

Penny stared. 'I'm not the bride. I don't need to make a ceremonial exit.'

Leslie sighed. 'I meant, do you need a ride out? The dance will go on all night, you know. And nobody in the house will get a wink of sleep. I know several people who are pushing off early. I just wondered if you'd like a lift back to town with one of them.'

'I hadn't thought,' Penny said slowly. 'Wouldn't Mummy mind?'

'Probably—if she knew. Who's going to tell her?'

Penny succumbed. 'It would be heaven.' A thought struck her. 'But I've got my car here. Damn. I suppose I could drive myself,' she said doubtfully.

Leslie looked faintly annoyed. 'Don't even think about it. You'll be much too tired, after last night's drama and all. I'll get someone to drive your car up tomorrow.'

'*Would* you?'

Leslie gave her an affectionate smile. 'Leave it with me. You deserve a break.'

Penny was touched. She was also enormously grateful.

She was even more grateful at midnight when Leslie came and touched her on the arm.

Penny had originally agreed to go to the dance out of family solidarity. She had never expected to enjoy it. For the critical hour while she was getting dressed in her new long gown she had thought that she might, after all, have fun. If Zoltan was there. If he danced with her. If they talked . . .

'I'm palpitating like a schoolgirl,' Penny told her reflection. 'This is ridiculous.'

But she couldn't stop the slight, sweet tremor of her body at the prospect.

The tremor was rapidly calmed. Registering arrival after arrival in the marquee, Penny slowly realised that Zoltan was not going to show up. She debated. She could not remark on his absence to her sisters without causing more comment than she could handle. But her new brother-in-law was a different matter.

Cautiously she remarked to Mike that his old teacher was taking a long time to get to the dance floor from his room under the eaves.

'Oh, Zoltan's gone,' Mike said.

He dragged her on to the dance floor and began to windmill his arms energetically.

'Gone?' Penny was blank. She began to dance on autopilot. 'He didn't say he was leaving.'

'He rang his secretary in Cambridge and she had some message for him,' Mike said without interest. 'He's always been like that. On the move all over the world at the drop of a hat.'

'Oh,' said Penny. After a pause she said carefully, 'Do you know where he is this time?'

'Haven't a clue,' said Mike cheerfully. 'Has he left something behind?'

'Not as far as I know.'

'Then there's no problem, is there?'

'No,' said Penny hollowly.

After that the sparkle went out of the evening. So she was relieved when Leslie tapped her on the arm.

'Get your coat,' her sister said briskly. 'Your chauffeur's leaving in ten minutes. Big dark car under the copper beech.'

'Thanks,' said Penny.

Leslie hugged her suddenly. 'Good luck.'

Surprised and moved, Penny hugged her back. 'Weddings seem to make everyone soggy,' she said, her eyes filling. 'You're a love.'

'Yes, I am. Hang on, Mummy's looking this way. I'll put up the smokescreen while you get your toothbrush.'

Penny nodded, retreating to the tented door.

'And don't forget to give me a ring,' Leslie hissed after her. 'I want to know if you get home safely.'

It was only later that Penny realised how oddly that explanation had been phrased.

CHAPTER TEN

BUT at the time Penny just darted back to her room and picked up her overnight case. She swung her frilled woollen serape round her bare shoulders against the chill of the summer evening. The edge of it caught something on the window ledge. It fell to the floor. Stooping, Penny picked it up.

It was the handkerchief Zoltan had given her. Crumpled and more than a little grubby now, it made her heart lurch. Her fingers closed round it convulsively.

'Has he left something behind?' Mike had asked.

Well, he had, hadn't he?

Here, if she wanted it, was the perfect excuse to get in touch with him again. Penny bit her lip. Did she want it?

She looked down at the scrap of crumpled linen. Oh, she did, she did. But was she brave enough to risk hurt again? 'Chances don't come round twice,' Aunt Catherine had said. She didn't want to spend the rest of her life wondering what would have happened if she had been brave enough, she realised suddenly. She stuffed the handkerchief in her pocket and tumbled downstairs.

Dropping her overnight case at the bottom, she sprinted back to the marquee. She scanned the crowd for Mike and soon located him. He had discarded his dinner jacket and was partying with enthusiasm.

'Mike,' she said, attracting his attention by the simple expedient of grabbing a handful of the back of his white shirt and pulling him backwards.

'Good lord, Pen, you going?'

'Never mind that. Where can I get hold of Zoltan Guard?'

He grinned. 'Old magic still working?' he asked admiringly. 'Don't know how the man does it.'

Penny ignored that. 'His address in Cambridge. Or better still a phone number.'

Mike shook his head. 'And I thought you were a sensible girl,' he mourned.

'We all lose our senses sometimes,' Penny said drily. 'Come on Mike. Give.'

'Huntingdon College,' he said. 'Don't remember the number. It's in the book. They'll know where to find him. He has rooms there.'

'Thank you,' said Penny. On impulse she kissed his cheek.

He looked pleased. 'Be careful,' he warned.

'Too late for that.' Penny suddenly found she felt inordinately cheerful. 'I'll let you know what happens.'

He shuddered. 'Cilly will kill me.'

Penny laughed and danced out into the night.

Her bag was undisturbed. She hooked it on to her shoulder and went in search of the car under the copper beech.

She wondered idly whom Leslie had instructed to drive her home. There were plenty of older couples who would be looking for their beds before dawn, she thought. She just hoped it wasn't going to be anyone who wanted to engage her in conversation all the way to London. She had too much thinking to do to make small talk.

It was, as Leslie had said, a big dark car. Penny did not know much about cars, but the sleek lines of this one were the height of expensive style. Good old Leslie, she thought with a private grin.

It was empty. Penny looked round, from the house to the marquee, wondering where her companions were coming from, when a hand came out of the darkness and unhooked the bag from her shoulder.

'You won't want that,' said a voice she knew.

Penny went absolutely still. For a moment she did not dare to turn round in case it was a fantasy.

'But you've left,' she croaked.

'I came back.'

'But—did you leave something behind?'

'Yes,' said Zoltan Guard with a soft laugh.

Penny began to tremble. She turned round. He was a tall shadow. She could not see his eyes. But somehow, through her whole body, veins and nerves and muscles, she could feel his laughter. And a fierce determination.

'What is it? I'll get it for you. Tell me where to look...' She was babbling and she knew it.

'Get in the car,' he said quietly.

'But I'll get it for you.'

There was that deep, achingly familiar note of amusement in his voice. 'You have.'

For a wild moment she thought he could see his handkerchief, scrunched up in her pocket. Then common sense reasserted itself. She blushed in the darkness.

'I don't understand,' said Penny untruthfully.

'Yes, you do.' He took her face between his hands and feathered the lightest of kisses against her mouth. 'You damned well do,' he said under his breath. 'And I'm going to prove it to you.'

A crazy happiness seemed to burst over her heart. At the same time a little forlorn wistfulness touched the moment.

'Quite temporarily,' she muttered.

'What?'

He raised his head and looked searchingly down at her in the darkness. From the marquee there came a burst of raucous laughter, then a surge of music, renewed at double amplification. It had the effect of isolating them in their corner of stillness under the copper beech.

'We'd better be moving,' Zoltan said. 'That doesn't sound like a party that's going to stay indoors for long.'

'Yes,' said Penny. She knew that she was agreeing to more than a car ride. It filled her with a reckless joy. 'Let's go.'

He tossed her bag on the capacious back seat. Then he helped her into the passenger seat, tucking her satin skirts around her, and closed the door on her. He swung into the driving seat and turned on the engine.

'We've got a lot to talk about,' he said. 'But not in imminent danger of being jumped by too many of my old students.'

He let the clutch in and the car moved forward with a luxurious purr. He looked sideways at her.

'I gather Ian has already maligned me,' he said casually.

Penny looked down at her hands, locked nervously in her lap. Why am I nervous? she thought, I've decided to do this.

She said coolly, 'He filled me in on your previous history with ladies.'

'I was afraid of that.' For once Zoltan didn't sound amused. Or very sure of himself, she noted with amazement. 'Did he tell you I was the greatest rake since Casanova?'

'Something along those lines.'

'It's not true,' he said urgently.

'It sounded awfully credible.'

He sent her another look. 'You're laughing at me,' he said on a note of discovery.

She shook her head. 'Maybe at both of us.'

'Why?'

'Well, I've steered clear of involvement since my marriage ended. It's completely out of character for me to be driving off at midnight with the greatest rake since Casanova, bound for God knows where. Or are you,' she added, injecting a faintly curious note into her voice, 'going to take me back to my flat as negotiated?'

'I'll take you wherever you want.' His voice was warm.

'You mean, it's my decision?'

'Of course.'

'Oh,' said Penny.

'You don't want it to be your decision?' He sounded bemused.

'Casanova had many faults. Or so I'm told. The great thing about his technique, though,' said Penny carefully, 'was that he swept a girl off her feet.'

'Ah. You want to be swept off your feet.' He sent her a quick look. 'Fine. I can arrange that.'

'I thought,' said Penny, with something of a snap, 'that you *had* arranged it. And that this was it.'

He reached out and brushed the back of his fingers down her cheek.

'Sweetheart, I haven't even started.'

He was driving through the lanes as if he had known them—and the car—all his life.

Penny said, 'Aren't we going a little fast?'

Zoltan chuckled. 'Faster than I've ever gone before.'

Penny did not pretend to misunderstand him. 'Is that wise?'

'Probably not.' He didn't sound worried.

Aunt Catherine, Penny thought with a sudden giggle, would approve.

'What are you laughing at?'

'Something one of my aunts said to me this evening.' She looked at him under her lashes. 'She told me not to let you get away, if I wanted you.'

'I'll second that.'

She was slightly put out. 'Yes, but do I?' she said captiously.

He turned the car on to the big dual carriageway. In the sudden light of the overhead streetlamps he looked deceptively serious, she thought.

'It's up to me to see you do.'

He didn't say much for the next hour. He was obviously concentrating on directions. Penny, to whom the road was unfamiliar, did not offer to help. Well, at least he wasn't taking her back to London, she thought, pleased.

'Where did you get the car?' she asked at one point, as they hit a motorway and he put his foot down. 'I didn't think they rented out cars of this quality in case they got beaten up.'

The car glided smoothly into hyperspeed. The engine noise stayed at the same drowsy purr. Zoltan shrugged.

'It's mine. I'm over here so much I keep a car in the UK.'

Penny sat up. 'Then why did I have to meet you at the station?' she demanded, put out.

'A friend had borrowed it. I had someone drive it over to Shrewsbury for me. I picked it up this afternoon.'

'Oh,' said Penny, digesting this. She snuggled down again in luxury upholstery.

Luxury cars that he used less than half the year. A car delivery service to all corners of the country. It added up to an unnervingly expensive lifestyle. She had realised he was not a hungry academic. But this?

'Are you terribly rich?' she said with foreboding.

Zoltan laughed. 'I pay my bills and I buy the toys I want. Like the car. I can earn as much as I want. I choose my own jobs. Apart from that, I'm a free man.'

Penny digested that.

'I don't understand,' she said mischievously, looking at him from under her lashes.

He reached out and squeezed her fingers hard. It made her catch her breath in a sudden flash-flood of desire. From the taut look on his face, it had the same effect on him.

'Does it matter how much money I have?' he said, sounding strangled.

Penny hesitated. 'I don't think I'd like to be a millionaire's mistress,' she said at last in a small voice. 'I'm sorry but——'

'*What*?'

'I dare say it seems very silly to you but——'

'We are not,' said Zoltan grimly, 'talking about mistresses.'

'Oh,' said Penny again, in an entirely different voice.

'I'm not talking about it in the car,' he told her hastily. 'You're a severe enough trial to my blood-pressure as it is.'

'Oh,' said Penny, pleased. 'No one has ever told me I'm a trial to their blood-pressure before.'

'You probably just didn't understand them,' Zoltan said maliciously. He reached out a long arm and tucked the woollen wrap more securely round her. 'Or they hadn't sat next to you for hours while your damned shawl slid off your bare shoulders. It's extremely disquieting.'

Penny blushed deeply. 'Good,' she said.

'I'm glad you think so. I am seriously considering confiscating that dress permanently when we arrive.'

'Arrive where?' she asked, to cover her confusion.

'My house in Cambridge. Since you expressed a desire to be swept off your feet, that's the best I can do at a moment's notice.' He touched her face again, as if he wanted to keep assuring himself that she was actually in the car beside him. 'Tomorrow any South Sea paradise you care to name.'

Penny choked. 'Don't be ridiculous. I've got a job.'

'I know. It's extremely inconvenient. But I have given it some thought and I think I've got the answer. Surely even hospital administrators are allowed time off for honeymoons?'

Penny went very still. All of a sudden all desire to laugh left her.

'Honeymoons?'

'Well, I was only thinking of one,' Zoltan told her amused. 'With me.'

'You did say honeymoon?' Penny said gropingly. 'As in legal matrimony?'

'That's the one.'

'But—you don't believe in permanence.'

'Twenty-four hours ago,' Zoltan said superbly, 'I didn't believe in love at first sight either. We can all learn from our mistakes.'

Penny drew a sharp breath.

'Can't we?' he asked softly.

She bit her lip. 'I don't know,' she said honestly. 'I seem to have made so many.'

'I can only think of one.'

He turned the car off the big road and swung it round a succession of roundabouts. A shadowed signpost said Cambridge. Penny's hands clenched tight in her lap.

'No, make that two,' he added in a thoughtful voice.

They were travelling down a tree-lined street with big gothic villas on either side, set back amid gardens like woodland groves. Without warning Zoltan turned the car in under a laburnum tree. The catkins were gold in the headlights for a moment. Then they died as he cut the engine and the lights.

Into the silence Penny said in an unnaturally bright voice, 'Only two?'

'Yup. One, when you married Alan Dane in the first place.'

He reached back and hefted her overnight bag from the back seat. He leaned in front of her and opened her door for her. He kissed her briefly.

'And two, not going to bed with me last night.'

Penny swallowed deafeningly in the silence of the car. She couldn't think of a thing to say.

'Never mind,' he told her forgivingly. 'We're going to put that right now.'

He took her into the house with one arm round her shoulders, as if he was afraid to let her go. It was a tall house with winding stairs and odd corners, full of pictures and books. Not unlike her own flat, Penny thought, startled, although he obviously had more money to spend. But the feeling of favourite things and untidy comfort was the same.

Perhaps it was for that reason that she suddenly clutched the serape tight around her. She found herself hoping desperately that Zoltan was not going to stampede her up to bed at once. She felt too strange in this familiar and yet not familiar house. He sensed her unease.

'Come into the study and warm up,' he said softly.

He did not take his arm from around her shoulders. Penny began to feel the tension easing. She even leaned her head briefly against his shoulder as he pushed open a doorway off the hall.

'I work in here,' he said, gesturing with the other hand. 'To prove it, to the left you will see my collected works.'

Penny gasped. She saw at once where he was pointing. For there, along the oak shelves, were two lines of them. Thin books, tall books, immensely fat books. In every language she could think of and some she couldn't. All of them saying on their spines 'Zoltan Guard'. It was oddly intimidating. Penny looked at him with astonishment—and reluctant awe. She suddenly felt horribly out of her depth.

But she said as lightly as she could manage, 'I see what you mean, Professor.'

The arm round her tightened.

'Don't look like that,' he said irritably. 'I told you— I do what I'm interested in. I have a lot of energy, there aren't many people in my field, so I get a lot of work. It's chance. Being a professor is largely chance too.'

Penny stared round the room. It was a large room and apart from his own works books filled all the wall space that wasn't taken up by windows or the fireplace. There were more books and papers on a battered oak desk.

'That's not what it looks like,' she said wryly.

'Don't be taken in by Dracula's Castle Library,' he said. 'It comes with the job description. That's what it means to be a professor. By the time you get to professor you've done the subject to death.'

There was a slight hint of defensiveness in his voice. Penny considered the handsome face above her and reached a conclusion.

'Are you embarrassed about all these books?' she demanded.

She could feel his heart beating under her shoulderblade.

'They must look stuffy to a gorgeous creature like you.'

Penny turned in his arms and looked up into his face.

'Are you joking?' she said incredulously.

He looked down at her, the blue eyes for once uncertain.

'Not stuffy?'

'The greatest rake since Casanova,' Penny told him firmly, 'is not stuffy.' When he did not seem reassured,

she reached up and kissed his chin. 'You promised you'd
warm me up.'

'Oh.' He looked disconcerted. 'Yes, of course. It's
chilly in here. I'll light the fire.'

'I was not,' said Penny, blushing furiously but keeping
her head high and her voice conversational, 'thinking of
a fire. Or of staying in here either.'

He didn't seem to be able to speak. He seemed to have
turned to stone. It was clearly going to be up to her to
make matters progress, Penny realised.

Ignoring her heated cheeks, she went on bravely, 'To
be honest, I was rather hoping you'd take me to bed.'

His arms went round her convulsively. They tightened
like a vice, knocking the breath out of her.

'Oh, my darling,' said Zoltan, shaken.

They kissed long and passionately. At last he released
her. Penny's head swam. Her serape had fallen to the
rug where it spilled over a pile of books and papers. So
great was the oxygen deprivation, she thought, amused,
that she felt the world swaying round her.

And then she realised that it really was swaying. Zoltan
had put one hand behind her knees, the other like a bar
across her shoulders, and swung her up to lie across his
chest.

'This is ridiculous,' gasped Penny, hanging on to him
in alarm.

He laughed down at her, the blue eyes dancing.

'You wanted to be swept off your feet. Here we go.'

His bedroom was right at the top of the house. By the
time they reached it they were both helpless with laughter.
Still holding her, Zoltan collapsed on the bed.

'The lady's fantasies fulfilled,' he said smugly.

Penny struggled up on one elbow. 'No, they jolly well
aren't. You've got a lot more to do before you can start
putting that in your autobiography.'

His eyes glinted down at her. 'It will,' he said softly, 'be my pleasure.' His mouth tilted in a smile that was entirely wicked. 'But first of all I'm confiscating that damned provocative dress as a matter of public safety.'

He began to kiss her, laughing. Then, as their clothes fell, and the first fingers of light signalled the dawn, they laughed no more.

Later Penny lay in his arms, dazed into silence. Zoltan, she had found, made love with an intensity of concentration that made her feel like the most precious creature in the whole world. He had brought her exquisitely alive in every atom of her being and then had taken that being to heights of quivering sensation she had not even imagined could be possible.

And then he had told her that he loved her.

'Oh, darling,' said Penny, overwhelmed.

He looked down at her, absorbedly combing her hair round the curve of her neck.

'It's never happened before. I didn't really think it could,' he confessed. 'I thought that only not very bright people fell in love.'

Penny gave a choke of laughter. He looked reproachful.

'I know. I know. But I thought I knew so much about the human condition, human feelings. And I knew all about my own. I've been trained to analyse all my life, after all. I just didn't think there was room for people to feel like this.'

He kissed her. Penny kissed him back.

'And now that you do?'

'I'd like to get married,' he said soberly. 'I told you in the car. I—know you may have reservations. But not all the men in the world are like Alan. I'm sure given time...'

He stopped. Penny had bounced into a sitting position.

'Are you saying you thought I wouldn't marry you?' she demanded. 'That I was the one with objections to marriage, I mean.'

'Well, yes. You said—this afternoon——'

'Yesterday afternoon,' Penny corrected.

'All right, pedant. Yesterday afternoon. You said it wasn't a very good idea.'

Penny drew a deep calming breath. Otherwise she would have screamed.

'But that was because I thought you were going to love and leave me, you stupid man,' she said in exasperation.

Zoltan looked blank. 'What?'

'That was your reputation,' she pointed out. 'And it was you yourself who told me you weren't into permanence. What would you have thought in my place?'

'Exactly what you did,' he admitted after a moment.

'And I spent a miserable afternoon wishing that I'd been braver. And then I found the hankie you'd lent me when I was crying and I thought, That's all the excuse I need. I'll follow him to the ends of the earth and see if he'll give me another chance.'

Zoltan stared into her eyes, fascinated. '*Did* you?'

'Yes, I did. I was going to sink my pride completely for you. And you don't seem to appreciate it at all,' Penny said, glaring.

He reached up for her and pulled her down to him firmly.

'I do. I do. I'm luckier than I deserve and I'm never going to let you go. I didn't realise. My darling, you are quite right; I'm a stupid man.'

Penny sighed and wriggled against him, pulling the covers over both of them again.

'No, you aren't,' she said blissfully. 'You're wonderful. You just don't notice when people are madly in love with you. I'm going to marry you and make sure you never make the same mistake again.'

He gathered her against his chest. She could feel the rumble of laughter as he sought her mouth.

'I rely on that,' he said.

Harlequin Romance ®

Delightful

Affectionate

Romantic

Emotional

Tender

Original

Daring

Riveting

Enchanting

Adventurous

Moving

Harlequin Romance—the
series that has it all!

HROM-G

HARLEQUIN PRESENTS®

HARLEQUIN PRESENTS
men you won't be able to resist falling in love with...

HARLEQUIN PRESENTS
women who have feelings just like your own...

HARLEQUIN PRESENTS
powerful passion in exotic international settings...

HARLEQUIN PRESENTS
intense, dramatic stories that will keep you turning
to the very last page...

HARLEQUIN PRESENTS
The world's bestselling romance series!

Harlequin® Historical

If you're a serious fan of historical romance,
then you're in luck!

Harlequin Historicals brings you
stories by bestselling authors, rising new stars
and talented first-timers.

Ruth Langan & Theresa Michaels
Mary McBride & Cheryl St. John
Margaret Moore & Merline Lovelace
Julie Tetel & Nina Beaumont
Susan Amarillas & Ana Seymour
Deborah Simmons & Linda Castle
Cassandra Austin & Emily French
Miranda Jarrett & Suzanne Barclay
DeLoras Scott & Laurie Grant...

You'll never run out of favorites.

Harlequin Historicals...they're too good to miss!

HH-GEN

HARLEQUIN®

I N T R I G U E®

THAT'S INTRIGUE—DYNAMIC
ROMANCE AT ITS BEST!

Harlequin Intrigue is now bringing you more—more men and mystery, more desire and danger. If you've been looking for thrilling tales of contemporary passion and sensuous love stories with taut, edge-of-the-seat suspense—then you'll *love* Harlequin Intrigue!

Every month, you'll meet four new heroes who are guaranteed to make your spine tingle and your pulse pound. With them you'll enter into the exciting world of Harlequin Intrigue—where your life is on the line and so is your heart!

Harlequin Intrigue—we'll leave you breathless!

INT-GEN

LOOK FOR OUR FOUR FABULOUS MEN!

Each month some of today's bestselling authors bring
four new fabulous men to Harlequin American Romance.
Whether they're rebel ranchers, millionaire power brokers
or sexy single dads, they're all gallant princes—and
they're all ready to sweep you into lighthearted fantasies
and contemporary fairy tales where anything is possible
and where all your dreams come true!

You don't even have to make a wish...Harlequin American
Romance will grant your every desire!

Look for Harlequin American Romance wherever Harlequin
books are sold!